Advances in

HEMATICAL

RAMMING

Recent Advances in

MATHEMATICAL

PROGRAMMING

Edited by

Robert L. Graves

Associate Professor of Applied Mathematics
Graduate School of Business
University of Chicago

Philip Wolfe

Mathematician, the RAND Corporation

McGRAW-HILL BOOK COMPANY, INC.

New York   San Francisco   Toronto   London

RECENT ADVANCES IN MATHEMATICAL
PROGRAMMING

Introduction

The growth of mathematical programming since its birth in 1947 has been marked — and stimulated — by a distinguished series of Symposia at which the major part of the research workers in the field have presented their work. The quality of these meetings has been ensured by a certain continuity of participants and supporters. The first such meeting was held in Chicago in 1949, sponsored by The RAND Corporation; selected papers from it appeared as "Activity Analysis of Production and Allocation", (1951), edited by Tjalling C. Koopmans. The first meeting to bear the title "Symposium" was held in Washington, D. C. in 1951 under the sponsorship of the National Bureau of Standards and the U. S. Air Force; abstracts and selected papers were published in "Symposium on Linear Inequalities and Programming" by the Air Force (1952). The "Second Symposium in Linear Programming" was held in Washington in 1955, under the same sponsorship as the first; its Proceedings, edited by Henry A. Antosiewicz, were published by the sponsors in 1955 The third symposium, "A Symposium on Mathematical Programming: Linear Programming and Recent Extensions" was held in Santa Monica, California in 1959; a report, "The RAND Symposium on Mathematical Programming", was published by The RAND Corporation in 1960.

The fourth symposium, on which this volume reports, was held in Chicago, Illinois, under the joint sponsorship of the Association for Computing Machinery, the Graduate School of Business of the University of Chicago, and The RAND Corporation, on June 18-22, 1962. The organizers of the present conference were drawn from the membership of SIGMAP, the Special Interest Group for Mathematical Programming in the Association for Computing Machinery. SIGMAP is devoted to furthering all aspects of mathematical programming.

Forty-three papers were presented at the Symposium, to an audience of more than 240 persons, from five continents. Papers were given in each of eight areas of mathematical programming. In four of these, especially invited survey papers gave the audience a broad view of the methods and problems of that area. The surveys are among the twenty-three papers appearing in full in these Proceedings. The remaining papers, whose appearance in full here has been sacrificed to the requirement that this volume be of reasonable size and to some authors' commitments to publish elsewhere, are given as abstracts. Full copies of such papers can generally be obtained

* Pub. by Cowles Commission for Research in Economics,

from the authors. Papers 14, 16, and 38 were edited by the authors from transcriptions made at the Symposium.

The first nine papers deal with the general theory of mathematical programming. The survey paper by Tucker, which begins this group, presents the theory of linear programming in its most powerful current form. The eight papers which follow deal with various aspects of the theory of both linear and nonlinear programming.

Papers 10 through 13 deal with nonlinear programming — with "nonlinear" used in the accepted sense as referring to "reasonably smooth" nonlinear objective functions and constraints. The first paper of these, by Wolfe, is a survey of most of the proposals which have been made for solving such problems.

Papers 14 through 18 are devoted to stochastic programming — mathematical programming problems whose data may be random variables. Such problems require careful statement if meaningful results are to be obtained. The first paper of these, by Madansky, surveys the outstanding problems of this field.

Papers 19 through 22 are concerned with computational procedures for very large linear programming problems. Such problems always have some regularity of structure that appropriately designed algorithms can take advantage of. The papers of this group constitute four different methods of attack on aspects of that regularity.

Papers 23 through 26 are concerned more intimately with the computational processes of mathematical programming, examining in detail, ways in which variations of the simplex algorithm — the most effective current tool for linear programming — can be made even more effective.

Papers 27 through 33 lie in the area of applications of mathematical programming. Since entire series of books are being written on this subject, these papers can no more than sample the area by showing some of the latest uses of currently available methods.

Papers 34 through 37 are devoted to integer programming problems. The first of these is Gomory's 1958 paper, now almost a classic, which established the subject of integer programming. It has been substituted for his paper presented at the Symposium because, still in great demand, it has been out of print for some time.

The last group of papers, 38 through 43, are concerned with problems of network flow, a special class of linear programming problem which, because of its rich structure, has given rise to an extensive and elegant theory. The first paper, by Fulkerson, surveys this area, reviewing its main tools and its outstanding problems.

Contents

Recent Advances in

MATHEMATICAL

PROGRAMMING

Combinatorial Theory Underlying Linear Programs[†]

Albert W. Tucker

The simplex method of G. B. Dantzig is much more than the basic computational tool of linear programming. It is also a combinatorial algorithm which provides constructive means of establishing fundamental theorems, not only in programming, but also in cognate areas, such as Farkas' theorem for linear inequalities and von Neumann's minimax theorem for matrix games. In an effort to discover the underlying theoretical structure, the author has been led to develop a <u>combinatorial linear algebra</u> which employs pivot steps (Gauss–Jordan elimination) and interchanges of rows and of columns to generate finite equivalence–classes of "dual linear systems." Such a class embraces in palpable form all the information needed to treat many theoretical and practical matters customarily handled by more elaborate linear algebra. Over an ordered field this algebra seems to provide a unified and simplified means of dealing with linear inequalities, linear programs, matrix games, etc.

DUAL LINEAR SYSTEMS.

The schema

$$(1)$$

is a succinct joint representation of two systems of linear equations. One

---

†This paper has been prepared with the assistance of Drs. Michel L. Balinski and Robert R. Singleton and with the support of the Office of Naval Research, Logistics Branch.

system arises by forming the inner products of the vector X^1 with the columns of the matrix A, and setting each inner product equal to the corresponding component of X^2. This leads to a system of n linear equations in the m + n variables x_i:

$$x_1 a_{11} + \ldots + x_m a_{m1} = x_{m+1}$$
$$\vdots \qquad\qquad \vdots \qquad \vdots$$
$$x_1 a_{1n} + \ldots + x_m a_{mn} = x_{m+n} \qquad\qquad (2)$$

The second system arises by forming the inner products of Y^2 with the rows of A, and setting each equal to the corresponding component of $-Y^1$. This yields a system of m linear equations in the m + n variables y_i:

$$a_{11} y_{m+1} + \ldots + a_{1n} y_{m+n} = -y_1$$
$$\vdots \qquad\qquad \vdots \qquad \vdots$$
$$a_{m1} y_{m+1} + \ldots + a_{mn} y_{m+n} = -y_m \qquad\qquad (3)$$

In matrix notation these systems are written

$$X^1 A = X^2 \text{ and } A Y^2 = -Y^1$$

where X^1, X^2 are row vectors and Y^1, Y^2 are column vectors.

The two systems are dual, in the sense that any solution X of the x-system is orthogonal to any solution Y of the y-system. This is because

$$XY = x_1 y_1 + \ldots + x_m y_m + x_{m+1} y_{m+1} + \ldots + x_{m+n} y_{m+n}$$
$$= X^1 Y^1 + X^2 Y^2 = X^1 (-A Y^2) + (X^1 A) Y^2 = 0 \qquad\qquad (4)$$

For solutions X and Y which are nonnegative (i.e., $x_i \geq 0$ and $y_i \geq 0$, i = 1, $\ldots$, m + n), the orthogonality XY = 0 yields a strong condition on individual components: namely, $x_i = 0$ or/and $y_i = 0$ for i = 1, $\ldots$, m + n. This is because the inner product XY is then a sum of nonnegative terms $x_i y_i$, which sum equals zero only if each individual term $x_i y_i$ equals zero.

By a natural generalization of ordinary analytic geometry, solutions X and Y may be regarded as (m + n)-tuples of coordinates specifying points in an (m + n)-dimensional space. Then the set of all solutions X and the set of all solutions Y constitute two complementary orthogonal linear subspaces in the (m + n)-space. The system $X^2 = X^1 A$ specifies an m-dimensional linear subspace because the m components of X^1 can be taken arbitrarily and then the components of X^2 are determined. Similarly, $A Y^2 = -Y^1$ specifies an n-dimensional linear subspace because the n components of Y^2 can be taken arbitrarily and then the components of Y^1 are determined. The two linear subspaces are orthogonal because of (4); they are complementary because the sum of their dimensions is m + n, the dimension of the containing space. Thus, each linear subspace determines the other.

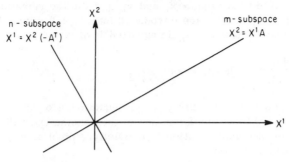

Fig. 1

The complementary-orthogonal nature of the two subspaces is indicated schematically in Figure 1, where the matrix equation $Y^1 = -AY^2$ for the n-dimensional subspace has been rewritten as $X^1 = X^2 (-A^T)$ by transposing and then substituting X^1, X^2 for Y^{1T}, Y^{2T}.

In plane analytic geometry two orthogonal straight lines through the origin have equations $y = ax$ and $x = -ay$, where $a = y/x$ is the usual slope of the first line and $-a = x/y$ is the reciprocal slope of the second line. By analogy, the matrix A can be regarded as the "$X^2 : X^1$-slope" of the linear subspace specified by $X^2 = X^1 A$ and the negative-transpose matrix $-A^T$ as the "$X^1 : X^2$-slope" of the complementary-orthogonal linear subspace specified by $X^1 = X^2 (-A^T)$.

COMBINATORIAL EQUIVALENCE.

We will now see that the process of Gauss-Jordan elimination can be applied simultaneously to the x-system (2) and the y-system (3) to pass from one pair of dual linear systems to a second pair of dual linear systems which are equivalent in the sense that the second systems have the same solutions as the first systems. Suitably organized, this use of Gauss-Jordan elimination leads to the concept of "combinatorial equivalence," so called because each equivalence class contains just a finite number of members.

If a coefficient $a_{ij} \neq 0$ in schema (1), the two equations in which it enters,

$$x_1 a_{1j} \quad + \ldots + x_i a_{ij} \quad + \ldots + x_m a_{mj} = x_{m+j}$$

$$a_{i1} y_{m+1} + \ldots + a_{ij} y_{m+j} + \ldots + a_{in} y_{m+n} = -y_i \qquad (5)$$

can be solved for x_i and y_{m+j} to give

$$-x_1 \frac{a_{1j}}{a_{ij}} - \ldots + x_{m+j} \frac{1}{a_{ij}} - \ldots - x_m \frac{a_{mj}}{a_{ij}} = x_i$$

$$\frac{a_{i1}}{a_{ij}} y_{m+1} + \ldots + \frac{1}{a_{ij}} y_i + \ldots + \frac{a_{in}}{a_{ij}} y_{m+n} = -y_{m+j}$$

These can be used to eliminate x_i and y_{m+j} from the remaining equations, but of course x_{m+j} and y_i are introduced into the left sides. When this is done, the new coefficient for x_h in equation k of (2) is

$$a_{hk} - \frac{a_{hj}\, a_{ik}}{a_{ij}} \qquad h \neq i,\; k \neq j$$

which is <u>also</u> the coefficient for y_{m+k} in equation h of (3).

We are thus led to a transformation of the schema (1), called an "elementary pivot transformation" (or briefly, "pivot step"), which may be represented as follows:

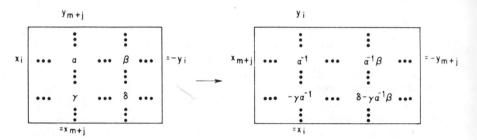

The pivot α is any element $a_{ij} \neq 0$, β is any other entry a_{ik} in the pivot's row, γ is any other entry a_{hj} in the pivot's column, and δ is the entry a_{hk} in β's column and γ's row. In the margins x_i and x_{m+j} have been interchanged, as have y_i and y_{m+j}. In the interchange of the y's the minus sign stays with the row. All other marginal variables remain unchanged.

In addition to pivot steps we admit two other types of elementary transformations on a schema: interchange of any two rows and interchange of any two columns. These are trivial modifications corresponding merely to the interchange of two equations in one system and of corresponding terms in the other system. Clearly the solutions of the two systems are not changed except for the order in which the variables appear.

Note that the schema (1) imposes an ordered partition

$$(1, \ldots, m \mid m+1, \ldots, m+n)$$

of the subscripts of the variables. An interchange of two rows permutes two of the subscripts $1, \ldots, m$; an interchange of two columns permutes two of the subscripts $m+1, \ldots, m+n$; a pivot step permutes one subscript from $1, \ldots, m$ with one from $m+1, \ldots, m+n$.

A finite succession of elementary transformations of the three types results in a transformed partition

$$(\overline{1}, \ldots, \overline{m} \mid \overline{m+1}, \ldots, \overline{m+n})$$

and transformed schema

$$
(X_\pi^1) \quad
\begin{array}{c}
 \\[2pt]
(Y_\pi^2) \\[4pt]
\begin{array}{ccc}
y\overline{_{m+1}} & \cdots\cdots & y\overline{_{m+n}} \\
\end{array} \\
\begin{array}{c}
x\overline{_1} \\[2pt] \vdots \\[2pt] x\overline{_m}
\end{array}
\left[
\begin{array}{ccc}
\overline{a}_{11} & \cdots\cdots & \overline{a}_{1n} \\
\vdots & (\overline{A}) & \vdots \\
\overline{a}_{ml} & \cdots\cdots & \overline{a}_{mn}
\end{array}
\right]
\begin{array}{c}
= -y\overline{_1} \\[2pt] \vdots \\[2pt] = -y\overline{_m}
\end{array} \\[6pt]
\begin{array}{ccc}
= X\overline{_{m+1}} & \cdots\cdots & = X\overline{_{m+n}}
\end{array} \\[4pt]
(= X_\pi^2)
\end{array}
\quad (= -Y_\pi^1), \qquad (6)
$$

where π denotes the permutation of $m+n$ objects which carries $(1, \ldots, m+n)$ into $(\overline{1}, \ldots, \overline{m+n})$.

The new dual linear systems

$$X_\pi^1 \overline{A} = X_\pi^2 \quad \text{and} \quad \overline{A} Y_\pi^2 = -Y_\pi^1$$

are equivalent respectively to the original dual linear systems

$$X^1 A = X^2 \quad \text{and} \quad A Y^2 = -Y^1$$

in that they have the same solutions—subject to the understanding that the correspondence between the solutions of one system and those of the equivalent system is a one-to-one correspondence established by the permutation π.

Define any two schemata

$$
\begin{array}{c}
Y^2 \\
X^1 \; \boxed{A} \; = -Y^1 \\
= X^2
\end{array}
\qquad\qquad
\begin{array}{c}
Y_\pi^2 \\
X_\pi^1 \; \boxed{\overline{A}} \; = -Y_\pi^1 \\
= X_\pi^2
\end{array}
$$

to be combinatorially equivalent if the dual linear systems $X_\pi^1 \overline{A} - X_\pi^2$ and $\overline{A} Y_\pi^2 = -Y_\pi^1$ have the same solutions as the dual linear systems $X^1 A = X^2$ and $A Y^2 = -Y^1$, where $X_\pi = [X_\pi^1, X_\pi^2]$ arises from $X = [X^1, X^2]$ by a permutation π of the $m+n$ component variables and Y_π arises similarly from Y. Then, as seen above, a finite succession of elementary transformations of the three types leads from a schema (1) to a combinatorially equivalent schema (6). Conversely, it can be shown that it is always possible to find a finite succession of elementary transformations of the three types leading from a schema to any combinatorially equivalent schema.

Table 1 shows a numerical example of combinatorially equivalent schemata, generated in this case by a single cycle of pivot steps. The set shown is essentially complete, in the sense that all other schemata combinatorially equivalent to these may be found by permutations only. The pivots are starred to permit the reader to check the transformations, the

Table 1

A SMALL EXAMPLE OF COMBINATORIALLY EQUIVALENT DUAL LINEAR SYSTEMS

(1)

	y_3	y_4	y_5	
x_1	0	3	4	$= -y_1$
x_2	$-2*$	5	9	$= -y_2$
	$= x_3$	$= x_4$	$= x_5$	

describes the following pair of dual systems of linear equations:

$$- 2x_2 = x_3$$
$$3x_1 + 5x_2 = x_4$$
$$4x_1 + 9x_2 = x_5$$

$$3y_4 + 4y_5 = -y_1$$
$$-2y_3 + 5y_4 + 9y_5 = -y_2.$$

From the schema (1) the following combinatorially equivalent schemata are formed by successive pivot steps, employing the starred entries as pivots.

(2)

	y_2	y_4	y_5	
x_1	0	6/2	8/2	$= -y_1$
x_3	$-1/2$	$-5/2*$	$-9/2$	$= -y_3$
	$= x_2$	$= x_4$	$= x_5$	

(3)

	y_2	y_3	y_5	
x_1	$-3/5$	$6/5$	$-7/5$	$= -y_1$
x_4	$1/5$	$-2/5$	$9/5*$	$= -y_4$
	$= x_2$	$= x_3$	$= x_5$	

(4)

	y_2	y_3	y_4	
x_1	$-4/9*$	$8/9$	$7/9$	$= -y_1$
x_5	$1/9$	$-2/9$	$5/9$	$= -y_5$
	$= x_2$	$= x_3$	$= x_4$	

(5)

	y_1	y_3	y_4	
x_2	$-9/4$	$-8/4$	$-7/4$	$= -y_2$
x_5	$1/4$	0	$3/4*$	$= -y_5$
	$= x_1$	$= x_3$	$= x_4$	

(6)

	y_1	y_3	y_5	
x_2	$-5/3$	$-6/3*$	$7/3$	$= -y_2$
x_4	$1/3$	0	$4/3$	$= -y_4$
	$= x_1$	$= x_3$	$= x_5$	

(7)

	y_1	y_2	y_5	
x_3	$5/6$	$-3/6$	$-7/6$	$= -y_3$
x_4	$2/6$	0	$8/6*$	$= -y_4$
	$= x_1$	$= x_2$	$= x_5$	

(8)

	y_1	y_2	y_4	
x_3	$9/8$	$-4/8$	$7/8*$	$= -y_3$
x_5	$2/8$	0	$6/8$	$= -y_5$
	$= x_1$	$= x_2$	$= x_4$	

(9)

	y_1	y_2	y_3	
x_4	$9/7$	$-4/7$	$8/7$	$= -y_4$
x_5	$-5/7$	$3/7$	$-6/7$	$= -y_5$
	$= x_1$	$= x_2$	$= x_3$	

These nine schemata, along with those formed by row and column permutations, constitute the finite equivalence class (108 in all).

Table 2

A UNIMODULAR EXAMPLE OF COMBINATORIALLY EQUIVALENT
DUAL LINEAR SYSTEMS

(123:456)

	y_4	y_5	y_6	
x_1	0	-1	1	$=-y_1$
x_2	-1	-1	1	$=-y_2$
x_3	1	1	-1	$=-y_3$

$$= x_4 = x_5 = x_6$$

(124:356)

	y_3	y_5	y_6	
x_1	0	-1	1	$=-y_1$
x_2	1	0	0	$=-y_2$
x_4	1	1	-1	$=-y_4$

$$= x_3 = x_5 = x_6$$

(125:346)

	y_3	y_4	y_6	
x_1	1	1	0	$=-y_1$
x_2	1	0	0	$=-y_2$
x_5	1	1	-1	$=-y_5$

$$= x_3 = x_4 = x_6$$

(126:345)

	y_3	y_4	y_5	
x_1	1	1	0	$=-y_1$
x_2	1	0	0	$=-y_2$
x_6	-1	-1	-1	$=-y_6$

$$= x_3 = x_4 = x_5$$

(134:256)

	y_2	y_5	y_6	
x_1	0	-1	1	$=-y_1$
x_3	1	0	0	$=-y_3$
x_4	-1	1	-1	$=-y_4$

$$= x_2 = x_5 = x_6$$

(135:246)

	y_2	y_4	y_6	
x_1	-1	1	0	$=-y_1$
x_3	1	0	0	$=-y_3$
x_5	-1	1	-1	$=-y_5$

$$= x_2 = x_4 = x_6$$

(136:245)

	y_2	y_4	y_5	
x_1	-1	1	0	$=-y_1$
x_3	1	0	0	$=-y_3$
x_6	1	-1	-1	$=-y_6$

$$= x_2 = x_4 = x_5$$

(235:146)

	y_1	y_4	y_6	
x_2	-1	-1	0	$=-y_2$
x_3	1	1	0	$=-y_3$
x_5	-1	0	-1	$=-y_5$

$$= x_1 = x_4 = x_6$$

(236:145)

	y_1	y_4	y_5	
x_2	-1	-1	0	$=-y_2$
x_3	1	1	0	$=-y_3$
x_6	1	0	-1	$=-y_6$

$$= x_1 = x_4 = x_5$$

(245:136)

	y_1	y_3	y_6	
x_2	0	1	0	$=-y_2$
x_4	1	1	0	$=-y_4$
x_5	-1	0	-1	$=-y_5$

$$= x_1 = x_3 = x_6$$

(246:135)

	y_1	y_3	y_5	
x_2	0	1	0	$=-y_2$
x_4	1	1	0	$=-y_4$
x_6	1	0	-1	$=-y_6$

$$= x_1 = x_3 = x_5$$

(345:126)

	y_1	y_2	y_6	
x_3	0	1	0	$=-y_3$
x_4	1	-1	0	$=-y_4$
x_5	-1	0	-1	$=-y_5$

$$= x_1 = x_2 = x_6$$

(346:125)

	y_1	y_2	y_5	
x_3	0	1	0	$=-y_3$
x_4	1	-1	0	$=-y_4$
x_6	1	0	-1	$=-y_6$

$$= x_1 = x_2 = x_5$$

The full equivalence class contains 468 (= 13 × 36) schemata, i.e. the
above 13 and all their row and/or column permutations.

fractional entries being left unreduced as a futher aid. The complete equivalence class consists of all row and column permutations of these nine representations, or

$$9 \times 2! \times 3! = 9 \times 12 = 108$$

in all. The maximum possible number for a 2×3 matrix is $(2 + 3)! = 120$. However, because of the zero entry in schema (1), one representation and its 12 permutations are lacking.

Table 2 shows a second example which is convenient for computation, since its entries and all subdeterminants that can be formed from it have the value 1, -1 or 0, so that denominators do not occur. The reader may check that different sequences of elementary transformations may result in the same schema. Thus

$$(123:456) \rightarrow (124:356) \rightarrow (134:256)$$

and

$$(123:456) \rightarrow (143:256) \rightarrow (134:256).$$

DUAL LINEAR PROGRAMS.

We will now see that the algebra of dual linear systems, pivot steps, combinatorial equivalence, etc., developed above in <u>homogeneous</u> form (for an arbitrary number-field), can be employed in <u>nonhomogeneous</u> form (for an ordered number-field, such as real numbers or rational numbers) to treat dual linear programs and the Dantzig simplex method.

Let it be required to

minimize $UB + d$ constrained by $U \geqq 0$, $UA \geqq C$,   and

maximize $CV + d$ constrained by $AV \leqq B$, $V \geqq 0$

We reformulate these dual linear programs in the following schema:

(7)

where $a_{00} = -d$, $a_{0j} = -c_j$, $a_{i0} = -b_i$, $\xi = -UB - d$, $\eta = -CV - d$, $X^1 = U$, $X^2 = UA - C$, $Y^1 = AV - B$, $Y^2 = V$. The instructions minimize and maximize are interchanged because maximizing ξ and minimizing η are equivalent to minimizing $UB + d = -\xi$ and maximizing $CV + d = -\eta$. Note that the schema (7) differs from schema (1) in just two respects: the x's and y's are required to be nonnegative, and non-homogeneity is introduced by the border column with marginal labels 1 and ξ and by the border row with marginal labels 1 and η.

The Dantzig simplex algorithm consists of a non-repeating sequence of pivot steps, using pivots not in the border row and column. Hence it must end in some terminal schema after a finite number of steps, since it remains within a finite (combinatorial equivalence) class of schemata. The four possible terminal schemata are given in the following theorem.†

Theorem:

By a finite succession of pivot steps, excluding pivots in the border row and column, it is always possible to pass to a (combinatorially equivalent) terminal schema

which has one of the following four forms:

†A compact inductive proof (to be published elsewhere) has recently been devised by the author along lines suggested by the paper of R. E. Gomory and M. L. Balinski presented at this Symposium, and by G. B. Dantzig's inductive proof [see IBM Journal **4**, 1960, pp. 505–506] which assumes $B \geqq 0$.

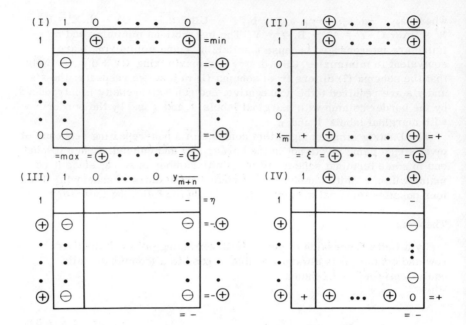

Here $+$, $\oplus$, $\bigcirc$, $\ominus$, and $-$ symbolize quantities which are positive, non-negative, zero, nonpositive, negative, respectively. Inside the four boxes above, they represent the actual nature of the entries $\bar{a}$ in the terminal schema (7). At the left and top margins, they represent values of $x_{\bar{1}}, \ldots,$ $x_{\bar{m}}$ and $y_{\overline{m+1}}, \ldots, y_{\overline{m+n}}$ which we will assign to determine the corresponding values of $x_{\overline{m+1}}, \ldots, x_{\overline{m+n}}$ and $y_{\bar{1}}, \ldots, y_{\bar{m}}$ at the bottom and right.

Terminal form (I) is the "successful" one, yielding optimal solutions to both programs. As indicated in the border row and column of (I), $-\bar{B} \leqq 0$ and $-\bar{C} \geqq 0$. If the marginal variables at the left and top are set equal zero, nonnegative x's and y's are determined at the bottom and right, while ξ and η take on the common value $\bar{a}_{00}$. Such feasible solutions with $\xi = \eta$ are necessarily optimal.

In terminal form (II) the border row $-\bar{C}$ is again nonnegative, but there is another row (shown above as the last row) which is nonnegative and has a positive entry in the border column $-\bar{B}$. The x-program is feasible but its objective function ξ is not bounded above. To see this take

$$x_{\bar{1}} = \cdots = x_{\overline{m-1}} = 0 \text{ and any } x_{\bar{m}} \geqq 0$$

to determine nonnegative x's at the bottom, and

$$\xi = \bar{a}_{00} + x_{\bar{m}} \bar{a}_m 0, \quad \bar{a}_m 0 > 0.$$

Then $\xi \longrightarrow +\infty$ as $x_{\bar{m}} \longrightarrow +\infty$, so no maximum exists. At the same time the y-program is infeasible, because $y_{\bar{m}} < 0$ for any assignment of nonnegative y's at the top.

Terminal form (III) is just the "negative transpose" of form (II). The x-program is now infeasible and the y-program is feasible but with objective η not bounded below.

In terminal form (IV) there is a nonnegative row (shown as the last row) with positive entry in the border column and a nonpositive column (shown as the last column) with negative entry in the border row. Any assignment of nonnegative x's at the left and nonnegative y's at the top makes $x_{\overline{m+n}} < 0$ and $y_{\overline{m}} < 0$. Hence neither program is feasible.

ANALYTIC GEOMETRY OF DUAL LINEAR PROGRAMS.

The constraint equations of the x-program in schema (7) specify a linear manifold

$$P : X^2 = X^1 A - C$$

in m+n-space. P is an m-dimensional linear manifold which can be obtained by translating the m-dimensional linear subspace $X^2 = X^1 A$ parallel to itself until it intercepts "the X^2-axis" (i.e., the n-subspace $X^1 = 0$) at the point $X^1 = 0$, $X^2 = -C$. Similarly the constraint equations of the y-program in schema (7) specify a linear manifold

$$Q : X^1 = X^2(-A^T) + B^T$$

in the $(m + n)$-space, where this matrix equation is obtained from $Y^1 = -AY^2 + B$ by transposing and then substituting X^1, X^2 for Y^{1T}, Y^{2T}. Q is an n-dimensional linear manifold which can be obtained by translating the n-dimensional linear subspace $X^1 = X^2(-A^T)$ parallel to itself until it intercepts "the X^1-axis" (i.e., the m-subspace $X^2 = 0$) at the point $X^1 = B^T$, $X^2 = 0$. Hence P and Q are linear manifolds of complementary dimensions, m and n, which are orthogonal because they are parallel, respectively, to the linear subspaces $X^2 = X^1 A$ and $X^1 = X^2(-A^T)$ that were seen to be orthogonal in our earlier discussion of (homogeneous) dual linear systems. Thus, in summary, P and Q are <u>complementary orthogonal</u> linear manifolds of dimensions m and n.

With respect to the partitioning $(x_1, \ldots, x_m \mid x_{m+1}, \ldots, x_{m+n})$ of the m+n coordinates into X^1 and X^2, indicated schematically in Fig. 2, P has the matrix A as "$X^2 : X^1$-slope" and $X^1 = 0$, $X^2 = -C$ as "X^2-intercept," while Q has the negative transpose matrix $-A^T$ as "$X^1 : X^2$-slope" and $X^1 = B^T$, $X^2 = 0$ as "X^1-intercept." Passing from

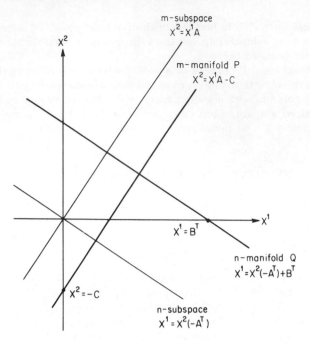

m−subspace
$x^2 = x^1 A$

m−manifold P
$x^2 = x^1 A - C$

x^2

$x^1 = B^T$

x^1

n−manifold Q
$x^1 = x^2(-A^T) + B^T$

$x^2 = -C$

n−subspace
$x^1 = x^2(-A^T)$

Fig. 2

by any succession of elementary transformations, excluding pivots in the border row and column, we get another ''slope-intercept'' representation,

$$X_\pi^2 = X_\pi^1 \overline{A} - \overline{C} \quad \text{and} \quad X_\pi^1 = X_\pi^2(-\overline{A}^T) + \overline{B}^T \tag{9}$$

of the <u>same</u> linear manifolds P and Q, because combinatorial equivalence leaves invariant the solution sets specifying P and Q. With respect to the new partitioning $(x_{\overline{1}}, \ldots, x_{\overline{m}} | x_{\overline{m+1}}, \ldots, x_{\overline{m+n}})$ of the m+n coordinates into X_π^1 and X_π^2, P has the matrix $\overline{A}$ as ''$X_\pi^2 : X_\pi^1$-slope'' and $X_\pi^1 = 0$, $X_\pi^2 = -\overline{C}$ as ''X^2-intercept,'' while Q has the negative-transpose matrix $-\overline{A}^T$ as ''$X_\pi^1 : X_\pi^2$-slope'' and $X_\pi^1 = \overline{B}^T$, $X_\pi^2 = 0$ as ''X_π^1-intercept.''

In terms of this analytic geometry, the aim of the Dantzig simplex method is to pass, if possible, from the initial ''slope-intercept'' represen-tation of P and Q, based on schema (7), to a terminal ''slope-intercept'' representation (9), based on schema (8), in which the intercepts $-\overline{C}$ and $\overline{B}^T$ will both be <u>nonnegative</u>. In terminal form (I) this aim is achieved. In terminal form (II) we fail because Q does not intersect the ''nonnegative (m+n)-orthant'' R, consisting of all points $X \geqq 0$, and so cannot have a nonnegative intercept at all; in terminal form (III) P does not intersect the orthant R; and in terminal form (IV) neither P nor Q intersects the orthant R.

HOMOGENEOUS LINEAR PROGRAMS.

The schema

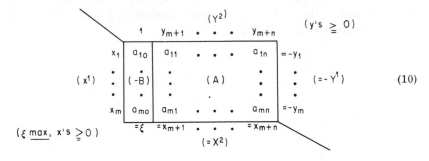

$$(10)$$

obtained by deleting the border row of schema (7), presents a mixed form of dual linear systems, one homogeneous and one not. Here the x-program, to maximize $\xi = -X^1 B$ (or minimize $X^1 B = -\xi$) constrained by $X^1 \geq 0$, $X^1 A = X^2 \geq 0$, is a "homogeneous linear program" with homogeneous objective-function and homogeneous constraints; and the y-program, to solve $B - AY^2 = Y^1 \geq 0$, $Y^2 \geq 0$, is merely a nonhomogeneous "feasibility program."

In this case the terminal schema (8) <u>with border row deleted</u> has one of just two possible forms:

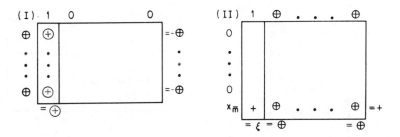

Form I shows that max $\xi = 0$ since $\xi \leq 0$ for any nonnegative x's and $\xi = 0$ trivially for all x's zero, and that the y-program has a feasible solution obtained by taking $y_{\overline{m+1}} = \cdots = y_{\overline{m+n}} = 0$. Form II shows that ξ is unbounded above since $\xi \to +\infty$ for $x_{\overline{1}} = \cdots = x_{\overline{m-1}} = 0$ and $x_{\overline{m}} \to +\infty$, and that the y-program is infeasible since $y_{\overline{m}} < 0$ for any assignment of non-negative values to $y_{\overline{m+1}}, \cdots, y_{\overline{m+n}}$.

These two mutually exclusive terminal forms provide simple construc-tive means of establishing transposition-duality theorems such as Farkas' theorem for linear inequalities. In particular, these two alternative forms can be used to prove the author's lemma [Ref. 2, page 5] from which classical and sharpened transposition-duality theorems follow [in Ref. 2].

MULTIPLICITY OF SOLUTIONS.

We now look again at form (I) of the terminal schema (8)—the "successful" form, in which the dual linear programs possess optimal solutions. If none of the m+n border entries (excluding $\bar{a}_{00}$) is zero, then the terminal schema has the form

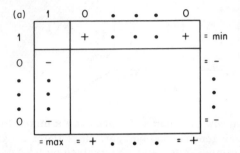

In this case both programs have unique optimal solutions.

On the other hand, if at least one of the m+n border entries is zero, then at least one of the dual programs has a multiplicity of solutions. In this event, it can be shown that a further succession of elementary transformations (excluding border entries as pivots) leads to a <u>normal</u> form of one of the following three types:

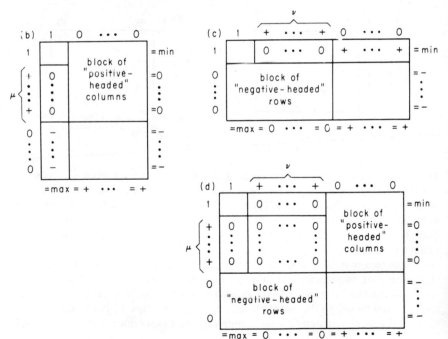

In a block of "positive-headed" columns each column has its first entry positive or a later entry positive which is preceded by zero entries only. In a block of "negative-headed" rows each row has its first entry negative or a later entry negative which is preceded by zero entries only.

In normal form (b), with its $\mu + 1$ by n block of "positive-headed" columns, the x-program has a μ-dimensional closed convex set of optimal solutions and the y-program has a unique optimal solution. The symbols + for the marginal x's indicate an optimal solution in the (relative) interior of the μ-dimensional convex set. The existence of such an optimal solution can be inferred from the block of "positive-headed" columns.

In normal form (c), with its m by $\nu + 1$ block of "negative-headed" rows, the x-program has a unique optimal solution and the y-program has a ν-dimensional closed convex set of optimal solutions: The symbols + and − for the marginal y's at top and −y's at right indicate an optimal solution in the (relative) interior of the ν-dimensional convex set. The existence of such an optimal solution can be inferred from the block of "negative-headed" columns.

In normal form (d), with its $\mu + 1$ by $n - \nu$ block of "positive-headed" columns and its $m - \mu$ by $\nu + 1$ block of "negative-headed" rows, the x-program has a μ-dimensional closed convex set of optimal solutions and the y-program has a ν-dimensional closed convex set of optimal solutions. Marginal symbols indicate (relative) interior solutions, as previously described.

The four forms (a), (b), (c), (d) exhaust the possibilities for optimal solutions in the "successful" case. For a specific pair of dual linear programs having optimal solutions, only one of the four forms can occur.

Note the full "complementary slackness" in the four forms (a), (b), (c), (d). Opposite each positive or zero component of the optimal x-solution indicated there is, without exception, a zero or positive component of the optimal y-solution indicated.

REFERENCES (to related papers of the author)

1. Gale, D., H. W. Kuhn, and A. W. Tucker, "Linear Programming and the Theory of Games," in Activity Analysis of Production and Allocation, T. C. Koopmans (ed.), Wiley, 1951.
2. "Dual Systems of Homogeneous Linear Relations," Linear Inequalities and Related Systems, H. W. Kuhn and A. W. Tucker (ed.), Annals Study 38, Princeton, 1956, pp. 3-18.
3. "A Combinatorial Equivalence of Matrices," Combinatorial Analysis, R. Bellman and M. Hall (ed.), Proceedings of Symposia in Applied Mathematics 10, American Mathematical Society, 1960, pp. 129-140.
4. "Abstract Structure of the Simplex Method," The RAND Symposium on Mathematical Programming, P. Wolfe (ed.), RAND Report R-351, 1960, pp. 33-34.

5. "Abstract Structure of Linear Programming," Information Processing
(Proceedings of the International Conference on Information
Processing, UNESCO, Paris, June 1959), UNESCO, Paris, 1960,
pp. 99-100.
6. "Solving a Matrix Game by Linear Programming," IBM Journal, Vol. 5,
Nov. 1960, pp. 507-517.
7. "Combinatorial Equivalence of Fair Games," Recent Advances in Game
Theory, M. Maschler (ed.), Princeton University Conference
publication, Princeton, 1962, pp. 277-282.
8. "Simplex Method and Theory," Mathematical Optimization Techniques,
R. Bellman (ed.), The University of California Press, 1963,
pp. 213-231.

A Mutual Primal-Dual Simplex Method

Michel L. Balinski
Ralph E. Gomory

1. SIMPLEX METHODS

A pair of dual linear programs

Primal (Row) Program

Minimize

$$y_0 \;\; = a_{00} \; + a_{01}y_{m+1} \; + \cdots + a_{0n}y_{m+n}$$

constrained by

$$^-y_1 \; = a_{10} \; + a_{11}y_{m+1} \; + \cdots + a_{1n}y_{m+n} \leqq 0$$

$$\vdots$$

$$^-y_m = a_{m0} + a_{m1}y_{m+1} + \cdots + a_{mn}y_{m+n} \leqq 0$$

$$y_{m+1} \geqq 0$$

$$\vdots$$

$$y_{m+n} \geqq 0$$

Dual (Column) Program

Maximize

$$x_0 \;\; = a_{00} \; + x_1 a_{10} \; + \cdots + x_m a_{m0}$$

constrained by

$$x_1 \geqq 0 \qquad\qquad (1.1)$$

$$\vdots$$

$$x_m \geqq 0$$

$$x_{m+1} = a_{01} \; + x_1 a_{11} \; + \cdots + x_m a_{m1} \geqq 0$$

$$\vdots$$

$$x_{m+n} = a_{0n} + x_1 a_{1n} + \cdots + x_m a_{mn} \geqq 0$$

is conveniently exhibited in the tableau

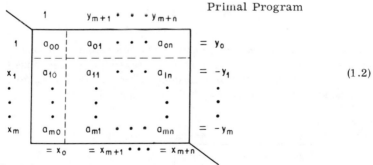

Primal Program

Dual Program

$$(1.2)$$

In the dual linear programs (1.1) or their tableau (1.2) $y_0, y_1, \ldots, y_m$, the <u>basic variables</u> of the primal program are expressed in terms of $y_{m+1}, \ldots, y_{m+n}$, the <u>nonbasic variables</u>; similarly, $x_0, x_{m+1}, \ldots, x_{m+n}$, the <u>basic variables</u> of the dual program, are expressed in terms of $x_1, \ldots, x_m$, the <u>nonbasic variables</u>.

A <u>pivot step</u> on (1.1) or (1.2) with pivot entry $a_{ij} \neq 0$ $(i, j \neq 0)$ is a

Gauss–Jordan or complete elimination step which simultaneously solves the ith (row) equation of the primal for y_{m+j} and the jth (column) equation of the dual for x_i, and uses these equations to eliminate y_{m+j} and x_i from the remaining row and column equations at the cost of introducing y_i and x_{m+j}. The y_{m+j} and x_i thereby become basic variables and y_i and x_{m+j} nonbasic variables. The pivot step with pivot entry $\alpha = a_{ij} \neq 0$ takes the tableau

$$
\begin{array}{c|cccc}
 & \cdots \; y_{m+j} \; \cdots & & \cdots & \\
\hline
 & & & & \\
x_i & \cdots \; \overset{*}{\alpha} \; \cdots \; \beta \; \cdots & & = -y_i & \\
 & & & & \\
 & \cdots \; \gamma \; \cdots \; \delta \; \cdots & & & \\
 & & & & \\
\hline
 & \cdots = x_{m+j} \cdots & & \cdots &
\end{array}
\tag{1.3}
$$

into the tableau

$$
\begin{array}{c|cccc}
 & \cdots \quad y_i \quad \cdots & & \cdots & \\
\hline
 & & & & \\
x_{m+j} & \cdots \; \alpha^{-1} \; \cdots \; \alpha^{-1}\beta \; \cdots & & = -y_{m+j} & \\
 & & & & \\
 & \cdots \; -\gamma\alpha^{-1} \; \cdots \; \delta - \gamma\alpha^{-1}\beta \; \cdots & & & \\
 & & & & \\
\hline
 & \cdots = x_i \; \cdots & & \cdots &
\end{array}
\tag{1.4}
$$

the other marginal variables and labels remaining in the same positions. Successive tableaus obtained by pivot steps simply reexpress the original pair of dual linear programs through different partitions into sets of basic and nonbasic variables. Any such tableau has the form

$$
\begin{array}{c|ccccc}
 & 1 & y'_{m+1} & \cdots & y'_{m+n} & \\
\hline
1 & a'_{00} & a'_{01} & \cdots & a'_{0n} & = y_0 \\
\hline
x'_1 & a'_{10} & a'_{11} & \cdots & a'_{1n} & = -y'_1 \\
\vdots & \vdots & \vdots & & \vdots & \vdots \\
x'_m & a'_{m0} & a'_{m1} & \cdots & a'_{mn} & = -y'_m \\
\hline
 & = x_0 & = x'_{m+1} & \cdots & = x'_{m+n} &
\end{array}
\tag{1.5}
$$

where the primed variables are a rearrangement of the original variables and the primed entries are determined by the succession of preceding pivot steps. Basic solutions to both programs are associated with any tableau (1.5); they obtain by setting the nonbasic variable equal to zero, thereby determining values for the basic variables $y_1' = -a_{10}', \ldots, y_m' = -a_{m0}'$, $y_0 = a_{00}' = x_0$, $x_{m+1}' = a_{01}', \ldots, x_{m+n}' = a_{0n}'$. If $-a_{10}' \geqq 0, \ldots, -a_{m0}' \geqq 0$ a basic feasible primal solution obtains; if $a_{01}' \geqq 0, \ldots, a_{0n}' \geqq 0$ a basic feasible dual solution obtains. If both primal and dual basic feasible solutions obtain, then they constitute optimal solutions to the programs.

A simplex method for solving a pair of dual linear programs is a finite sequence of tableaus exhibiting equivalent pairs of dual linear programs obtained by successive pivot steps, with prescribed pivot entry choice rules, which obtain a tableau exhibiting optimal solutions to both programs, or the noncompatibility of the primal and/or dual constraints. Letting $\oplus$ denote nonnegative entries, and $\ominus$ nonpositive entries, these cases can be exhibited in tableau form:

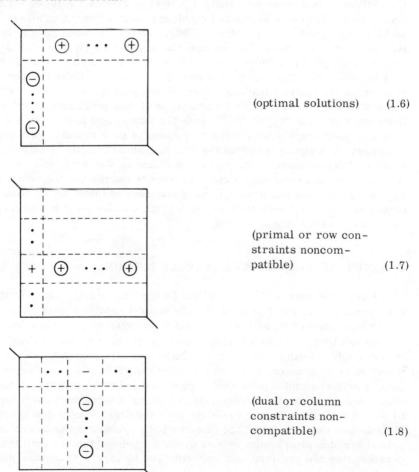

(optimal solutions)   (1.6)

(primal or row constraints noncompatible)   (1.7)

(dual or column constraints noncompatible)   (1.8)

A <u>primal (dual) simplex method</u> is a simplex method beginning with a tableau exhibiting a primal (dual) basic feasible solution with pivot steps which maintain primal (dual) feasibility in each succeeding tableau. A primal (dual) <u>pivot choice rule</u> is as follows:

If a tableau (1.5) does not exhibit optimal solutions to both programs there must exist a $a'_{0j} < 0$ for some j (a $a'_{i0} > 0$ for some i). Either (a) every entry in the column of $a'_{0j} < 0$ is nonpositive (every entry in the row of $a'_{i0} > 0$ is nonnegative) or (b) there exist positive (negative) entries. (a) The tableau exhibits the noncompatibility of the dual constrains (of the primal constraints).
(b) Choose as pivot entry $a'_{kj} > 0$ ($a'_{i\ell} < 0$) satisfying

$$\frac{a'_{k0}}{a'_{kj}} = \max_{a'_{sj} > 0} \frac{a'_{s0}}{a'_{sj}} \quad \left(\frac{a'_{0\ell}}{a'_{i\ell}} = \max_{a'_{is} < 0} \frac{a'_{0s}}{a'_{is}} \right)$$

If an initial tableau does not exhibit a primal (dual) basic feasible solution some special device is introduced enabling consideration of an allied problem whose solution provides a primal (dual) basic feasible solution for the original problem. The original Dantzig method [1] is a primal simplex method; the Lemke paper [5] describes a dual simplex method.

The proofs for termination of a simplex method in a finite number of pivot steps use the fact that any tableau is uniquely determined by its associated nonbasic variables (of primal or of dual programs) and that there exist at most $\binom{n+m}{m} = \binom{n+m}{n}$ possible sets of nonbasic variables. Then any pivot steps assuring that no tableau is ever repeated guarantees finiteness. The finiteness proof for a primal (dual) simplex method in which no "degeneracies" occur, i.e., in which $a'_{i0} < 0$, $i \neq 0$, ($a'_{0j} > 0$, $j \neq 0$) is clear, for each pivot step strictly decreases (increases) the value of a'_{00} and thereby assigns an order to the sequence of tableaus. If, however, degeneracy occurs, some form of lexicographic order must be introduced to avoid the possibility of cycling.

2. A MUTUAL PRIMAL-DUAL SIMPLEX METHOD

We describe here a simplex method for directly solving any pair of dual linear programs (1.1) or (1.2). The method specifies pivot choices for any tableau whether feasible or not, and degenerate or not, which lead to a tableau exhibiting a primal feasible solution (or, primal infeasibility) and then to a tableau exhibiting optimal solutions to both programs (or, primal objective unboundedness and dual infeasibility). This is accomplished by using a primal simplex pivot choice rule until primal degeneracies occur; then a dual simplex pivot choice rule is used on a subtableau corresponding to primal zero valued basic variables until the degeneracies are resolved. If "sub-dual degeneracies" are or come to be present in the subtableau, a primal simplex pivot choice rule is used on a sub-subtableau until these degeneracies are resolved, and so forth. The hierarchy of tableau, sub-

tableau, sub-subtableau, etc., is used to establish a hierarchy of goals
which are associated with every tableau. Every pivot step leads to a
strict "improvement" in one of the goals, with goals higher in the
hierarchy remaining unaffected. This serves to order the sequence of
tableaus, thus assuring termination of the method in a finite number of
pivot steps.

Every tableau (1.5) in the sequence of tableaus obtained by successive
pivot steps has associated with it a hierarchy of numbered subtableaus each
with a distinguished entry (and hence row and column). Odd numbered subtableaus k have the form

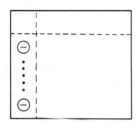

("primal or row
feasible form")   (2.1)

with $\alpha(k) \geq 1$, the number of rows, and $-\beta(k)$, the value of the distinguished
entry. Even numbered subtableaus k have the form

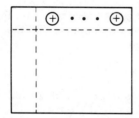

("dual or col-
umn feasible
form")   (2.2)

with $\alpha(k) \geq 1$, the number of columns, and $\beta(k)$, the value of the distinguished entry.

The hierarchy of subtableaus associated with a tableau is initiated as
follows. Subtableau 1 consists of all columns and all rows of (1.1) with
$a_{i0} \leq 0$, with distinguished entry some $a_{h0} > 0$ (if all $a_{i0} \leq 0$ and the entire
tableau is in primal feasible form, the entire tableau is taken as "sub-
tableau 1"). Given any tableau suppose a subtableau k in primal (dual)
feasible form has been defined with distinguished row R and column C.
If C (if R) contains zeros and R is not all nonnegative (C is not all nonpositive), a subtableau k + 1 in dual (primal) feasible form is defined as
consisting of rows (columns) corresponding to the zeros of C (of R),
columns (rows) corresponding to the nonnegative entries of R (nonpositive entries of C), with distinguished entry some negative entry of R
(some positive entry of C). Schematically,

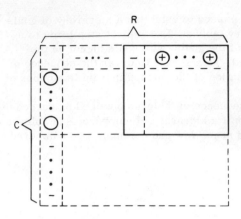

where the whole diagram represents a primal feasible form subtableau k, and the subdiagram enclosed in solid lines a dual feasible form subtableau k + 1.

Associate with any tableau and its subtableaus a hierarchy of goals with goal k (k = 1, 2, ...) being to pivot to obtain a new tableau whose new subtableau k (if it exists) has $\alpha(k)$ larger, or, has $\alpha(k)$ unchanged but $\beta(k)$ larger; while $\alpha(i)$, $\beta(i)$ for i < k remain unchanged.

Suppose, now, that we have reached the pth tableau with entries a_{ij}^p, along with its well-defined hierarchy of subtableaus and their associated values $(\alpha_p(k), \beta_p(k))$. We describe the choice of pivot entry to obtain the $(p + 1)^{-th}$ tableau and the hierarchy of subtableaus associated with the $(p + 1)^{-th}$ tableau.

Rules

Suppose the subtableau with highest index K is in primal (dual) feasible form.

(a) Apply the primal (dual) simplex pivot choice rule (see above) to the subtableau K. Maintain same hierarchy of subtableaus, except K. Redefine K and any subsequent ones if possible.

    If rule (a) is not applicable then one of the two possibilities (b) or (c) must hold.

(b)

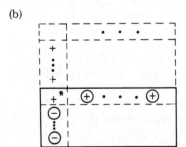 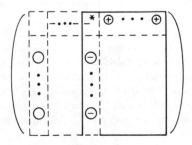

Choose as pivot entry the distinguished entry. Maintain same hierarchy of subtableaus, except $K-1$ and K. Redefine $K-1$ and any subsequent ones if possible.

(c)

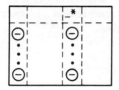 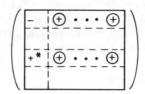

Choose as pivot entry the negative (positive) entry in the distinguished row (column) whose column is nonpositive (whose row is nonnegative). Maintain same hierarchy of subtableaus except K. Redefine K and any subsequent ones if possible.

Finally, if ever the choice of pivot entry is an element of the first row (some a_{0j}^p) or of the first column (some a_{i0}^p), <u>stop</u>.

If the process is stopped because the choice of pivot entry is a_{00}^p, solutions to both programs obtain; if it is stopped because the choice of pivot entry is some a_{i0}^p, the primal or row program has no feasible solution; if it is stopped because the choice of pivot entry is some a_{0j}^p, the primal program is in feasible form but the dual or column program has no feasible solution.

If the pivot entry is chosen according to (a) either there is no Kth subtableau or $\alpha_{p+1}(K) \geqq \alpha_p(K)$ and if $\alpha_{p+1}(K) = \alpha_p(K)$ then $\beta_{p+1}(K) > \beta_p(K)$ (due to the absence of "Kth degeneracies"); while $\alpha_{p+1}(i) = \alpha_p(i)$ and $\beta_{p+1}(i) = \beta_p(i)$ for $i < K$ since the pivot entry has zeros in rows and columns that could have an effect on these values. If the pivot is chosen according to (b) either there is no $(K-1)$th subtableau or $\alpha_{p+1}(K-1) > \alpha_p(K-1)$ [see subtableau in (b)]; while again, and for the same reason, $\alpha_{p+1}(i) = \alpha_p(i)$ and $\beta_{p+1}(i) = \beta_p(i)$ for $i < K-1$. Finally, if the pivot is chosen according to (c), either there is no Kth subtableau or $\alpha_{p+1}(K) > \alpha_p(K)$ [see subtableau in (c)], while again $\alpha_{p+1}(i) = \alpha_p(i)$ and $\beta_{p+1}(i) = \beta_p(i)$ for $i < K$. Therefore, this choice of pivot entry and assignment of subtableaus always leads to strict improvement in some goal, thereby ordering the sequence of tableaus obtained in successive pivot steps. As noted above, this suffices to assure termination of the method in a finite number of pivot steps.

A. W. Tucker has pointed out that the inductive counterpart of this construction leads to a particularly simple and appealing proof of termination. The induction is made on the number $m+n$ of primal (or dual) variables.

3. SOME REMARKS

It is perhaps of interest to review the primal-dual algorithm of Dantzig, Ford, and Fulkerson [2] to enable comparison with the algorithm proposed here. By our definition the primal-dual algorithm is a simplex method applied not directly to the problem as stated but to an "extended" problem and with rather special pivot choice rules.

The problem to be solved and its dual as posed in [2] is

Primal (Row) Program

Minimize   Maximize

$y_0 = a_{01}y_{m+1} + \cdots + a_{0n}y_{m+n}$ $x_0 = x_1a_{10} + \cdots + x_ma_{m0}$

constrained by   constrained by   (3.1)

$a_{10} = a_{11}y_{m+1} + \cdots + a_{1n}y_{m+n} \geq 0$ $x_{m+1} = -a_{01} + x_1a_{11} + \cdots + x_ma_{m1}$

$\vdots$ $\vdots$

$a_{m0} = a_{m1}y_{m+1} + \cdots + a_{mn}y_{m+n} \geq 0$ $x_{m+n} = -a_{0n} + x_1a_{1n} + \cdots + x_ma_{mn}$

$y_{m+1} \geq 0, \ldots, y_{m+n} \geq 0$ $x_{m+1} \geq 0, \ldots, x_{m+n} \geq 0$

where it is assumed that the dual program has a feasible solution (if not, the extra variable $y_{m+n+1} \geq 0$ and constraint $y_{m+1} + \cdots + y_{m+n} + y_{m+n+1} = a_{m+1,0}$ with $a_{m+1,0}$ arbitrarily large can be added to the primal program, thus assuring an easily found initial feasible solution to the new dual problem). An "extended" problem and its dual is then defined which can be exhibited in the tableau

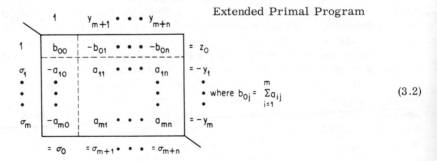

Extended Primal Program

where $b_{0j} = \sum_{i=1}^{m} a_{ij}$ (3.2)

Dual to
Extended Primal Program

Here $z_0 = y_1 + \cdots + y_m$ is to be minimized subject to the row equations and $y_1 \geq 0, \ldots, y_{m+n} \geq 0$, and σ_0 is to be maximized subject to the column equations and $\sigma_1 \geq 0, \ldots, \sigma_{m+n} \geq 0$. Since $a_{i0} \geq 0$, (3.2) is in primal feasible form. Notice that a feasible solution exists to the primal program (3.1) only if min $z_0 = 0$.

The primal-dual algorithm can be described as consisting of a finite sequence of tableaus, starting with (3.2), obtained by successive pivot steps. With every tableau is associated a (not necessarily basic) feasible solution $\{x_0, x_1, \ldots, x_{m+n}\}$ to the dual or column program (3.1). Then, given any tableau and its associated $\{x_0, x_1, \ldots, x_{m+n}\}$ a primal pivot choice rule is used on a subtableau consisting of all columns except for those corresponding to y_{m+j} for which $x_{m+j} > 0$ ($j = 1, \ldots, n$). If a primal pivot choice cannot be made the subtableau can only be in ("optimal") form (1.6) and one of three cases for the complete tableau must hold:

(a) The distinguished entry has value 0
(b) The distinguished entry has positive value and the distinguished row some negative entry
(c) The distinguished entry has positive value and the distinguished row all nonnegative entries.

If (a) occurs the values exhibited for $y_{m+1}, \ldots, y_{m+n}$ in the tableau and the associated values for $\{x_0, x_1, \ldots, x_{m+n}\}$ constitute optimal solutions to the dual programs (3.1). This is easily established since these values are feasible and they make $x_0 = y_0$. If (b) occurs then a new feasible solution to the dual program (3.1) with values $\{\bar{x}_0, \bar{x}_1, \ldots, \bar{x}_{m+n}\}$ is associated with the whole tableau, with $\bar{x}_0 > x_0$. Namely,

$$\bar{x}_k = x_k + \Theta\sigma_k, \qquad \Theta = \min_{\substack{\sigma_{m+j} < 0 \\ (j = 1, \ldots, n)}} -\frac{x_{m+j}}{\sigma_{m+j}} \quad (> 0) \tag{3.3}$$

where σ_k is the value exhibited by the tableau of the variable σ_k. (This step can easily be described as a "partial pivot step" in which the values of the x_k are altered by the values of the σ_k). If (c) occurs then the minimum value of z_0 is attained but is positive, implying no feasible solution to the primal problem (3.1) exists.

In "geometric language" the primal–dual algorithm defines a sequence of successive neighboring vertices or extreme points of the convex polyhedron defined by the constraints of the extended primal program (3.2). It also defines a sequence of feasible points in the dual program (3.1) space which are not, in general, extreme. In fact the straight line joining two successive such dual feasible points [defined by (3.3)] usually lies in the interior of the dual convex polyhedral region (3.1), while the points themselves (except possibly the first) lie on some face of the polyhedron. In contrast, the mutual primal–dual simplex method defines a sequence of successive neighboring points (vertices after feasibility is achieved) of the convex polyhedron defined by the constraints of the original primal problem and visits only extreme points. Although there is no logical basis for comparison, intuition would seem to indicate that the computational advantage resides with "sticking to extreme points of the original problem."

Of course, the primary interest of these methods is in their application to highly "degenerate" problems, for example the assignment and trans-portation problems. The primal-dual algorithm applied to an assignment or transportation problem is the Hungarian method [4] (though it must be said that it was the ideas of the Hungarian method which led to the development of the primal-dual algorithm). Contrary to widely held beliefs, the Hungarian method (as described in [6]) can be described as a simplex method in much the same way as the primal-dual algorithm has been above. In fact, every operation as given in [6] has its simplex method counterpart. It is hoped (and expected) that the application of the idea of the mutual primal-dual simplex method to the assignment and transportation problems will lead to a new computational method which may better the efficiency of the Hungarian method, for in these problems the geometric considerations alluded to above appear to be important. Finally, the application of these ideas to the network flow algorithms, and particularly the "out of kilter" method of Fulkerson [3], should lead to further insight concerning the relationship between these specialized algorithms and simplex methods.

REFERENCES

1. Dantzig, G. B., "Maximization of a Linear Function of Variables Subject to Linear Inequalities," Chapter XXI of Activity Analysis of Production and Allocation (edited by T. C. Koopmans), Cowles Commission Monograph No. 13, Wiley, New York, 1951.
2. Dantzig, G. B., L. R. Ford, and D. R. Fulkerson, "A Primal-Dual Algorithm for Linear Programs," Paper 7 of Linear Inequalities and Related Systems (edited by H. W. Kuhn and A. W. Tucker), Annals of Mathematics Study No. 38, Princeton University Press, Princeton, 1956.
3. Fulkerson, D. R., "An Out of Kilter Method for Minimal Cost Flow Problems," RAND Corporation, P-1825, April 5, 1960.
4. Kuhn, H. W., "The Hungarian Method for the Assignment Problem," Naval Research Logistics Quarterly, Vol. 2, 1955, pp. 83-97.
5. Lemke, C. E., "The Dual Method of Solving the Linear Programming Problem," Naval Research Logistics Quarterly, Vol. 1, 1954, pp. 48-54.
6. Munkres, J., "Algorithms for the Assignment and Transportation Problems," Journal of the Society for Industrial and Applied Mathematics, Vol. 5, 1957, pp. 32-38.

On Cone Functions

Edmund Eisenberg

I. INTRODUCTION

In what follows we shall be concerned with generalizations of the following "feasibility" theorem of Fan, Glicksberg, and Hoffman:

Theorem 1: Let K be a convex subset of R^n, let $f_i : K \rightarrow R$, $i = 1, \ldots, m$, be convex functions, then one, and only one, of the following conditions holds:

There is an x in K such that

$$f_i(x) < 0 \quad \text{for all } i = 1, \ldots, m. \tag{1}$$

There exists a $y = (y_1, \ldots, y_m) \in R^m$ such that

$$y \neq 0, \ y_i \geq 0 \quad \text{for all } i, \quad \text{and}$$

$$\sum_{i=1}^{m} y_i f_i(x) \geq 0 \quad \text{for all } x \in K. \tag{2}$$

The concept underlying our discussion is that of "convexity with respect to a fixed cone C in R^m" of a function $F : K \rightarrow R^m$ (K being a convex subset of R^n). This definition turns out to be a natural extension of the case where each component of F is convex in the usual sense, the last being essentially the assumption of Theorem 1. One can then generalize Theorem 1 and its variants to a system of "cone" inequalities (Theorems 3 and 4).

The results discussed here can be shown to hold in a more general framework than that imposed here, e.g., R^n and R^m may be replaced by normed linear spaces satisfying appropriate conditions. However, to be specific, we limit our discussion to the more restricted situation.

---

†This research has been partially supported by the Office of Naval Research under Contract Nonr-222(83) with the University of California. Reproduction in whole or in part is permitted for any purpose of the United States Government.

II. BASIC DEFINITIONS

For each positive integer k we denote by R^k the set of all real k-tuples $x = (x_1, \ldots, x_k)$; we sometimes write R in place of R^1. If K is a subset of R^k we say K is <u>convex</u> providing $\lambda x + (1 - \lambda)x'$ is in K whenever x and x' are both in K, λ is in R, and $0 \leq \lambda \leq 1$. If C is a nonempty subset of R^k we say that C is a <u>(convex) cone</u> providing C is convex and λx is in C whenever x is in C and λ is non-negative real number. Henceforth, we shall use "cone" and "convex cone" interchangeably. Equivalently, C is a cone providing $\lambda x + \mu x'$ is in C whenever x and x' are in C and λ and μ are both non-negative real numbers. If x and z are in R^k, $x = (x_1, \ldots, x_k)$, $z = (z_1, \ldots, z_k)$ we write xz^T for the inner product of x and z, i.e.,

$$xz^T = \sum_{i=1}^{k} x_i z_i$$

We say that $x \leq z$ providing $x_i \leq z_i$ for all $i = 1, \ldots, k$. For any subset S of R^k we define the <u>polar</u> of S to be:

$$S^* = R^k \cap \{z \mid zx^T \leq 0 \quad \text{for all } x \in S\}$$

It is clear that S^* is always a closed, convex cone.

Whenever we use topological concepts such as "open set," "closed set," etc., it will always be with respect to the usual norm, i.e., $\|x\| = (xx^T)^{1/2}$. We shall use the following fundamental separation theorem, the proof of which may be found in the literature (cf. [1] or [4]).

Theorem 2: Let K be a convex subset of R^n, x_0 a point in R^n but x_0 not contained in K. Then there must exist $a \in R^n$, $\alpha \in R$, such that $a \neq 0$ and

$$ax_0^T \geq \alpha$$

$$ax^T \leq \alpha \quad \text{for all } x \in K \tag{3}$$

If, in addition, K is closed, then we may assume that $ax_0^T > \alpha$.

III. CONE FUNCTIONS

The fact that the conclusion of Theorem 1 holds does not depend, in the last analysis, so much on the properties of each of the functions $f_1, \ldots, f_m$ individually but rather on the way f_i are inter-related, that is the relevant properties are those of the vector valued function $F(x) = (f_1(x), \ldots, f_m(x))$. Specifically, to say that each f_i is convex on K is equivalent to saying that:

for each $x, z \in K$, $\quad \lambda \in R$, $\quad 0 \leq \lambda \leq 1$, $\quad G(x, z, \lambda) \leq 0$ $\qquad$ (4)

where

$$G(x, z, \lambda) = F(\lambda x + (1 - \lambda)z) - \lambda F(x) - (1 - \lambda)F(z) \qquad (5)$$

One observes that (4) simply states that $G(x, z, \lambda)$ is in R_+^m, the non-negative orthant of R^m, whenever $x, z \in K$ and $\lambda \in [0,1]$. It is clear then that a very natural generalization of (4) is the requirement that $G(x, z, \lambda)$ always be in some fixed cone C in R^m. For functions F satisfying that condition one would expect an analog of Theorem 1 to hold with "$f_i(x) < 0$ all i," replaced by "$F(x) \in$ Interior (C)" and "$y_i \geq 0$" replaced by "$y \in C*$." This turns out to be the case and is formalized in Theorem 3. Accordingly, we have:

Definition: Let K be a convex subset of R^n. Let C be a cone in R^m, $F : K \to R^m$. We say that F is a C-function providing $G(x, z, \lambda) \in C$ whenever $x, z \in K$, $\lambda \in [0,1]$ and G is as in (5).

Let us illustrate the preceding definition. For $m = 1$, the only cones C in R^m are the origin, closed rays from the origin, and the whole line. In the first case a C-function is a linear function; in the second case, a C-function is convex or concave according to whether C is the negative or positive ray; in the last case, any function $F : K \to R^m$ is a C-function. In general, if $C = R^m$ then every function is a C-function, however Theorem 3 is then of no interest because $F(x)$ is in the interior of C for any x in R^n.

For $m = 2$, the class of C-functions does not provide a great amount of new information either, primarily because the closed cones in R^2 are rather simple; they are all finite cones (i.e., the sum of a finite number of rays).

In general, whenever C is a finite cone in R^m, that is there exists an $m \times k$ matrix A such that $C = R^m \cap \{y \mid yA \leq 0\}$, C-functions may be characterized quite simply as follows: let $a^1, \ldots, a^k$ be the column vectors of A then $F : K \to R^m$ is a C-function if, and only if, each of the functions $F(x)a^1, \ldots, F(x)a^k$ is convex on K. Thus, if C is a finite cone, then questions concerning C-functions can be formulated in terms of a finite collection of convex functions, which may, in turn, be accomplished by reference to Theorem 1 or variants of it.

In case C is not a finite cone (and thus $m \geq 3$) the property that F is a C-function can no longer be stated in terms of convexity of each of a finite collection of functions. In fact, a way of looking at Theorem 3 in case C is not a finite cone is that it represents a generalization of Theorem 1 to a system with infinitely many inequalities.

IV. OPEN FEASIBILITY

The analog of Theorem 1 for C-functions is:

Theorem 3: Suppose C is a cone in R^m with nonempty interior. Let K be a convex subset of R^n and $F : K \to R^m$ be a C-function. We conclude that one, and only one, of the following statements holds:

There is an x such that

$$x \in K \text{ and } F(x) \in \text{Interior } (C) \tag{6}$$

There exists a $y \in C^*$ such that

$$y \neq 0 \text{ and } F(x)y^T \geq 0 \text{ for all } x \in K \tag{7}$$

Before proving Theorem 3 we require two simple preliminary results:

    Lemma 1: Suppose C is a convex cone in R^m, $y \in$ Interior (C), $z \in C^*$, $z \neq 0$. Conclusion: $yz^T < 0$.

    Proof: Suppose y,z are as above and $yz^T \geq 0$. Since $y \in$ Interior (C), there exists a $\delta > 0$ such that $w \in C$ whenever $||w - y|| \leq \delta$. Let w be any such vector, then $v = 2y - w$ is also in C because $||v - y|| = ||y - w|| \leq \delta$. Now $y = \frac{1}{2}(v + w)$, $v, w \in C$ and $z \in C^*$; thus $0 \leq yz^T = \frac{1}{2}(vz^T + wz^T) \leq 0$ and $wz^T = 0$. We have just demonstrated that $wz^T = 0$ for all w in some neighborhood of y, contradicting $z \neq 0$.

    Lemma 2: Let C be a convex cone in R^m, $y \in$ Interior (C), $z \in C$, $\lambda \in R$, $\lambda > 0$. Conclusion: $y + z \in$ Interior (C) and $\lambda y \in$ Interior (C).

    Proof: Since y is in the interior of C we know there exists a $\delta > 0$ such that $u \in C$ whenever $||u - y|| \leq \delta$; however if $||(y + z) - w|| \leq \delta$ then $||y - (w - z)|| \leq \delta$ and $w - z \in C$. But then $w = (w - z) + z \in C$ because C is a cone. Thus $y + z$ is in the interior of C. For the statement: $\lambda y \in$ Interior (C) we have the following sequence of implications: $||\lambda y - w|| \leq \lambda \delta \Longrightarrow ||y - \lambda^{-1}w|| < \delta \Longrightarrow \lambda^{-1}w \in C \Longrightarrow w \in C$, and thus λy is in the interior of C.

    Proof of Theorem 3: The proof that (6) and (7) cannot hold simultaneously follows from Lemma 1 because if (6) and (7) both hold then $y \in C^*$, $x \in K$, $F(x) \in$ Interior (C) and from Lemma 1 we have $F(x)y^T < 0$, contradicting (7). To show that either (6) or (7) holds, let us assume that (6) is false and consider the set:

$$Y = \{y \mid \text{there exist } x \in K \text{ and } \bar{y} \in \text{Int}(C) \text{ with } y = \bar{y} - F(x)\}$$

The fact that (6) is false is equivalent to saying that $y = 0$ is not a member of Y. We intend to show that Y is convex, then apply Theorem 2 to Y, knowing it does not contain the origin, and thus obtain a y satisfying (7). Suppose we have $y_1, y_2 \in Y$, i.e., there exist $\bar{y}_1, \bar{y}_2 \in \text{Int}(C)$, and $x_1, x_2 \in K$ with $y_k = \bar{y}_k - F(x_2)$, $k = 1, 2$. Now if $\lambda \in (0, 1)$ we wish to show $y = \lambda y_1 + (1 - \lambda)y_2 \in Y$. Let $u = \lambda \bar{y}_1 + (1 - \lambda)\bar{y}_2$, $v = F(\lambda x_1 + (1 - \lambda)x_2) - \lambda F(x_1) - (1 - \lambda)F(x_2)$ then $y = u + v - F(\lambda x_1 + (1 - \lambda)x_2)$. However, $\bar{y}_1 \in$ Interior (C) and $(1 - \lambda)\bar{y}_2 \in C$ thus, by Lemma 2, $u \in \text{Int}(C)$. Also, because F is a C-function, $v \in C$ and thus by Lemma 1 we have $u + v \in$ Interior (C), showing that Y is convex.

    Next, we know that Y is convex and $y_0 = 0$ is not an element of Y.

Applying Theorem 2 we know that there exists an $a \in R^m$, $a \neq 0$, $\alpha \in R$ such that:

$$0 \geq \alpha$$

$$a[\bar{y} - F(x)]^T \leq \alpha \qquad \text{all } \bar{y} \in \text{Int}(C), \, x \in K \tag{8}$$

From Lemma 2 we know that $\lambda \bar{y} \in \text{Interior } (C)$ whenever $\lambda > 0$ and $y \in \text{Interior } (C)$, thus we may infer from (8) that:

$$\bar{y}a^T \leq 0 \qquad \text{all } \bar{y} \in \text{Int}(C) \tag{9}$$

Now, by assumption there is a $\bar{y}_0 \in \text{Interior } (C)$, so that if $y \in C$, $\lambda \geq 0$ then by Lemma 2 $\lambda y + y_0 \in \text{Interior } (C)$. We see then, using (9), that

$$\lambda y a^T + \bar{y}_0 a^T \leq 0 \qquad \text{all } \lambda \geq 0, \, y \in C$$

Thus, $ya^T \leq 0$ whenever $y \in C$ and consequently $\underline{a \in C^*}$. Furthermore, for each $\lambda > 0$ we have by Lemma 2 $\lambda \bar{y}_0 \in \text{Interior } (C)$, thus from (8) we have

$$\lambda \bar{y}_0 a^T - F(x)a^T \leq \alpha \leq 0 \qquad \text{all } \lambda > 0, \, x \in K$$

whence it follows that $\underline{F(x)a^T \geq 0}$ for all $x \in K$ and of course $a \neq 0$; thus $y = a$ satisfies all the conditions in (7).

As an immediate corollary of Theorem 3 one obtains Theorem 1 by letting C be the nonpositive orthant and $F(x) = (f_1(x), \ldots, f_m(x))$.

V. CLOSED FEASIBILITY

The statement of Theorem 1, and similarly of Theorem 3, is in many respects inadequate. Frequently, one encounters situations where it is required, within the framework of Theorem 1 as an example, to find an $x \in K$ with $f_i(x) \leq 0$ for all i, rather than the strict inequalities of (1). It would seem reasonable, given that K is closed, to replace (1) by weak inequalities and correspondingly replace (2) by a statement of the form: "there is a $y = (y_1, \ldots, y_n) \in R^m$ such that $y \geq 0$ and $\sum_{i=1}^{m} y_i f_i(x) > 0$ for all $x \in K$," and expect a true statement. This turns out to be indeed the case when K is a linear variety and all the f_i are linear. In general, with the f_i being convex, it may happen that there is no $x \in K$ such that $f_i(x) \leq 0$ for all i, and yet there is no $y \in R_+^m$ with $\sum_i y_i f_i(x) > 0$ for all $x \in K$. This is illustrated by: $m = 2$, $n = 2$, $K = R_+^2$, $f_1(x_1, x_2) = x_2 - 1$, $f_2(x_1, x_2) = 1 - x_1 x_2(x_1 + x_2)^{-1}$ $(f_2(0) = 0)$. It is readily checked that f_1 and f_2 are convex; furthermore if $f_1(x) \leq 0$ and x in K then either $x_1 x_2(x_1 + x_2)^{-1} < x_2 \leq 1$ or $x_2 = 0$, in each case we have $f_2(x) > 0$. However, if there exist $y_1, y_2 \geq 0$ such that $y_1 f_1(x) + y_2 f_2(x) > 0$ for all x in K, i.e.,

$$y_1(x_2 - 1) + y_2\left[1 - \frac{x_1 x_2}{x_1 + x_2}\right] > 0 \quad \text{all } x_1, x_2 \geq 0$$

then, letting $x_2 = 0$, $x_1 = 1$, we get $y_2 > y_1$. On the other hand, letting x_1 become arbitrarily large, we must have: $y_1(x_2 - 1) + y_2(1 - x_2) > 0$ for all $x_2 \geq 0$, and thus $y_1 = y_2$, a contradiction.

It thus follows, in particular, that the rephrasing of Theorem 3 in terms of weak inequalities, i.e., replacing "Interior (C)" in (6) and "$F(x)y^T \geq 0$" by "$F(x)y^T > 0$" in (7), need not always hold. We can show, however, that under certain regularity assumptions on C, K and F the statement in question does hold:

Theorem 4: Let C, K and F be as in Theorem 3, let

$$H = \{y \mid \text{there exist } x \text{ in } K \text{ and } \bar{y} \text{ in } C \text{ with } y = \bar{y} - F(x)\}$$

then H is a convex set. Furthermore, if H is also closed and the statement:

There is an x such that

x is in K and F(x) is in C   (10)

is false, then the statement:

There is a $y \in C^*$ such that

$F(x)y^T > 0$ for all x in K   (11)

is a true statement.

Proof: As in the proof of Theorem 3, the convexity of H is a direct consequence of the assumptions on C, K and F. The fact that (10) is false is equivalent to saying that $y_0 = 0$ is not in H, thus if H is <u>closed</u> and convex then, from Theorem 2, it follows that there must exist an $a \in R^m$ and $\alpha \in R$ such that:

$$ay^T \leq \alpha < ay_0^T = 0, \quad \text{all } y \in H \tag{12}$$

i.e.,

$$a\bar{y}^T - F(x)a^T \leq \alpha < 0, \quad \text{all } \bar{y} \in C, x \in K \tag{13}$$

However, $0 \in C$ and also $\lambda y \in C$ whenever $y \in C$ and $\lambda \geq 0$ and thus we infer from (13) that:

$$ay^T \leq 0 \qquad \text{all } y \in C$$

$$-F(x)a^T \leq \alpha < 0 \qquad \text{all } x \in K \tag{14}$$

and (14) states that the vector a is precisely the one required for (11). Q.E.D.

Note: We have stated Theorem 4 in slightly different form than Theorem 3; however it is quite obvious that (10) and (11) cannot be simultaneously true.

It is worth noting that the condition that H be closed though certainly sufficient in order that (11) hold in case (10) is false, is by no means necessary. For one thing, as is clear from the proof of Theorem 4, we can actually get a positive lower bound for $F(x)y^T$ on K (namely the number $-\alpha$) when H is closed; however, consider the case $m = n = 1$, $K = R_+$, $C = R_-$ and $F(x) = (1 + x)^{-1}$. Then F is a C-function (because F is convex) but $x \in K$, $F(x) \in C$ has no solution because $F(x) > 0$ for all $x \in K$. Now $C^* = R_+$ and in fact any $y \in C^*$ will satisfy (11). Nevertheless, no matter what $y \in C^*$ we take, $F(x)y^T$ has no positive lower bound as x ranges over K (by letting x become arbitrarily large we can make $F(x)$ arbitrarily close to zero). Thus, in this case, H is not closed. Other situations where the closedness of H is not necessary arise when K itself is not closed.

In a future note it is intended to relate to cone functions the following characterization of differentiable convex functions: Suppose K is an open convex set in R^n, $f : K \rightarrow R$ has all second partial derivatives then f is convex if, and only if, the quadratic form $[f_{ij}(x)]$ is positive-semi-definite for each x in K.

REFERENCES

1. Berge, Claude, Espaces Topologiques, Dunod, Paris, 1959.
2. Dantzig, George B., Linear Programming and Extensions, to be published soon by the Princeton University Press.
3. Fan, Ky, Irving Glicksberg and A. J. Hoffman, "Systems of Inequalities Involving Convex Functions," Proc. Amer. Math. Soc., Vol. 8, 1957, pp. 617-622.
4. Fenchel, W., "Convex Cones, Sets and Functions," Princeton University Lecture Notes, Spring 1953.

THE MAXIMUM TRANSFORM

R. E. Bellman and *W. Karush*

ABSTRACT

Let the <u>maximum</u> (additive) <u>convolution</u> of two functions f and g on n nonnegative real variables $x = (x_1, x_2, \ldots, x_n)$ be defined by $(f \oplus g)(x) = \max_{u+v=x} [f(u) + g(v)]$, $u \geq 0$, $v \geq 0$, $x \geq 0$. This operation arises in optimization problems and prompts the consideration of transformations Tf having the "disassociative" property $(*) T(f \oplus g) = Tf + Tg$.

Let the <u>maximum transform</u> $Mf = \varphi$ be defined by $\varphi(\xi) = - \sup_{x \geq 0} [-(\xi,x) + f(x)]$, where $(\xi,x) = \sum_{i=1}^{n} \xi_i x_i$. Then (1) M has property (*); (2) $Mf = M\bar{f}$, where $\bar{f}$ is the concave increasing "cap" of f; (3) if $Mf = \varphi$, then $M\varphi = \bar{f}$. [For closely related results, see W. Fenchel, "Convex Cones, Sets, and Functions," Lecture notes (1953), Department of Mathematics, Princeton University; there, φ is called the conjugate of f, for f concave.] Let T be an arbitrary transformation with property (*). Then (i) $Tf = T\bar{f}$; (ii) $T = \lambda M$ for some transformation λ such that $\lambda(\varphi_1 + \varphi_2) = \lambda\varphi_1 + \lambda\varphi_2$. This shows that M is a "best" transformation T. Similar results apply to the product convolution $(F \otimes G)(x) = \max_{u+v=x} [F(u) \times G(v)]$.

The paper also includes a discussion of applications and of certain extensions of the theory.

REPRESENTATIONS FOR THE GENERALIZED INVERSE OF MATRICES PARTITIONED AS A = [U,V]

R. E. Cline

ABSTRACT

The generalized inverse of a matrix has been used by L. D. Pyle in the development of an "interior gradient projection method" for solving linear programming problems. It is of interest, therefore, to have techniques for determining the generalized inverse of a matrix.

Let A designate any m by n matrix with complex elements. Partition A arbitrarily as $A = [U,V]$ where the submatrices U and V have k and $n - k$ columns, respectively, $1 \le k \le n - 1$. Designating the generalized inverse of any matrix, X, as X^+ and the conjugate transpose as $X*$ then

Theorem 1

Let $C = (I - UU^+)V$

and

$$K = [I + (I - C^+C)V*U^{+*}U^+V(I - C^+C)]^{-1}$$

Then

$$A^+ = \begin{bmatrix} U^+ - U^+VC^+ - U^+V(I - C^+C)KV*U^{+*}U^+(I - VC^+) \\ C^+ + (I - C^+C)KV*U^{+*}U^+(I - VC^+) \end{bmatrix}$$

Proceeding in the opposite direction, suppose that $A = [U,V]$ and that A^+ is known. Partition A^+ as $A^+ = \begin{bmatrix} G \\ H \end{bmatrix}$ where G has the dimensions of U* and H has the dimensions of V*. Then

Theorem 2

$$U^+ = G[I + V(I - HV)^+H]\{I - [H - (I - HV)$$
$$\times (I - HV)^+H]^+[H - (I - HV)(I - HV)^+H]\}$$
$$V^+ = H[I - U(I - GU)^+G]\{I - [G - (I - GU)$$
$$\times (I - GU)^+G]^+[G - (I - GU)(I - GU)^+G]\}$$

Using Theorems 1 and 2 and various corollaries derived therefrom, it is possible to combine the interior gradient projection method and the simplex method into a technique for solving linear programming problems.

REFERENCES

1. Greville, T. N. E., "Some Applications of the Pseudoinverse of a
    Matrix," SIAM Review, Vol. 2, 1960.
2. Penrose, R., "A Generalized Inverse for Matrices," Proceedings of the
    Cambridge Philosophical Society, Vol. 51, 1955.
3. Pyle, L. D., "The Generalized Inverse in Linear Programming,"
    Doctoral Thesis, Purdue University, Lafayette, Ind., January 1960.
[This material will be contained in the author's Ph.D. thesis at Purdue
University.]

On Unimodular Sets of Vectors

Isidore Heller

The definition of the concept of a unimodular set (Section 2) is followed by a discussion of some of its properties (Sections 3-5) and a study of inter-relations between classes of maximal unimodular sets (Sections 6-9). The main result is a theorem on the union of two unimodular sets (Section 9). The paper constitutes an introductory presentation on the subject.

1. INTRODUCTION

In order to relate the definition to some familiar concept we recall that given a group G of transformations on a set (say a vectorspace) V, and given a subset S of V, it is frequently of interest to study the structure of the subgroup H of G which is defined as the set of all those transformations that leave S invariant, that is

$$H = \{T \in G \mid T(S) \subset S\} \tag{1.1}$$

where $T(S)$ is a short notation for the image of S under T. Conversely, given a subgroup H of G one may be interested in those subsets S of V for which H is the associated subgroup defined by (1.1).

It is a slight generalization of (1.1) if, instead of the subgroup H, we consider the subset H' of all those elements of G which map a specified subset S_0 of S into S, that is

$$H' = \{T \in G \mid T(S_0) \subset S\} \tag{1.2}$$

where H' will in general no longer be a group.

Conversely, having specified an S_0 for each S of V, and given a subgroup H of G, one may ask: for which subsets S of V is the [by definition (1.2)] associated H' contained in H. This question, for a special choice of S_0, G and H, leads to the definition of unimodular sets.

---

†This work was sponsored in part by the RAND Corporation and in part by the National Science Foundation.

2. DEFINITION

For the purpose of this paper V is assumed to be a vector space of finite dimension over the field of real numbers. The G denotes the group of nonsingular linear transformations on V, U the unimodular subgroup of G, that is, the group of transformations whose determinants have absolute value 1. Without further loss of generality, the consideration is restricted to those subsets of V which are not contained in a proper subspace of V; then each such subset S contains some basis B of V.

Definition: In V, a subset S containing some basis B of V is unimodular iff every nonsingular linear transformation that maps B into S is a unimodular transformation. Or, briefly:

S is unimodular iff, for some basis $B \subset S$,
$$\{T \in G \mid T(B) \subset S\} \subset U. \tag{2.1}$$

This definition does not depend on the particular choice of B in S. That is, if B and C are two bases in S,

$$H_1 = \{T \in G \mid T(B) \subset S\}, \qquad H_2 = \{T \in G \mid T(C) \subset S\}$$

and $H_1 \subset U$, then $H_2 \subset U$. To see this, let $T(C) \subset S$ and $T_1(B) = C$. Then $T_1 \in U$, and from $T(C) = TT_1(B) \subset S$ it follows that $TT_1 \in U$. Hence, T $= TT_1 T_1^{-1} \in U$. This proves the asserted independence from the choice of basis, and thereby the equivalence of definition (2.1) to the formally more restrictive definition:

S is unimodular iff $\{T \in G \mid T(B) \subset S$ for some basis $B \subset S\} \subset U$ (2.2)

or, in other words:

S is unimodular iff every two bases in S are related by a unimodular transformation.   (2.3)

3. PROPERTIES

The motivation for the study of the concept will become clear from its properties. We shall discuss a few which are characteristic, that is, constitute necessary and sufficient conditions for a set S to be unimodular and can therefore serve as alternative definitions.

Let $B = \{b_1, b_2, \ldots, b_n\}$ be a basis in S, and

$$d = \sum \lambda_i b_i \tag{3.1}$$

be the representation of a vector d of S in terms of B.

If $\lambda_j \neq 0$, replacement of b_j in B by d yields a new basis D in S. If T is a linear transformation mapping B onto D, the matrix $\overline{T}$ of T with respect to the basis B is a permutation matrix except for the column of the jth unit vector which is replaced by the sequence of the λ_i. Therefore, the determinant of $\overline{T}$ and hence of T equals $\pm \lambda_j$.

If S is unimodular, then T is a unimodular transformation, and hence λ_j must equal ± 1. Since λ_j was assumed $\neq 0$ but otherwise arbitrary, we have for unimodular S the property that in (3.1) $\lambda_i \in \{0, 1, -1\}$ for $i = 1, 2, \ldots, n$ and for every pair d, B in S.

Conversely, if a set S has that property, a linear transformation T satisfying $T(B) = D$ will certainly have determinant ± 1 and hence be unimodular whenever the two bases B and D of S coincide in all but one vector (and trivially so when they coincide in all). If B and D have less or no vectors in common, it is readily seen that appropriate successive replacement of vectors in B by vectors of D leads to a sequence of bases $B = B_0, B_1, B_2, \ldots, B_k = D$, where every two consecutive ones differ in only one vector. Hence, T can be represented as a product of unimodular transformations $T = T_k \ldots T_2 T_1$, where $T_i(B_{i-1}) = B_i$ $(i = 1, 2, \ldots, k)$. Therefore, T is unimodular.

The two statements combine to this:

S is unimodular iff, for every basis $B \subset S$, and every $d \in S$,
the coordinates of d with respect to B equal 0, 1, or -1.   (3.2)

Considering a fixed basis in S, it becomes immediate from (3.2) that a unimodular set in V_n contains at most 3^n vectors. It should also be noted that weakening the conditions of (3.2) to read "some" instead of "every" in either one of the two occurrences would render them insufficient. However, the following weaker form still holds:

S is unimodular iff, for every basis $B \subset S$ and every $d \in S$,
the coordinates of d with respect to B are integers.   (3.3)

To see that the condition of (3.3) implies the condition of (3.2), assume that the latter is not satisfied; that is, that for some basis B and element d of S, the representation (3.1) contains some $\lambda_i \neq 0, 1, -1$. But then replacement of b_i in B by d yields a new basis in which b_i has the representation

$$b_i = \frac{1}{\lambda_i} (d - \sum_{r \neq i} \lambda_r b_r)$$

where the coefficient of d is not an integer. Hence, the condition of (3.3) is not satisfied either.

For later reference we mention some other formulations of (3.3). If J(S) denotes the integral span of S, that is, the set of all linear combinations of elements of S with integral coefficients, then (3.3) reads

S is unimodular iff, for every basis B of S, $S \subset J(B)$.   (3.4)

Further, since $J(B) \supset S \Leftrightarrow J(B) \supset J(S)$, and since $B \subset S$ implies $J(B) \subset J(S)$, we have

S is unimodular iff, for every basis B in S, $J(B) = J(S)$.   (3.5)

Each of the last two statements can be taken as the definition of unimodular sets S in a free abelian group of rank n, if B denotes a set of n linearly independent elements in S (and hence in general not necessarily a basis for the entire group).

If S is in Euclidean R^n, it is convenient to interpret a basis B, in some arrangement of its vectors, as matrix, $\bar{B}$, and to represent a linear transformation T by its matrix $\bar{T}$. Then the relation $T(B) = D$ implies $\bar{T} \bar{B} = \bar{D} \bar{P}$ where $\bar{P}$ is an adequately chosen permutation matrix. Since the determinant $|\bar{P}| = \pm 1$, T is unimodular iff $|\bar{B}| = \pm |\bar{D}|$. Hence, by (2.3),

S is unimodular iff the determinants associated with bases in
S have the same absolute value.   (3.6)

In R^n the set S itself can, of course, for some arrangement of its vectors as columns, be interpreted as matrix. However, care must be taken not to confuse the concept of a unimodular set with the (classical) concept of a unimodular transformation. To enforce the necessary distinction in cases where the set S takes visually the form of a matrix A, we shall have to specify whether we are concerned with A as representative of a set of vectors or as matrix of a linear transformation, whenever this is not clear from the context. In order to avoid too lengthy terminology, we propose that

In conjunction with a matrix, "set" shall mean "set of
columns"   (3.7)

so that when D is a matrix, expressions like "the set D is unimodular," "D is a unimodular set," will have a clear meaning.

To obtain still another property of unimodular sets, we consider the system of linear equations

$Ax = b$ (3.8)

where A is a matrix of n rows and of rank n, and hence the number of columns $k \geq n$.

Solving (3.8) can be interpreted as finding a representation of b in terms of the set A. If the columns of A entering a particular representation with nonzero coefficients are linearly independent, then b appears represented in terms of some basis B of A, and the solution is called "basic."

The existence of an integral solution is equivalent to $b \in J(A)$. If the set A is unimodular and $b \in J(A)$, then (3.5) asserts $b \in J(B)$ for every basis B in A, that is, all basic solutions are integral. Conversely, if for every $b \in J(A)$ all basic solutions are integral, that is, $b \in J(B)$ for every B in A, then $J(A) = J(B)$ for every B in A, and, by (3.5), A is a unimodular set. Hence, we have

> The set A is unimodular iff the system $Ax = b$ has the property
> that all its basic solutions are integral whenever b is such that
> an integral solution exists, that is, for every $b \in J(A)$.   (3.9)

Properties (3.2) and (3.9) suggest the role of the concept in applications. Heuristically, the concept actually arose from these properties; (3.9) has to do with the existence of integral-valued solutions to systems of linear equations, matrix games and linear programs; (3.2) relates to the possibility of simplified computational algorithms for the solution of such systems: it states that the unimodular property amounts to the absence of division in those iterative computational algorithms where each step involves transition from one basis to another by the exchange of a vector in the basis.

4. GENERAL DEFINITION

The definition (2.1) was restricted to those sets S in V_n which contain a basis of V_n. If S in V_n is of dimension $k < n$, the restriction in (2.1) is circumvented by considering S in its linear span $L(S)$ which is a V_k. Then the definition (2.1) reads:

> In V_n a set S of dimension $k \leq n$ is unimodular iff, for a given
> subset B_k of k linearly independent vectors of S, every
> nonsingular linear transformation on the subspace $V_k = L(S)$,
> which maps B_k into S is a unimodular transformation on V_k.   (4.1)

This definition obviously includes (2.1) as the special case $k = n$.

Of the statements in Sections 2 and 3, all but one remain true for $k < n$ if "transformation" is taken to mean "transformation on $L(S)$," [hence, in particular, U is taken to denote the group of unimodular transformations on $L(S)$], and "basis" is taken to mean "basis of $L(S)$," that is, a maximal set of linearly independent vectors in S. The excepted statement is (3.6), which, for the general case $k \leq n$, will receive a more direct formulation in (4.3) and (4.4) below. For this purpose, we first note:

> If a linear transformation T on V_n preserves the dimension of
> S, then S is unimodular iff $T(S)$ is unimodular.   (4.2)

Proof. The restriction of T to $V_k = L(S)$, as isomorphism between V_k

and $W_k = L(T(S))$, preserves linear relations both ways. Hence, (3.2) implies (4.2).

If now A is a matrix of rank k, $A_k = \{a_{i_1}, a_{i_2}, \ldots, a_{i_k}\}$ is a set of k independent rows of A and T is the orthogonal projection on the linear span of the set of unitvectors $\{e_i \mid a_i \in A_k\}$, then (4.2) yields

> If A is of rank k and A_k is a submatrix consisting of k linearly independent rows of A, then A is a unimodular set iff A_k is a unimodular set. (4.3)

Application of (3.6) to A_k of (4.3) yields

> If A is of rank k, then the set A is unimodular iff in each set A_k of k rows in A, the nonvanishing minors of order k have the same absolute value. (4.4)

It should be noted that this value may vary with the choice of A_k. Application of (4.4) to A and its transpose A' suggests:

> If A is of rank k, then the sets A and A' are both unimodular iff all nonvanishing minors of order k have the same absolute value. (4.5)

Proof. To see that the condition is necessary, let M_1, M_2 be nonsingular minors of order k, R_1 and C_1 the set of rows and the set of columns of A which contain M_1. Then the minor P common to R_1 and C_2 is nonsingular, since the k by k coefficient matrix D representing C_1 in terms of C_2, that is, satisfying $C_2 D = C_1$, also satisfies $PD = M_1$. If the sets A and A' are both unimodular, then by (4.4) $||P|| = ||M_1||$ and $||P|| = ||M_2||$.

Of methodological interest for subsequent investigations is

> If S is unimodular, every subset of S is unimodular. (4.6)

Proof. Let S be of dimension k, R a subset of dimension $r \leq k$, and $d \in R$ represented in terms of a basis B in R by $d = \lambda_1 b_1 + \lambda_2 b_2 + \cdots + \lambda_r b_r$. Obviously d has the same representation in a basis of S which contains B. If S is unimodular, the λ_i satisfy (3.2) and hence R is unimodular.

As a statement on matrices, (4.6), in conjunction with (4.3) and (4.4), reads: Let A be a matrix of rank k and let C, a submatrix consisting of columns of A, have rank r. If the nonvanishing minors of order k in some fixed set A_k of k linearly independent rows of A have the same absolute value, then, in each set C_r of r rows of C, the nonvanishing minors of order r have the same absolute value. It should be noted that the conclusion is not generally true for A_r instead of C_r. Hence, A_r need not be a unimodular set when the set A is unimodular.

5. TOTALLY UNIMODULAR SETS

Let S be a set of dimension n in V_{n+k}. If n linearly independent vectors in S are chosen as basis for a coordinate system in $L(S)$, then S appears represented by a set $\bar{S}$ in R^n and $\bar{S}$ contains the unit vectors of R^n. Since the transition from $L(S) = V_n$ to R^n is an isomorphism, it is obvious that S is unimodular iff $\bar{S}$ is unimodular. Hence, the study of unimodular sets reduces to the study of those unimodular sets in R^n which contain the unit vectors of R^n (and hence, in particular, are of dimension n). Such a set, viewed as matrix (for some arrangement of its vectors), is of the form $A = [I_n \mid D]$ where I_n denotes the identity matrix of order n.

$A = [I_n \mid D]$ is a unimodular set iff every nonvanishing minor in D (in A) has absolute value 1. (5.1)

Proof. Sufficiency is obvious. Necessity follows from (3.6) and the observation that the k columns of A which contain a given minor of order k can be completed to a basis by columns of I_n.

Originally the connotation "unimodular" was used by A. J. Hoffman and J. B. Kruskal [2] to characterize sets satisfying the condition of (5.1). In the context of our definition (2.1) it now becomes desirable to distinguish the special character of these sets. Following a suggestion of C. Berge and A. J. Hoffman, we define

In R^n, the set A is totally unimodular iff every nonvanishing minor in A has absolute value 1. (5.2)

The following two statements are obvious:

If A is a matrix and A' its transpose, then the set A' is totally unimodular iff the set A is totally unimodular. (5.3)

In R^n the set A is unimodular iff there exists a nonsingular linear transformation T such that T(A) is a totally unimodular set. (5.4)

6. CLASSES OF MAXIMAL UNIMODULAR SETS

For brevity of exposition we return again to the practice adopted in Section 2: for a given V_n consideration shall be restricted to sets of dimension n.

Since subsets of a unimodular set are unimodular, the question as to which sets are unimodular reduces to the question as to which are the maximal unimodular sets. Clearly, a maximal unimodular set contains the nullvector and with each vector also its negative.

Further, since nonsingular linear transformations preserve the unimodular and maximality property of a set, two sets related by such transformation can be considered as equivalent, thus leading, for each dimension n, to a collection of equivalence classes of maximal unimodular sets.

For a given dimension the number of distinct classes is finite, as is immediate from (3.2).

One particular class, which we shall term "Class I," is well known. A member of Class I is, if we disregard the nullvector, a set D of the form

$$D = \{a_i - a_j\} \quad (i \neq j; \; i,j = 1, 2, \ldots, n+1) \tag{6.1}$$

where the a_i are n+1 affine independent vectors, that is

$$\sum_{i=1}^{n+1} \lambda_i a_i = 0, \; \sum_{i=1}^{n+1} \lambda_i = 0 \Longrightarrow \lambda_i = 0 \quad (i = 1, 2, \ldots, n+1) \tag{6.2}$$

Geometrically D can be interpreted as the set of edges of an n-simplex in affine space (each edge taken in both orientations).

In R^n a member D of Class I which contains the unit vectors can be viewed graphtheoretically as the set of paths in an oriented tree of n+1 vertices, if a path is represented by an incidence column which characterizes the edges of the tree that are contained in the path.

Major facts on Class I are the following:

(i) A unimodular set of dimension n belongs to Class I iff it consists of $n(n+1)$ vectors (not counting the nullvector).

(ii) A maximal unimodular set of dimension n which is not in Class I consists of less than $n(n+1)$ vectors; such sets exist iff $n \geq 4$. \hfill (6.3)

For proofs and further details see [3] and [4]. For another graph-theoretical interpretation and related facts see [2], [5] and [6]; for related concepts [7].

While the preceding sections dealt with properties of an individual unimodular set, the consideration now turns to properties that inter-relate distinct classes of unimodular sets; it is the objective of the remaining sections to obtain a fundamental property of this nature, namely the theorem of Section 9. This is achieved by a series of auxiliary statements concerning the representation of vectors in terms of certain bases (Section 7), the structure of the intersection of two unimodular sets (Section 8) and finally a comparison of classes of unimodular sets (Section 9).

7. REPRESENTATIONS

Notation.

When $A \cap B = 0$, we shall write $A + B$ instead of $A \cup B$, and when $A \subset B$, we will write $B - A$ for the complement of A in B. Conversely, the use of this notation shall mean that the assumptions are satisfied.

Further, for a set consisting of a single element x, we shall write x instead of $\{x\}$ whenever the meaning is clear from the context. Thus, if $B = \{b_1, b_2, \ldots, b_n\}$, the notation $A = B - b_1 + a$ shall mean $A = \{a, b_2, \ldots, b_n\}$.

Finally, if B is a basis and x a vector in V_n, $R(x,B)$ denotes the set of vectors in B that enter, with nonzero coefficients, the representation of x in terms of B. That is, if $x = \Sigma\lambda_i b_i$, then $R(x,B) = \{b_i \mid \lambda_i \neq 0\}$.

For later reference we first translate a few trivial facts into this notation.

$$\text{If } B \text{ and } C \text{ are bases, then } R(x,B) = R(x,C) \Longleftrightarrow R(x,B) \subset C \qquad (7.1)$$

If B is a basis, and $C = B - b + x$, then C is a basis iff
$b \in R(x,B)$ $\qquad\qquad (7.2)$

If B is a basis, $b \in R(x,B) \cap R(y,B)$, and $C = B - b + x$, then C is a basis and

(i) $R(y,C) \supset R(x,B) \cup R(y,B) - R(x,B) \cap R(y,B) + x$

(ii) $R(y,C) \subset R(x,B) \cup R(y,B) - b + x$

(iii) $R(y,C) \cap [B - R(y,B)] = R(x,B) \cap [B - R(y,B)]$

(iv) $R(y,C) \cap [B - R(x,B)] = R(y,B) \cap [B - R(x,B)]$ $\qquad (7.3)$

In (7.3) the last two relations are immediate consequences of the first two. We shall have use for the following form of (iii) and (iv):

If B is a basis, $B^+ \subset B$, $b \in R(x,B) \cap R(y,B)$, $b \in' B^+$ and $C = B - b + x$, then C is a basis such that $B^+ \subset C$ and

(i) $R(x,B) \cap B^+ = 0 \Rightarrow R(y,C) \cap B^+ = R(y,B) \cap B^+$

(ii) $R(y,B) \cap B^+ = 0 \Rightarrow R(y,C) \cap B^+ = R(x,B) \cap B^+$. $\qquad (7.4)$

The following statement concerns representations within a unimodular set.

Let B be a basis in S, $x \in S$, $y \in S$, and

$$R(x,B) \cap R(y,B) = B^0 \neq 0,$$

so that in the representations

$$x = L_1(B^0) + L_2(B - B^0)$$
$$y = L_3(B^0) + L_4(B - B^0),$$

the linear combinations L_1 and L_3 have all nonzero coefficients. If S is unimodular, then

$$L_3(B^0) = \pm L_1(B^0).\tag{7.5}$$

Proof. By (3.2) all nonzero coefficients are ± 1. Hence, (7.5) can be violated only when B^0 contains at least two vectors, say b_1, b_2, and

$$x = \epsilon_1 b_1 + \epsilon_2 b_2 + \cdots$$
$$y = \epsilon_1 b_1 - \epsilon_2 b_2 + \cdots$$

where $\epsilon_i = \pm 1$. But then in the basis $C = B - b_1 + x$, the representation of y would be

$$y = x - 2\epsilon_2 b_2 + \cdots$$

where b_2 has the coefficient ± 2, in contradiction to (3.2). Hence, (7.5) must hold.

We note that for unimodular sets (7.5) implies a sharper form of (7.3), namely,

If S is unimodular, B a basis in S, $x \in S$, $y \in S$, and $b \in R(x,B) \cap R(y,B)$, then, for the basis $C = B - b + x$, $R(y,C) = R(x,B) \cup R(y,B) - R(x,B) \cap R(y,B) + x$. $\tag{7.6}$

8. INTERSECTION OF TWO UNIMODULAR SETS

Assumptions and notation.

Throughout this section we are concerned with two sets, F and G, such that

    (i)   both are unimodular

    (ii) each contains with x also $-x$

    (iii) their intersection $F \cap G = D$ contains a common basis B

    (iv) there exist $f \in F$ and $g \in G$ such that $f \neq \pm g$ and
       $R(f,B) = R(g,B) = B^0$. $\tag{8.0}$

Without loss of generality, we may then assume

$$f = b_1 + b_2 + \cdots + b_k - (b_{k+1} + b_{k+2} + \cdots + b_{k+s})$$
$$g = b_1 + b_2 + \cdots + b_k + b_{k+1} + \cdots + b_{k+s}$$

for which we symbolically write

$$f = \Sigma B^+ - \Sigma B^-$$
$$g = \Sigma B^+ + \Sigma B^- = \Sigma B^0. \tag{8.1}$$

Obviously

$$f \in F - D, \ g \in G - D \tag{8.2}$$

since otherwise f and g would both belong to the same unimodular set, and (8.1) would contradict (7.5).

We denote by

$$\mathcal{B} = \{B \mid B \text{ is a basis and } B^0 \subset B \subset D\}. \tag{8.3}$$

For the intersection D the given assumptions imply a special structure which will emerge from the study of representations in the remainder of this section.

$$x \in D, \ B \in \mathcal{B}, \ R(x,B) \cap B^+ \neq 0 \Rightarrow R(x,B) \cap B^- = 0. \tag{8.4}$$

Proof. In the representation of x consider the nonzero coefficients of vectors in B^+ and B^- in conjunction with (7.5) and (8.1); since $x \in F$, those coefficients must be of opposite sign; since $x \in G$, they must be of the same sign. Hence, $R(x,B)$ cannot intersect both B^+ and B^-.

$$x \in D, \ y \in D, \ B \in \mathcal{B}, \ R(x,B) \cap B^+ \neq 0, \ R(x,B) \cap R(y,B) \neq 0$$
$$\Longrightarrow R(y,B) \cap B^- = 0. \tag{8.5}$$

Proof. Assume $R(y,B) \cap B^- \neq 0$. Then, by (8.4), $R(x,B) \cap B^- = 0$ and $R(y,B) \cap B^+ = 0$, hence $R(x,B) \cap R(y,B) \cap B^0 = 0$. If now $b \in R(x,B) \cap R(y,B)$, then $b \in' B^0$, hence $C = B - b + x \in \mathcal{B}$. Then (7.6) implies $R(y,C) \cap B^0 \supset [R(x,B) \cup R(y,B)] \cap B^0$, hence $R(y,C)$ intersects B^+ as well as B^-, in contradiction to (8.4).

If we define

$$D^+ = \{x \in D \mid R(x,B) \cap B^+ \neq 0 \text{ for some } B \in \mathcal{B}\}$$
$$D^- = \{x \in D \mid R(x,B) \cap B^- \neq 0 \text{ for some } B \in \mathcal{B}\}$$
$$D' = D - (D^+ \cup D^-) \tag{8.6}$$

then obviously $D^+ \supset B^+$ and $D^- \supset B^-$. Furthermore,

$$D^+, \ D^-, \ D' \text{ are pairwise disjoint.} \tag{8.7}$$

Proof. By its definition, D' is disjoint from D^+ and D^-. To show that D^+ and D^- are disjoint, assume $x \in D^+ \cap D^-$. Then, for some $A \in \mathcal{B}$ and some $C \in \mathcal{B}$, we will have $R(x,A) \cap B^+ \neq 0$, $R(x,C) \cap B^- \neq 0$. Let $H = B^0 \cup R(x,A) \cup K$ be a maximal independent set in $B^0 \cup R(x,A) \cup R(x,C)$, and B an extension of H to a basis in D. Then, noting that $R(x,B) = R(x,A)$, we have $H \subset B \in \mathcal{B}$, $R(x,B) \cap B^+ \neq 0$. Note that $B \not\supset R(x,C)$ since otherwise uniqueness of representation would imply $R(x,C) = R(x,B)$ and hence by (8.4), $R(x,C) \cap B^- = 0$.

Let $y \in R(x,C)$, $y \in' B$. The assumption on H implies $R(y,B) \subset H$. Then $R(x,B) \cap R(y,B) \neq 0$, since otherwise $y \in C$ and $R(y,B) \subset B^0 \cup K \subset C$ would imply $R(y,B) = R(y,C) = y \in B$, contradicting $y \in' B$. Hence, by (8.5), $R(y,B) \cap B^- = 0$. Therefore, if we pass from the representation of x in terms of C, $x = L(R(x,C))$, to the representation of x in terms of B, $x = L_1(R(x,B))$, by means of substituting for each y in $R(x,C)$ which is not in B its expression $y = L_2(R(y,B))$, then these substitutions will not affect elements in B^-, and hence lead to $R(x,B) \cap B^- = R(x,C) \cap B^- \neq 0$ in contradiction to (8.4). This completes the proof of (8.7).

$$x \in D, \ y \in D, \ B \in \mathfrak{B}, \ R(x,B) \cap B^+ \neq 0, \ R(x,B) \cap R(y,B) \neq 0$$
$$\Rightarrow y \in D^+. \tag{8.8}$$

Proof. $R(y,B) \cap B^+ \neq 0$ implies $y \in D^+$ by definition of D^+. $R(y,B) \cap B^+ = 0$ in conjunction with (8.5) implies $R(y,B) \cap B^0 = 0$. Hence, if $b \in R(x,B) \cap R(y,B)$, then $B - b + x = C \in \mathfrak{B}$, and by (7.4), $R(y,C) \cap B^+ = R(x,B) \cap B^+ \neq 0$. Thus, $y \in D^+$.

As a special case of (8.8), we note

$$x \in D, \ B \in \mathfrak{B}, \ R(x,B) \cap B^+ \neq 0 \Longrightarrow [x \cup R(x,B)] \subset D^+. \tag{8.8a}$$

We are now prepared to prove the essential statement of this section:

(i) $x \in D^+ \Rightarrow R(x,B) \subset D^+$ for all $B \in \mathfrak{B}$

(ii) $x \in D^- \Rightarrow R(x,B) \subset D^-$ for all $B \in \mathfrak{B}$ (8.9)

Proof of (8.9i). Note that $x \in D^+$ implies $R(x,B) \cap B^- = 0$ for all $B \in \mathfrak{B}$, and let

$$H = \{A \in \mathfrak{B} \mid R(x,A) \cap B^+ \neq 0\}. \tag{1}$$

Then, for $B \in H$, (8.8a) implies $R(x,B) \subset D^+$.

Now assume $B \in' H$ and $R(x,B) \not\subset D^+$. Then

$$R(x,B) = E + E^+, \ 0 \neq E \subset D - D^+, \ E^+ \subset D^+ - B^+. \tag{2}$$

Since $x \in D^+$, H is not empty. Let $C \in H$ be such that

$$B \cap C \text{ is maximal in } \{B \cap A \mid A \in H\}.$$

We first show

$$C \supset E \text{ and } R(x,C) \cap E = 0. \tag{3}$$

To see that $C \supset E$, assume $y \in E$, $y \in' C$. The first implies $y \in D^+$, hence $R(y,C) \cap B^+ = 0$. Note that there exists $c \in R(y,C)$ such that $c \in' B$, since otherwise $R(y,C) \subset B$ and $y \in B$ would imply $R(y,C) = R(y,B) = y$, contradicting $y \in' C$. Then in particular $c \in' B^0$, hence $C - c + y = C^* \in \mathfrak{B}$. Furthermore, $R(x,C^*) \cap B^+ = R(x,C) \cap B^+ \neq 0$; this is obvious when $c \in' R(x,C)$, and in the other case it follows from $c \in R(x,C) \cap R(y,C)$, $R(y,C) \cap B^+ = 0$ and (7.4i). Hence, $C^* \in H$. However, the relation $B \cap C^* = B \cap C + y$ contradicts the assumption that $B \cap C$ was maximal, since $y \in' C$ implies $y \in' B \cap C$. This proves $C \supset E$.

The assertion $R(x,C) \cap E = 0$ is a special case of $R(x,C) \subset D^+$ which follows from $C \in H$ and (8.8a). This completes the verification of (3).

We have thus

$$R(x,C) = Q + Q^+, \quad Q \subset C - E - B^0, \quad 0 \neq Q^+ \subset B^+. \tag{4}$$

Denoting by $\overline{B}$ the set of those elements of $R(x,B)$ which are not in C, it follows from (2) and $C \supset E$ that

$$\overline{B} = R(x,B) - C \cap R(x,B) \subset E^+. \tag{5}$$

Given the representation of x in terms of B, we can substitute for each $y \in \overline{B}$ its representation in terms of C. This substitution should yield the (unique) representation of x in terms of C. Since $R(x,B) \supset E$ while $R(x,C) \cap E = 0$, we must have $R(y,C) \cap E \neq 0$ for some $y \in \overline{B}$. However, this is not possible as we will show in the following two steps:

$$y \in \overline{B} \Rightarrow R(y,C) \supset Q^+ \tag{6}$$

$$y \in \overline{B} \Rightarrow R(y,C) \cap E = 0 \tag{7}$$

<u>Proof of (6)</u>. Assume $q \in Q^+$, $q \in' R(y,C)$. Let $c \in R(y,C)$, $c \in' B$; such c exists since otherwise $R(y,C) = R(y,B) = y$ and y would be in C. Then $C - c + y = C^* \in \mathfrak{B}$. Further, $q \in R(x,C)$ implies $q \in R(x,C^*)$; this is obvious when $c \in' R(x,C)$, and in the other case it follows from $q \in' R(y,C)$. Therefore $C^* \in H$. However, $B \cap C^* = B \cap C + y$ contradicts the assumption that $B \cap C$ was maximal, since $y \in' C$ implies $y \in' B \cap C$. This proves (6).

<u>Proof of (7)</u>. For $y \in \overline{B}$, (6) implies $R(y,C) \cap B^+ \neq 0$. Hence, by (8.8a), $R(y,C) \subset D^+$. Then, by definition of E in (2), $R(y,C) \cap E = 0$. This proves (7) and hence completes the proof of (8.9i).

<u>Proof of (8.9ii)</u>. By assumption (ii) of (8.0), $-f \in F$. Substitution of $-f$ for f in (8.1) interchanges B^+ and B^- and subsequently D^+ and D^-. Then (8.9i) implies (8.9ii). This completes the proof of (8.9).

$$x \in D' \Rightarrow R(x,B) \subset D' \text{ for all } B \in \mathfrak{B}. \tag{8.10}$$

Proof. If, for some $x \in D'$ and $B \in \mathfrak{B}$, $R(x,B) \not\subset D'$, let $b \in R(x,B)$ such that $b \in D - D' = D^+ + D^-$. If $b \in B^0 = B^+ + B^-$, then definition (8.6) implies $x \in' D'$, thus contradicting $x \in D'$. If $b \in' B^0$, then $B - b + x = C \in \mathfrak{B}$ and $x \in R(b,C)$. Hence, $R(b,C) \cap D' \neq 0$, which by (8.7) and (8.9) implies $b \in' (D^+ + D^-)$, contradicting our assumption on b. This proves (8.10).

The statements (8.9) and (8.10) combined achieve the aim of this section in the following assertion on the structure of the set D:

Let $V(S)$ denote the linear span of the set S.

Under the assumptions (8.0) and definition (8.6) the three subspaces
$V^+ = V(D^+)$, $V^- = V(D^-)$, $V' = V(D')$ are pairwise disjoint.   (8.11)

Proof. For an arbitrary but fixed $B \in \mathcal{B}$, let $Q^+ = B \cap D^+$, $Q^- = B \cap D^-$, $Q' = B \cap D'$. By (8.7), $B = Q^+ + Q^- + Q'$; then, by (8.9) and (8.10): $V^+ = V(Q^+)$, $V^- = V(Q^-)$, $V' = V(Q')$.

9. COMPARISON OF CLASSES

A comparison of two classes of maximal unimodular sets of the same dimension is effectuated by comparing a pair of representatives, F and G. To this end, the representatives are so chosen that their intersection is maximal. That is, if $\mathcal{L}$ denotes the group of nonsingular linear transformations, we assume, for given G, F so chosen that

$$F \cap G \text{ is maximal in } \{G \cap T(F) \mid T \in \mathcal{L}\}. \qquad (9.1)$$

Theorem.

Let two maximal unimodular sets, F and G, satisfy (9.1), let
$f \in F$, $g \in G$, and B be a common basis. Then $R(f,B)$
$= R(g,B) \Rightarrow f = \pm g$, and hence $\{f,g\} \subset F \cap G$.   (9.2)

Stated in other words, the theorem says: if f and g are not common elements, then $R(f,B) \neq R(g,B)$. To see the geometric meaning, note that $R(x,B)$ associates to each x a minimal subspace among the subspaces spanned by subsets of B. Then (9.2) asserts about the union of F and G: if a subspace V spanned by a subset A of B contains x,y of $F \cup G$, then either $x = \pm y$, or at least one of the two elements is in a subspace spanned by a proper subset of A.

Proof. We note first that each of F and G contains with x also $-x$ (since each is maximal unimodular) and that $F \cap G$ contains a basis, as easily follows from (9.1). Further, if we assume that under the conditions of (9.2) $f \neq \pm g$, then all assumptions of (8.0) appear satisfied. The special assumption (8.1) can be satisfied in replacing, if necessary, some of the vectors in B by their negatives so as to achieve nonnegative coefficients in the representation of g. Then (8.11) holds, and we define $T \in \mathcal{L}$ by $Tx = -x$ when $x \in V^-$ and $Tx = x$ when $x \in V^+ \oplus V'$. Then $T(D) = D$ and $Tf = g$. Hence, $G \cap T(F) \supset D + g$ in contradiction to assumption (9.1). This completes the proof of (9.2).

REFERENCES

1. Heller, I. and C. Tompkins, "An Extension of a Theorem of Dantzig's," Ann. Math. Study No. 38.
2. Hoffman, A. J. and J. B. Kruskal, "Integral Boundary Points of Convex Polyhedra," Ann. Math. Study No. 38.
3. Heller, I., "On Linear Systems with Integralvalued Solutions," Pac. Jour. Math., Vol. 7, No. 3.
4. _____, "Constraint Matrices of Transportation-Type Problems," Naval Res. Logistics Quarterly, Vol. 4, No. 1.
5. _____ and A. J. Hoffman, "On Unimodular Matrices," to appear in Pac. Jour. Math.
6. Auslander, L. and H. M. Trent, "Incidence Matrices and Linear Graphs," J. Math. Mech., Vol. 8, pp. 827-835.
7. Tutte, W. T., "Matroids and Graphs," Trans. Amer. Math. Soc., Vol. 90, pp. 527-552.

Dual Programs

Pierre Huard

1. INTRODUCTION

This article is a direct application of the Kuhn-Tucker optimality conditions [1], well known to those who are interested in nonlinear programming. These conditions, necessary (in return for a weak hypothesis) and often sufficient (under the hypothesis that the functions are concave), are naturally at the root of the principal algorithms for solving such nonlinear programs, particularly with respect to the optimality tests of these algorithms.

Another interesting aspect of nonlinear programs which has been of concern to certain authors in recent years is how to generalize the well known duality properties of linear programs to the nonlinear cases. Of particular interest are the definition of the program dual to a given program and the theorem on the existence of a solution to the dual program when the primal program has a finite solution. After the articles of Dennis [2] and Dorn [3] concerning quadratic programming (linear constraints and a quadratic objective function), some more general results appeared such as the articles of Dorn [4], Wolfe [5], and Hanson [6]. The goal of this article, whose principle results had been established in the beginning of 1961 [7], is essentially to complete the work by establishing the second part of the duality theorem. As will be seen later, this reciprocity (the existence of a solution to the dual implying the existence of a finite solution to the primal) necessitates a supplementary hypothesis S which distinguishes between the linear and nonlinear cases. This hypothesis S can be expressed by a regularity condition of a matrix. A sufficient condition that this hypothesis be satisfied is that the objective function or at least one of the constraints satisfied by the optimum of the dual program be strictly concave in the neighborhood of this optimum [9].

We have tried to generalize, that is, to weaken our supplementary hypothesis. But we have been able to do no better than to apply the hypothesis S only to the nonlinear parts of the concave functions; this result, nevertheless, permits the theorem to be applied to partly linear functions, so that linear programs appear simply as a limiting case.

Finally, to return to the conditions of Kuhn and Tucker, one ascertains that the use of these latter ideas considerably shortens the proofs.

Notation

Matrices are denoted by capital letters, vectors by small letters, and scalars by Greek letters. The transposition sign T is used to denote row vectors. If A is a matrix and i and j are indices, then A_i represents the ith row of A, A^j represents the jth column of A, and A_i^j represents the element in row i and column j of A. If a is a (column) vector and E a set of indices, then a_E is a subvector of a whose rows are defined by the indices of E. If the scalar, ϕ, and the column vector, a, are each functions of a vector, x, then $(d\phi/dx)$ is a row vector whose j^{th} component is $(\partial\phi(x)/\partial x_j)$ and (da/dx) is a matrix whose general element (i, j) is $(\partial a_i(x)/\partial x_j)$.

2. MATRIX EXPRESSIONS OF THE KUHN-TUCKER CONDITIONS

Let (P) be the following general program: Maximize $\phi(x)$ under the conditions †

$$a(x) \geq 0 \tag{2.1}$$

where ϕ is a scalar, a is a vector, and both are continuously differentiable functions of a vector x.

The following hypothesis H [1] has the role of eliminating possible singular points of the domain defined by (2.1).

Hypothesis H: Let $\hat{x}$ be the optimum of (P), E the set of indices of the constraints exactly satisfied by $\hat{x}$ (that is for which one has $a_E(\hat{x}) = 0$), and $\hat{K}$ the cone tangent at $\hat{x}$ defined by

$$(da_E/dx) \quad (x - \hat{x}) \geq 0$$

where the partial derivatives are evaluated at $x = \hat{x}$. It is assumed that for all points x in $\hat{K}$, there is an arc tangent to $(x - \hat{x})$ at the point $\hat{x}$ and entirely contained in the domain defined by (2.1).

Under hypothesis H, the following conditions are necessary for an optimum at $x = \hat{x}$.

There exists a vector u such that:

$$u \geq 0 \tag{2.2}$$

$$u^T(da/dx) + (d\phi/dx) = 0 \tag{2.3}$$

$$u^T a(\hat{x}) = 0 \tag{2.4}$$

The vector u is indexed like the vector a and the derivatives are evaluated at $x = \hat{x}$.

---

†The relations (2.1) may include nonnegativity constraints on certain components of x as well as equality relations. For example, b(x) = 0 may be written $b(x) \geq 0$ and $-b(x) \geq 0$.

If ϕ and a are concave functions of x_i then the Kuhn-Tucker conditions are also sufficient. The solution of the concave program (P) is equivalent to the solution of the system formed by the relations (2.1) to (2.4).

It is easy to give these conditions when the program (P) itself is of the form on the left:

Max ϕ (y,z)	Kuhn-Tucker conditions

$b(y,z) = 0$ (2.1a)   (v unrestricted)   (2.2a)

$c(y,z) \geq 0$ (2.1b) $w \geq 0$

$y \quad \geq 0$ (2.1c) $v^T (\partial b/\partial y) + w^T (\partial c/\partial y) + (\partial\phi/\partial y) \leq 0$ (2.3a)

(z unrestricted) $v^T (\partial b/\partial z) + w^T (\partial c/\partial z) + (\partial\phi/\partial z) = 0$ (2.3b)

$$w^T c = 0 \qquad\qquad (2.4a)$$

$$[v^T (\partial b/\partial y) + w^T (\partial c/\partial y) + (\partial\phi/\partial y)]\, y = 0 \qquad (2.4b)$$

The partial derivatives as well as y and c are all evaluated at $(y,z) = (\hat{y},\hat{z})$.

3. DEFINITION OF THE DUAL PROGRAMS

Let us consider the general program (P) considered in the previous section as max ϕ (x) under the conditions

$$a(x) \geq 0 \qquad\qquad\qquad\qquad\qquad\qquad (3.1)$$

where the functions ϕ and a are concave and twice continuously differentiable, and such that hypothesis H of Kuhn and Tucker is satisfied. We shall call the dual program of (P) the program (D) following:

$$\text{minimize } \theta(x,u) = \phi(x) + u^T a(x)$$

under the conditions

$$(d\phi/dx) + u^T (da/dx) = 0 \qquad\qquad\qquad\qquad (3.2)$$

$$u \geq 0 \qquad\qquad\qquad\qquad\qquad\qquad (3.3)$$

the program (P) being called the primal program of (D).

One can remark that the domain of (P), defined by (3.1), is convex since a is concave.

Further, since a and ϕ are concave, θ is a concave function of x for all fixed $u \geq 0$. But one can say nothing as such about the constraint (3.2).

Finally, for all given $u \geq 0$, but $u \neq 0$, the point x (if it exists) such that (x,u) belongs to the domain of (D), is unique if θ is strictly concave as a function of x. For that, it is sufficient that ϕ, or at least one of the components a_h of a, corresponding to $u^h > 0$, be strictly concave. In fact, under these conditions θ is strictly concave with respect to x, and the relations (3.2), which can be written

$$(\partial\theta/\partial x_j) = 0 \qquad \text{for all j in J}$$

admit a unique solution, corresponding to the maximum, for the given value of u, of the strictly concave function θ.

4. DUALITY THEOREM

The optimal solutions of the programs (P) and (D) defined in section 3 are described by the following theorem.

Theorem
1) If $\hat{x}$ maximizes the program (P), there exists a vector $\hat{u}$ such that $(\hat{x},\hat{u})$ is an optimal solution of program (D).
2) Conversely, if $(\bar{x},\bar{u})$ minimizes the program (D) and if, in addition, the following supplementary hypothesis (S) is satisfied

(S): The matrix $(\partial^2\theta/\partial x^2)$ is nonsingular at $(\bar{x},\bar{u})$,

then the vector $\bar{x}$ is a solution of the program (P).
3) In both cases one has

$$\text{maximum } \phi(x) = \text{minimum } \theta(x,u).$$

Proof
Part 1. If $\hat{x}$ is an optimal solution of (P) then there exists $\hat{u}$ such that

$$a \geq 0 \tag{4.1}$$

$$\hat{u} \geq 0 \tag{4.2}$$

$$\hat{u}^T(da/dx) + (d\phi/dx) = 0 \tag{4.3}$$

$$\hat{u}^T a = 0 \tag{4.4}$$

where a and the derivatives are evaluated at $x = \hat{x}$.

Relation (4.1) merely states that $\hat{x}$ is feasible for (P) while the other relations are those of Kuhn and Tucker.

It is clear that $(\hat{x},\hat{u})$ is a feasible solution of (D) from relations (4.2) and (4.3).

Further, if (x,u) is any feasible solution whatever of (D) we have:

$$\theta(\hat{x},\hat{u}) - \theta(x,u) = \phi(\hat{x},\hat{u}) - \phi(x,u) + \hat{u}^T a(\hat{x}) - u^T a(x) \qquad \text{by definition}$$

$$\phi(\hat{x},\hat{u}) - \phi(x,u) \leq (d\phi/dx)(\hat{x} - x) \qquad \text{because } \phi \text{ is concave}$$

$\hat{u}^T a(\hat{x}) = 0$	from (4.4)
$-u^T a(x) \le u^T (da/dx)(\hat{x} - x) - u^T a(\hat{x})$	because $a(x)$ is con-cave and $u \ge 0$
$-u^T a(\hat{x}) \le 0$	from (4.1) and (3.3), (x,u) being a feasible solution of (D)
$\theta(\hat{x},\hat{u}) - \theta(x,u) \le [d\phi/dx + u^T da/dx](\hat{x} - x)$	by addition

With (3.2) we obtain finally:

$$\theta(\hat{x},\hat{u}) - \theta(x,u) \le 0 \qquad (4.5)$$

The relation (4.5) being verified for any feasible solution (x,u) of (D), it follows that $(\hat{x},\hat{u})$ is the optimal solution of (D).

On the other hand,

$$\theta(\hat{x},\hat{u}) = \phi(\hat{x}) + \hat{u}^T a(\hat{x}) = \phi(\hat{x}) \qquad (4.6)$$

follows from (4.4), which concludes the proof of the first part of the theorem.

Part 2. The vectors $(\bar{x},\bar{u})$ form an optimal solution to (D) satisfying the relations

$$(d\phi/dx) + \bar{u}^T (da/dx) = 0 \qquad (4.7)$$

$$\bar{u} \ge 0 \qquad (4.8)$$

where the derivatives are evaluated at $x = \bar{x}$.

We shall suppose that hypothesis H of Kuhn and Tucker is satisfied for this point $(\bar{x},\bar{u})$ relative to the domain of D. Under this hypothesis, the conditions of Kuhn and Tucker are necessary and they can be written by applying the particularized formulas of section 2 to the program (D).

$$(da/dx)\bar{v} - a \le 0 \qquad (4.9)$$

$$(\partial[(d\phi/dx) + \bar{u}^T (da/dx)]/\partial x)\bar{v} = 0 \qquad (4.10)$$

$$\bar{u}^T[(da/dx)\bar{v} - a] = 0 \qquad (4.11)$$

The derivatives are evaluated at $x = \bar{x}$.

The supplementary hypothesis S, introduced in the second part of the statement of the theorem, assures us that the solution $\bar{v}$ of the homogeneous system (4.10) is unique, and therefore

$$\bar{v} = 0 \qquad (4.12)$$

Under these conditions, it is easy to verify that the relations (4.7) to (4.12) imply the optimality conditions (2.1) to (2.4) relative to the program (P), and for $x = \bar{x}$ and $u = \bar{u}$:

(4.9) and (4.12)	imply	(2.1)
(4.8)	implies	(2.2)
(4.7)	implies	(2.3)
(4.11) and (4.12)	imply	(2.4).

Since a and ϕ are concave functions, the optimality conditions (2.1) to (2.4) are sufficient, and thus $\bar{x}$ is the optimal solution of the program (P).

Further, (4.11) and (4.12) imply

$$\theta\,(\bar{x},\bar{u}) = \phi\,(\bar{x}) \tag{4.13}$$

which concludes the proof of the second part of the theorem.

5. MODIFICATION OF HYPOTHESIS S AND OF THE THEOREM FOR THE PARTIALLY LINEAR CASE.

The hypothesis S, introduced for the proof of the second part of the theorem is clearly too strong to select programs having suitable duality properties. This point appears clearly in the cases where ϕ and a are partially linear, that is when the functions can be put in the form

$$\phi\,(x,y) = \phi'\,(x) + f^T y \tag{5.1}$$

$$a(x,y) = a'\,(x) + Ay - a \tag{5.2}$$

where x and y form a partition of the vector variable. Here ϕ' and a' are concave scalar and vector functions, f and a are constant vectors, and A is a constant matrix.

The matrix of relation (4.10), which enters in hypothesis S, can be written in the form

$$\begin{bmatrix} (\partial[(d\phi'/dx) + u^T (da'/dx)]/\partial x) & 0 \\ 0 & 0 \end{bmatrix} \tag{5.3}$$

This matrix is clearly singular, and the hypothesis S is not satisfied. But in the limiting case where ϕ and a are completely linear the corresponding program of course satisfies the linear duality theorem, which, although different from the theorem established above, is rather analogous. The essential difference is that, in the linear case, the program (D) does not contain terms in x. As a consequence, only the first part of the theorem is always valid (the dual variable $\hat{u}$ is the optimal solution of (D), and the variable $\hat{x}$ simply becomes useless); as for the formulation of the second part, one sees clearly that it is insufficient to give the solution to (P) apart from that to (D), this latter not containing x.

It thus seems useful to formulate the duality theorem in a more general form which applies to all cases; linear, nonlinear, or partially linear. This result is obtained very simply by considering the functions ϕ and a written in the form of (5.1) and (5.2). The programs (P) and (D), as well as the corresponding Kuhn-Tucker conditions, become

Program (P)		Necessary and sufficient Kuhn-Tucker conditions

Max $\phi'(x) + f^T y$

$a'(x) + Ay - a \geq 0$ (5.4) $u \geq 0$

    (x unrestricted) $u^T(da'/dx) + (d\phi'/dx) = 0$ at $\hat{x}$

      (y unrestricted) $u^T A + f^T \quad\quad\quad = 0$

                             $u^T[a'(\hat{x}) + A\hat{y} - a] \quad = 0$

Program (D)		Necessary Kuhn-Tucker conditions

Min $\phi'(x) + u^T a'(x) - u^T a$

$u^T(da'/dx) + (d\phi'/dx) = 0$ (5.5)   (v' unrestricted)

$u^T A + f^T = 0$ (5.6)   (w unrestricted)

$u \geq 0$ (5.7) $(da'/dx)\bar{v}' + A\bar{w} - a' + a \leq 0$ (5.8)

    (x unrestricted) $(\partial[u^T(da'/dx) + (d\phi'/dx)]/\partial x)\bar{v}' = 0$ (5.9)

                      $\bar{u}^T[(da'/dx)\bar{v}' + A\bar{w} - a' + a] = 0$ (5.10)

[The expression for the objective function of program (D), which does not contain y, has been simplified in writing (5.6).]

[In the last three relations, a' and ϕ' and their derivatives are evaluated at $x = \bar{x}$.]

If one calls $(\bar{x}, \bar{u})$ the optimal solution of (D), and $(\bar{v}', \bar{w})$ the corresponding dual variables, one can verify easily that if the matrix of relation (5.9)

$$(\partial[u^T(da'/dx) + (d\phi'/dx)]/\partial x) \tag{5.11}$$

evaluated at $(\bar{x}, \bar{u})$ is nonsingular, then an optimal solution of (P) is given by

$$x = \bar{x}, \quad y = -\bar{w}$$

with the dual variable $u = \bar{u}$. Thus are found the properties of the duality theorem stated above for the nonlinear part, namely the functions ϕ' and a', and the classical duality properties of linear programs for the linear parts involving the variable y. In particular, the dual variable of (D), relative to the constraint (5.6) which is independent of x, represents the "linear" part of the optimal solution of (P).

The program (P) having its objective function and its constraints written in the form (5.1) and (5.2), the duality theorem may be modified as

Theorem

1) If $(\hat{x},\hat{y})$ maximize the program (P), there exists a vector $\hat{u}$ such that $(\hat{x},\hat{u})$ is the optimal solution of the program (D).

2) Conversely, if $(\bar{x},\bar{u})$ minimize the program (D), and under the limitation of the following supplementary hypothesis

(S) The square matrix $(\partial[\bar{u}^T(da'/dx) + (d\phi'/dx)]/\partial x)$ is nonsingular at $x = \bar{x}$,

there exists a vector $\bar{w}$ such that $(\bar{x}, -\bar{w})$ is an optimal solution of the program (P).

3) In both cases one has

$$\text{maximum } \phi(x,y) = \text{minimum } \theta(x,u)$$

It appears that the first and second parts have a more symmetric form as far as the extra variables are concerned.

REFERENCES

1. Kuhn, W. W. and A. W. Tucker, "Nonlinear Programming," Second Berkeley Symposium, pp. 481-492.
2. Dennis, J. B., "Mathematical Programming and Electrical Networks," Technology Press and John Wiley and Sons, New York, 1959.
3. Dorn, W. S., "Duality in Quadratic Programming," Quarterly of Applied Mathematics, Vol. XVIII, July 1960, pp. 155-162.
4. Dorn, W. S., "A Duality Theorem for Convex Programs," IBM Journal, Vol. IV, 1960, pp. 407-413.
5. Wolfe, P., "A Duality Theorem for Nonlinear Programming," Quarterly of Applied Mathematics, Vol. XIX, No. 3, 1961, pp. 239-244.
6. Hanson, M. A., "A Duality Theorem in Nonlinear Programming with Nonlinear Constraints," Australian Journal of Statistics, Vol. III, No. 2, 1961, pp. 64-72.
7. Huard, P., "Conditions de Kuhn et Tucker—Programme Dual—Couts Marginaux," Groupe de Travail Mathematique des Programmes Economiques, AFCALTI-SOFRO, Seances du 30.1.1961 et du 13.2.1961.
8. Huard, P., "Dual Programs," IBM Journal of Research, Vol. 6, No. 1, 1962, pp. 137-139.
9. Mangasarian, O. L., "Duality in Nonlinear Programming," Shell Development Co., Feb. 2, 1962, submitted to Quarterly of Applied Mathematics.

SYMMETRIC DUAL QUADRATIC PROGRAMS

Richard W. Cottle

ABSTRACT

The purpose of this paper is to exhibit a pair of quadratic programs which are symmetric, dual, and related to one which is self-dual. Symmetry, duality, and self-duality in quadratic programming have each been treated by W. S. Dorn in separate publications. It is believed that the programs offered here encompass all these features and hence tend to unify the theory.

Specifically, the programs are:

(1) Primal problem

$$\text{Minimize} \quad F(x,y) = \tfrac{1}{2}y'C*y + \tfrac{1}{2}x'Cx + p'x$$

$$\text{subject to} \quad C*y + Ax \geq -b$$

$$\text{and} \quad x \geq 0$$

(2) Dual problem

$$\text{Maximize} \quad G(u,v) = -\tfrac{1}{2}v'C*v - \tfrac{1}{2}u'Cu - b'v$$

$$\text{subject to} \quad -A'v + Cu \geq -p$$

$$\text{and} \quad v \geq 0$$

where C and $C*$ are symmetric, positive semi definite matrices.

The symmetric dual programs of linear programming can be obtained from (1) and (2) by setting C and $C*$ equal to zero matrices. Setting just $C*$ equal to zero yields the dual problems of Dorn.

The duality of (1) and (2) is proved by means of the duality theorem of linear programming. It is a consequence of the demonstration that

Theorem: If either problem (1) or (2) has an optimal solution, there exists a common optimal solution for (1) and (2).

Theorem: If both (1) and (2) are feasible, then both (1) and (2) have optimal solutions.

It is shown that there exists a (primal) quadratic program which is formally self-dual. Here the results are analogous to those in linear programming and, in a sense, generalize them.

ORTHOGONALITY, DUALITY, AND QUADRATIC TYPE PROBLEMS IN MATHEMATICAL PROGRAMMING

C. E. Lemke

ABSTRACT

In this paper a number of problems of near-linear and quadratic-like character are considered, all of which may be posed as linear programs subject to additional orthogonality side constraints. The aim is to effect a single general formulation embracing a wide class of programming problems. An extension of the duality notions of linear programming, and based thereon, is proposed for these problems.

Methods of Nonlinear Programming[†]

Philip Wolfe

1. INTRODUCTION

The problem of concern is that of maximizing the objective function $f(x)$ in the n variables $x = (x_1, \ldots, x_n)$ subject to the constraints

$$g_i(x) \leq 0 \qquad \text{for } i = 1, \ldots, m \tag{1}$$

Except for these constraints, it is supposed that each x_j may assume any real value. The term "nonlinear programming" is not appropriately used to refer to any programming problem which is not linear; the functions above must have some kind of smoothness. Problems having integer-valued variables, for example, while being problems of "not-linear programming," are not conventionally taken to be problems of nonlinear programming. The functions f and g_i will be assumed differentiable throughout, although nothing is lost from most of our work if only piecewise differentiability is assumed.

Most of the methods studied here aim at finding a local solution of the problem—a solution valid in the immediate neighborhood. If, however, f is assumed concave, and g_i convex, then any local solution is global—is the actual solution of the problem. Some of the procedures studied, in fact, require these properties in order that they arrive at even a local solution. There are two equivalent definitions for the convexity of a differentiable function g:

For any two points x,y and scalars $r,s \geq 0$, $r + s = 1$,

$$g(rx + sy) \leq rg(x) + sg(y); \tag{2}$$

For any two points x,y,

†This article is an abridgment of Recent Developments in Nonlinear Programming, The RAND Corporation, R-401-PR, May 1962. The research was sponsored by the United States Air Force under Project RAND. Views or conclusions contained in this article should not be interpreted as representing the official opinion or policy of the United States Air Force or The RAND Corporation. Permission to quote from or reproduce portions of this article must be obtained from The RAND Corporation.

$$g(y) - g(x) \geq \nabla g(x) \cdot (y - x), \tag{3}$$

where $\nabla g(x) = (\partial g/\partial x_1, \ldots, \partial g/\partial x_n)$ is the gradient of g, the vector pointing in the direction of its maximum rate of change.

Figure 1 will be used to illustrate the general nonlinear programming problem. The constraint set is bounded by five nonlinear constraints, whose boundaries $g_i(x) = 0$ intersect in the edges and vertices of the figure. Convexity of g_i entails convexity of the set, as shown. A suitable concave objective function is $f(x) = -\Sigma_j (x_j - P_j)^2$; the problem is then that of finding the point of the constraint set closest to P.

Table 1 summarizes some of the features of the procedures studied in the sequel: whether the procedure is designed for a quadratic (Q) or a general nonlinear (N) objective function; whether for linear (L) or nonlinear (N) constraints; whether further assumptions are needed to insure convergence to a local solution; and whether the procedure terminates in an exact solution if the constraints are linear and the objective either linear or quadratic.

Note that a procedure which can handle nonlinear constraints can always handle a nonlinear objective, since a constraint of the form $z - f(x) \leq 0$ may be added to the problem. The matter of termination in the linear and quadratic applications of the procedure is possibly not of great interest, but may bear on the speed of convergence in other cases. The term "convexity"

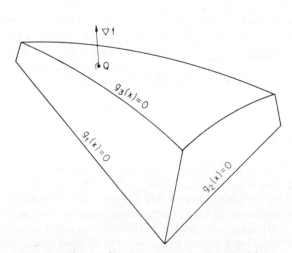

Fig. 1. The nonlinear programming problem

Table 1

FEATURES OF THE METHODS

	Objective	Constraints	Conditions for Convergence	Termination if Objective is . . . Lin.	Quad.
Direct differential gradient	N	N	not known	no	no
Lagrangian differential gradient	N	N	strict convexity	no	no
Simplex method for quadratic progr.	Q	L	convexity	yes	yes
Gradient Projection I	N	L	-	yes	no
Gradient Projection II	N	N	convexity	yes	no
Reduced-gradient	N	L	-	yes	no
Separable progr.	N	N	-	yes	no
Decomposition	N	N	convexity	yes	no
Cutting-plane	N	N	convexity	yes	no
Accelerated cutting-plane	N	L	convexity	yes	yes

is used in the table to refer to convexity of the constraints and concavity of the objective.

All these methods are discussed in the sections which follow. Computer routines for them and computational experience are cited wherever possible, but there is little to report. Lacking data which would permit the comparison of any of these methods, we nevertheless have opinions on the relative efficiencies of some of them. We trust that these opinions, which are delivered at the end of each section, will be readily distinguished from the more objective portion of this paper.

The present paper is a modest condensation of an unpublished report [1]. Discussion of a procedure [2] for quadratic programming which has been superseded by others [3, 4] has been omitted, as has a discussion of procedures for finding a feasible solution to a nonlinear problem, that is, a point x satisfying the constraints of Eq. (1). The latter discussion can be summarized in these two remarks: For linear constraints, the simplex method for linear programming provides a means for finding a feasible solution which is hard to improve upon; For nonlinear constraints, a procedure similar to that generally used with the simplex method can be employed—

apply the nonlinear procedure under consideration to the minimization of the function $\Sigma_i \{g_i(x) : g_i(x) > 0\}$, which will vanish when x is feasible.

2. DIRECT DIFFERENTIAL GRADIENT METHODS

The "differential gradient" procedures are best described by differential equations expressing the idea that a trial point x is to be moved in the direction of greatest increase of the objective f with appropriate alterations to enforce the constraints. Their basic form can be given as

$$\frac{dx}{dt} = \nabla f(x) - \sum_i \delta_i(x) \nabla g_i(x),$$ (4)

where

$$\delta_i(x) = \begin{cases} 0 \text{ if } g_i(x) \leq 0, \\ K \text{ if } g_i(x) > 0. \end{cases}$$ (5)

In Eq. (5), the number K is chosen sufficiently large to keep x from leaving the constraint set—for example, larger than the maximum of all $|\nabla f(x)| / |\nabla g_i(x)|$ for any x on the boundary. The terms of $\Sigma_i \delta_i(x) \nabla g_i(x)$ serve to "kick back" x when it tends to leave the constraint set.

It can be shown, under fairly general conditions, that these equations have a solution. Of course, one would not attempt to find it analytically, but rather by a digital procedure in which, with a suitable selected interval Δt chosen, the equations would be used to calculate a displacement Δx of the test point to $x + \Delta x$, and the process repeated.

The question of the convergence of the solution x(t) of the differential equations has not been studied in detail, as far as we know. Assuming, however, that $\bar{x} = \text{Lim}_{t \to \infty} x(t)$ exists, and that the functions δ_i have an average value

$$u_i = \underset{T \to \infty}{\text{Lim}} \frac{1}{T} \int_T^{2T} \delta_i(x(t)) \, dt$$

we can show that $\bar{x}$ solves the problem, for:

$$0 = \underset{T \to \infty}{\text{Lim}} \frac{x(2T) - x(T)}{T}$$

$$= \underset{T \to \infty}{\text{Lim}} \frac{1}{T} \left[\int_T^{2T} \nabla f(x) \, dt - \sum_i \int_T^{2T} \delta_i(x) \nabla g_i(x) \, dt \right]$$

$$= \nabla f(\bar{x}) - \sum_i \nabla g_i(\bar{x}) \underset{T \to \infty}{\text{Lim}} \frac{1}{T} \int_T^{2T} \delta_i(x) \, dt$$

$$= \nabla f(\bar{x}) - \sum_i u_i \nabla g_i(\bar{x})$$

The point $\bar{x}$ must satisfy the constraints, for if $g_i(\bar{x}) > 0$ then $u_i = K$, which is impossible, owing to the choice of K. Further, it is evident from the definition of δ_i that if $g_i(\bar{x}) < 0$ for any i then $u_i = 0$; and in general $u_i \geq 0$. We have thus proved the existence of the generalized Lagrange multipliers u_i introduced into nonlinear programming by Kuhn and Tucker [5]:

If $\bar{x}$ solves the nonlinear programming problem, then there exist non-negative u_i such that

$$\nabla f(\bar{x}) = \sum_i u_i \nabla g_i(\bar{x}) \quad \text{and} \quad g_i(\bar{x}) < 0 \text{ implies } u_i = 0 \tag{6}$$

It is easy to show that if f is concave and g_i convex then the existence of multipliers satisfying these conditions is sufficient for $\bar{x}$ to be a solution if it satisfies the constraints. Many other derivations of this result are available, and the multipliers themselves have considerable significance when suitably interpreted in applications.† They will appear here and there in the sequel for computational purposes.

There has been a certain amount of activity in differential gradient procedures for some twelve years; Brown [7] surveys in detail most of the work done before 1957, and the basic idea is periodically proposed afresh [8]. In view of the fact that no successful numerical experience on significant problems has yet been reported, we feel that this class of method is not promising. An important measure of the inefficiency of a digital procedure is certainly the number of evaluations of nonlinear functions it requires; and it appears that these methods require a great number. No doubt the fact that they cannot give exact answers to problems for which other methods can has also worked against their acceptance.

These objections are not important if analog, rather than digital, computation is considered; the analog computer is a natural setting for the basic differential equations, and several experiments in this direction have been made [9-11]. Solutions can be obtained almost instantaneously and parameters of the problem are readily changed. The possibilities of analog equipment, especially for problems of linear programming, do not seem to have been exploited to the degree they might; some reasons, probably, are the rather long setup time and the fact that, if general-purpose equipment is used, a large machine is needed for problems of reasonable size. The view that the accuracy of analog equipment is insufficient for mathematical programming is usually abandoned when the accuracy of the input data is carefully considered.

3. THE LAGRANGIAN DIFFERENTIAL GRADIENT METHOD

The Lagrangian differential gradient method uses differential equations, like Eqs. (4, 5) above, but explicitly introduces the Lagrange multipliers whose existence was inferred in Sec. 2. The process is governed by the differential equations

---

†See Gale [6], for example, for many illustrations of their usefulness.

$$\frac{dx}{dt} = \nabla f(x) - \sum_i u_i \nabla g_i(x) \tag{7}$$

and

$$\frac{du_i}{dt} = \begin{cases} g_i(x) & \text{if } \dot{u}_i > 0 \quad \text{or} \quad g_i(x) > 0, \\ 0 & \text{otherwise.} \end{cases} \tag{8}$$

It can be shown that if f is strictly concave and g_i are strictly convex, then the differential equations have solutions x(t), u(t) which converge to values $\bar{x}$, $\bar{u}$ as $t \to \infty$. It is then easily argued that $\bar{x}$ and $\bar{u}$ satisfy the Kuhn-Tucker conditions, Eq. (6), and thus solve the problem. Strict convexity is essential in this procedure; it will not converge, for example, if f and g_i are all linear.

The Lagrangian differential procedure has the odd property that the point x may depart from the constraint set during the computation; the terms u_i which eventually force it back in do not immediately become large. Only this method and the cutting-plane method below, of those studied here, thus operate at times outside the constraint set.

Most of the theoretical work on this method has been reported by Arrow, Hurwicz, and Uzawa [12]. Thomas Marschak [12]† reports some experiments programmed for the RAND JOHNNIAC computer on an ordinary linear programming problem. Using a high-precision scheme for obtaining the trajectory of the Eqs. (7, 8), that routine took an uncommonly long time to solve small problems. It does not appear that this procedure has been used as effectively as it might, since the exact trajectory x(t) is not of much interest, but we feel that it is not likely to behave a great deal better than the direct differential gradient method.

4. SIMPLEX METHODS FOR QUADRATIC PROGRAMMING

"Quadratic programming" now conventionally denotes the problem of maximizing a quadratic function under linear constraints. In the notation of Sec. 1:

$$f(x) = \sum_j p_j x_j - \sum_{j,k} Q_{jk} x_j x_k \quad (j, k = 1, \ldots, n) \tag{9}$$

$$g_i(x) = \sum_j a_{ij} x_j - b_i \quad (i = 1, \ldots, m) \tag{10}$$

If the function f is to be concave, the n by n matrix Q must be positive semidefinite. This problem has a unique property among nonlinear programming problems: an exact solution may be obtained, as in linear programming, by linear methods, essentially because the gradient of f is linear. There are two prominent "simplex methods" for quadratic pro-

---

†Pages 146–153.

gramming: that of Beale [3] and that of Wolfe [13]. While the first uses the ideas of the simplex method for linear programming in a more fundamental way, and thus has a better claim to the title of this section, and further yields a local solution even when the objective is not concave, unlike the second procedure; we shall describe the latter here, on the grounds of greater familiarity.

Assuming f concave, the conditions of Kuhn and Tucker, Eq. (6), are both necessary and sufficient. Letting $y_i = -g_i(x)$, for the quadratic problem they become

$$\sum_k a_{ik}x_k + y_i = b_i \quad \text{(all i)}$$

$$2\sum_k Q_{jk}x_k + \sum_i u_i a_{ij} + p_j z_j = p_j \quad \text{(all j)} \tag{11}$$

$$y_i \geq 0, \quad u_i \geq 0, \quad z_j = 0$$

Ignoring for the moment the requirement $z_j = 0$, they have the initial solution

$$x_k = 0, \quad u_i = 0, \quad y_i = b_i, \quad z_j = 1 \quad \text{(all i, j, k)} \tag{12}$$

Our task is to

$$\text{Minimize} \sum_j z_j$$

under the constraints of Eq. (11) and the restriction:

$$\text{If } u_i \neq 0, \text{ retain } y_i = 0; \text{ and vice versa} \tag{13}$$

The minimization is performed exactly as in the simplex method for linear programming, except that the restriction of Eq. (13) serves to restrict the choice of incoming variable. The procedure will terminate with $z_j = 0$, so that the x_j thus found will solve the problem.

The Beale procedure has been programmed for the Ferranti Mercury computer under the name "Quandary A." The version of November 1960, could accommodate 65 inequality constraints in 63 variables. The Wolfe procedure is used by the SHARE routine RSQP1 for the IBM 704 and 7090, accommodating problems for which the sum of the numbers of variables and constraints is less than 253. While both these procedures have steps not used in linear programming, the time taken for a quadratic problem does not seem to differ greatly from that taken for a linear problem of comparable size.

5. PROJECTED-GRADIENT METHODS

"Projected-gradient" methods can be viewed as resulting from the attempt to make a differential gradient method take steps as large as possible

while never allowing the point x to leave the constraint set. Several procedures of this sort have been proposed, both for linear and for nonlinear
constraints (labelled respectively "gradient projection I" and "gradient
projection II" in Table 1). We shall deal at greatest length with the procedure for linear constraints due to Rosen [14]. It is illustrated in Fig. 2,
beginning at the feasible point x^0 and leading to the sequence of points
x^1, x^2, ... In the discussion below, the word "plane" denotes the entirety
of a single hyperplane of the form $g_i(x) = 0$, whose intersection with the
constraint set yields, in general, one of its faces.

Starting with the point x^k in the constraint set, either one or two successors of x^k are determined by the following steps. A particular set of
planes is associated with x^k at all times; initially, let this be the set of all
planes which pass through x^k.

(1) Calculate $\nabla f(x^k)$.

(2) Find the projection of $\nabla f(x^k)$ onto the intersection of all the planes
associated with x^k. (In case there are no planes—as when x^k is
interior to the constraint set—this intersection is the whole space,
and thus the projection is $\nabla f(x^k)$ itself.)

(3) If the projection is different from zero, extend a ray from x^k in that
direction, and define x^{k+1} to be the farthest point along the ray be-
longing to the constraint set.

    (a) If $f(x^{k+1}) > f(x^k)$, then the cycle is complete.

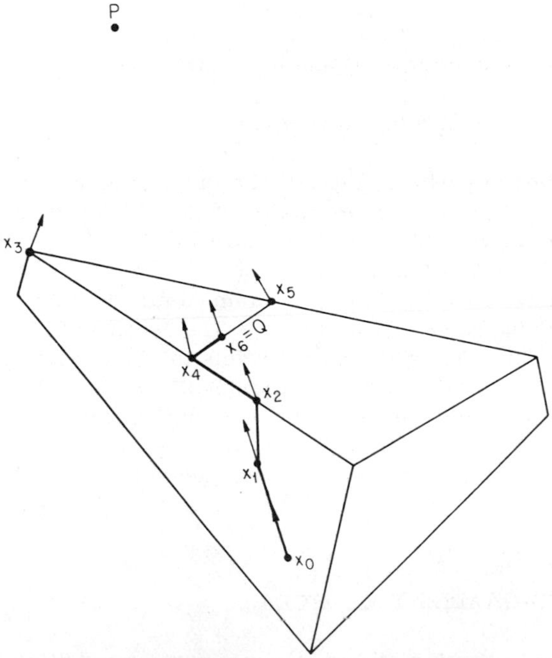

Fig. 2. Projected-gradient method

(b) Otherwise, choose x^{k+2} so as to maximize the function f on the
segment $\overline{x^k x^{k+1}}$; this completes the cycle.
(4) If the projection is equal to zero, then $\nabla f(x^k)$ may be written

$$\nabla f(x^k) = \sum_i u_i A_i$$

as a linear combination of <u>normals</u> A_i to the planes associated with
x^k (the A_i are chosen to point away from the constraint set).
(a) If all $u_i \geq 0$, then x^k is the solution of the problem, for the Kuhn-
Tucker conditions, Eq. (6), are satisfied.
(b) Otherwise, define a new set of planes to be associated with x^k by
deleting from the present set some one plane for which $u_i < 0$,
and return to step (2).
It is assumed that the one-dimensional maximization problem which
may have to be solved in step (3b) is not difficult to cope with, which is
usually the case. In Fig. 2, the points x^4 and x^6 have been obtained as the
result of minimizing on the segments $\overline{x^2 x^3}$ and $\overline{x^4 x^6}$; at these minima ∇f is,
of course, perpendicular to the segment in question. Convergence of the
procedure in the case of a linear objective is not difficult to show.
A procedure very closely related to the above, which need not actually
use $\nabla f(x^k)$ as a projection, can be given. The projection of $\nabla f(x^k)$ onto
the face in which x^k lies turns out to be precisely the direction of steepest
ascent for the function f per unit distance in the Euclidean metric, if that
direction is chosen so as to keep one in the constraint set. If, on the other
hand, some other metric were used, a different algorithm would be obtained.
The metric

$$||\Delta x|| = \max\{|\Delta x_1|, \ldots, |\Delta x_n|\},$$

for example, changes the work of step (2) from that of finding the projection of $\nabla f(x^k)$ onto the face of x^k to that of determining a point y that maximizes $\nabla f(x^k) \cdot y$ under the linear constraints of the original problem aug-
mented by the constraints $|x^k_j - y_j| \leq 1$; the direction of motion away from
x^k is then that of the ray from x^k through y. Several variants of this procedure have been proposed by Zoutendijk [15], and a related one by Lemke
[16]. Some of the work of Frisch [17] is close to this approach. An excellent
detailed survey of projected-gradient procedures by Witzgall [18] exhibits
the Rosen, Frisch, and Lemke methods as variants of a single basic scheme.
Rosen [14] has reported programming his method for the IBM 704 and
7090. Computational experience with these has not been reported, except
for the observation that the procedure does not seem as well-suited to the
linear programming problem as does the simplex method. The experiments
of Witzgall [19] support this observation, as well as indicating the possibility of numerical difficulties with this and with a Frisch procedure not
shared by the simplex method. No other experience with these methods
has been reported, although rumor has it that other Frisch and Zoutendijk
procedures have been tried.

Extensions of the gradient projection procedure to problems having non-linear constraints have been proposed by Rosen [20], and Fiacco, Smith, and Blackwell [21]. Both procedures operate roughly in this way: At any trial point $\bar{x}$ the function f and the constraints effective in the immediate neighborhood of $\bar{x}$ [i.e., those for which $g_i(\bar{x})$ is close to zero] are replaced by their first-order Taylor's series approximations. In the thus linearized local problem, a step of carefully selected length is taken in accordance with the rules above for the method with linear constraints. If the new trial point is still feasible, this process can be repeated; if not, a step in the direction of $-\nabla g_i(\bar{x})$ for those $g_i(x) > 0$ (i.e., back through the boundaries of those constraints which were violated) should yield a feasible point. Rosen reports having programmed this procedure, but computational experience has not been cited.

The projected-gradient methods seem to constitute a sound attack on the nonlinear programming problem, especially as they are not dependent on any properties of the functions involved other than reasonable smoothness. The likelihood of their efficiency is much more convincing in the case of linear constraints than for nonlinear constraints, where it is not clear that they will perform much better than a differential gradient method designed to take fairly large steps. Some hope has been held that they might be useful even for linear programming problems, since in a single step a projected-gradient method can pass from a trial point on one side of the constraint set clear to the other side, not being required to pass from vertex to adjacent vertex as with the simplex method. No evidence has appeared to support this hope, for which two reasons may be given. First, it appears that the graph-theoretic diameter—that is, the maximum number of steps needed to trace a path from one vertex to any other, which is a measure of the work required by the simplex method—of a typical constraint set is smaller than intuition leads us to expect. Second, even if a projected-gradient procedure were lucky enough to find the solution of the problem in one step, it would still require as many as m iterations to convince itself that no better point could be found. The fact that a procedure must not only solve a problem but also demonstrate that it has done so is often overlooked.

6. THE REDUCED-GRADIENT METHOD

The reduced-gradient method is like the projected-gradient methods in using the gradient of the objective function to give the desired direction of motion. It is designed only for linear constraints, its computational basis being the simplex method for linear programming. The simplex method does not, of course, provide for solutions other than vertices of the constraint set; this procedure may be viewed [13] as an extension of the simplex method which makes such provision. Since the gradient is not projected but is "reduced" in order to impose the constraints of the problem, as is the objective of a linear function for the simplex method, the procedure is not conveniently illustrated geometrically.

At the beginning of a typical step of the procedure there is a current feasible point x^k and a simplex method basis, which is essentially a partition $(y, z) = x$ of the variables of the linear constraints $Ax = b$ into a set of dependent (or basic) ·variables z and independent (or nonbasic) variables y, connected by the relations $z = \overline{b} - \overline{A}y$ which are equivalent to the original constraints. (Unlike the simplex method, $\overline{b} \geq 0$ is not required.) We suppose that the basic portion of x^k is positive.

(1) Calculate $\nabla f(x^k)$, and obtain (as with the simplex method, using $\nabla f(x^k)$ as the coefficients of the objective) the "reduced costs" $c_j = [\nabla f(x^k)]_j - \Sigma_i \overline{A}_{ij}[\nabla f(x^k)]_i$ for the nonbasic variables y_j (where i ranges over all the basic variables).

(2) Define Δy by $\Delta y_j = \text{Max}\{0, c_j\}$ for all nonbasic j, $\Delta z = -\overline{A}\Delta y$, and finally $\Delta x = (\Delta y, \Delta z)$; Δx is the "reduced gradient." If $\Delta x = 0$, the problem is solved.

(3) Determine the step length $\circledS$ as the smaller of the two values of θ achieving

$$\text{Max}_\theta \{x + \theta \Delta x \geq 0\}, \quad \text{Max}_\theta f(x + \theta \Delta x),$$

and replace x by $x + \circledS \Delta x$.

(4) If all basic variables of the new x are positive, return to step (1). Otherwise perform a simplex method pivot step, interchanging any vanishing basic variable with some non-vanishing nonbasic variable. Return to step (1).

This procedure is very close to the simplex method. Indeed, it becomes the simplex method if in step (2) the definition of Δy is altered so that $\Delta y_J = 1$ and $\Delta y_j = 0$ for $j \neq J$, where J is such that $c_J = \text{Max}_j c_j$; then only one nonbasic variable is increased at a time, and one basic variable vanishes, so that only basic solutions appear. The method has been shown to converge to a solution for a nonlinear objective function and to terminate for a linear objective function if the objective is bounded and the constraints of the problem are nondegenerate.

This recent procedure has not been tested computationally. It is expected to behave like the projected-gradient methods.

7. THE SEPARABLE PROGRAMMING METHOD

The separable programming method [22], like the decomposition method of the following section, makes use of a linear programming problem constructed to be a good approximation of the nonlinear problem. The data for the linear problem result from the evaluation of the functions of the nonlinear problem on a grid of points spanning a suitable portion of the space of the problem.

Let $x^1, x^2, \ldots, x^T$ be a collection of n-vectors. Any point x of the convex hull of this collection (the smallest convex set containing it) may be written

$$x = \sum_{t=1}^{T} \lambda^t x^t, \text{ where} \tag{14}$$

$$\sum_t \lambda^t = 1 \text{ and } \lambda^t \geq 0 \text{ (all t).} \tag{15}$$

Given any function h of x, the linearization of h on the grid $x^1, \ldots, x^T$ is attained through the approximation

$$h(x) = \sum_t \lambda^t h(x^t). \tag{16}$$

Any mathematical programming problem becomes a linear problem in the variables λ^t if x and h(x) are replaced throughout by their representations above. Using this representation, the mathematical programming problem may be stated in the approximate form:

$$\text{Maximize } \sum_t \lambda^t f(x^t) \text{ subject to} \tag{17}$$

$$\begin{cases} \lambda^t \geq 0, \sum_t \lambda^t = 1, \text{ and} \\ \\ \sum_t \lambda^t g_i(x^t) \leq 0 \text{ (all i).} \end{cases} \tag{18}$$

Let $\bar{\lambda}^1, \ldots, \bar{\lambda}^T$ be the solution of the problem stated in Eqs. (17) and (18). Then

$$\bar{x} = \sum_t \bar{\lambda}^t x^t \tag{19}$$

is offered as an approximate solution of the original problem. If the functions g_i are convex, we have

$$g_i(\bar{x}) = g_i \left(\sum \bar{\lambda}^t x^t \right) \leq \sum \bar{\lambda}^t g_i(x^t) \leq 0, \tag{20}$$

so that $\bar{x}$ satisfies its constraints. How closely $f(\bar{x})$ approximates the maximum obtained in the linear problem is determined by the fineness of the grid in general. But if f is concave, then

$$\sum_t \bar{\lambda}^t f(x^t) \leq f(\bar{x}), \tag{21}$$

so that $\bar{x}$ gives at least as high a value of the objective function as is indicated by the solution of the linear problem.

The observations above make grid linearization an effective tool for problems having the proper convexity; but where convexity does not obtain, a more refined technique must be used. This technique has so far been implemented only for problems in which each nonlinear function is separable, that is, may be written as the sum of separate functions of the components x_j of the point x:

$$f(x) = \sum_{j=1}^{n} f_j(x_j),$$

$$g_i(x) = \sum_{j=1}^{n} g_{ij}(x_j) \text{ (all i)}. \tag{22}$$

The linearization technique is applied separately to each variable x_j. Suppose that for each j a sequence of values $x_j^1, \ldots, x_j^T$ has been chosen (we suppose the same number T chosen for each j). Write

$$x_j = \sum_t \lambda_j^t x_j^t \tag{23}$$

The resulting linear programming problem, derived from Eqs. (17) and (18), is

$$\text{Maximize } \sum_j \sum_t \lambda_j^t f(x_j^t) \text{ subject to} \tag{24}$$

$$\begin{cases} \lambda_j^t \geq 0 \text{ (all j, t)}, \ \sum_t \lambda_j^t = 1 \text{ (all j), and} \\ \sum_j \sum_t \lambda_j^t g_{ij}(x_j^t) \leq 0 \text{ (all i)} \end{cases} \tag{25}$$

From the solutions $\bar{\lambda}_j^t$ of this problem the approximate solutions

$$\bar{x}_j = \sum_t \bar{\lambda}_j^t x_j^t \text{ (all j)} \tag{26}$$

of the original problem are obtained.

These solutions will <u>not</u> be good approximations unless the following condition is satisfied: For each j, $\bar{\lambda}_j^t$ must vanish except for, at most, two values of t, which must be adjacent. The condition ensures that the interpolation our formulas accomplish is always done between two adjacent grid points. (Curiously, for convex problems this automatically occurs.) In the separable programming algorithm, the condition is enforced by restricting the choice of incoming variable permitted to the simplex algorithm applied to the linearized problem: The nonbasic variable λ_j^t is a candidate for the basis only if either λ_j^{t+1} or λ_j^{t-1} is already a member of the basis.

If the grid is chosen suitably fine in the neighborhood of the solution, answers of good accuracy can be obtained, and the procedure can be augmented so that it automatically constructs its own refinements, in a manner like that of the decomposition procedure below. A version of the procedure for functions not necessarily separable into functions of single variables has also been given [22].

Separable programming is a feature of the mathematical programming routine SCM3, scheduled for release by the SHARE distribution agency in 1962. The Standard Oil Company of California has used the method for several years on a variety of nonlinear problems, although details of their computational experience have not been given.

8. THE DECOMPOSITION PROCEDURE

In the case of nonseparable nonlinear problems, any grid of reasonable fineness covering a large region will include a tremendous number of points, posing considerable data processing problems. In actual fact, however, only a small number of these points would ever actually be used in the computation. On account of the basic properties of the simplex method, the final solution of the approximating linear programming problem would involve only $m + 1$ points; and probably only some small multiple of this number would be used in the course of arriving at the final solution. These facts indicate that it would be well to investigate how grid points might be generated when needed, rather than all set down a priori. The decomposition algorithm for linear programming is a particular device for using the data of very large linear programming problems of a certain form to generate recursively only the needed data for a smaller linear programming problem whose iterated solutions solve the larger problem. What follows is essentially the application of this method to our nonlinear programming problem, conceived as being represented by a linear program of the form of Eqs. (17, 18) constructed from an arbitrarily fine grid.

Let a grid $x^1, \ldots, x^T$ be given, and let the associated linear programming problem, Eqs. (17, 18), be solved, yielding as well as the solution $\bar{\lambda}^1, \ldots, \bar{\lambda}^T$, the dual solution $\bar{u}_0, \ldots, \bar{u}_m$ (for convenience, the equation $\Sigma_t \lambda^t = 1$ is numbered 0). Allowing complete freedom in choice of grid points, we may pose the question: Of all possible points x^{T+1} that might be adjoined to the given grid as a further refinement, which point would the simplex method first choose as contributing the most to the solution of the thus extended linear programming problem?

The column added to the problem, Eqs. (17, 18), will have the objective coefficient $f(x^{T+1})$ and the remaining coefficients $(1, g_1(x^{T+1}), \ldots, g_m(x^{T+1}))$. Recalling that in the "revised form" of the simplex method, the reduced cost for a column is formed by subtracting from the objective coefficient the inner product of the dual solution of the current basis with the coefficients of the column, and recalling that the column of largest reduced cost is desired, then the column to be adjoined is given by the solution of the problem.

$$\text{Maximize } f(x) - \bar{u}_0 - \sum_i \bar{u}_i g_i(x) \qquad (x \text{ unconstrained}) \qquad (27)$$

Letting x^{T+1} be this solution, a new column for the linear programming problem is constructed, a new variable λ^{T+1} added, and the simplex method once more employed to find a new solution to the expanded linear programming problem.

The repeated application of the procedure just described constitutes the decomposition algorithm for nonlinear programming. It can be shown that, when the functions involved are appropriately convex, the process converges to a solution of the original nonlinear programming problem, in the sense that any limit point of the sequence

$$\sum_{t=1}^{T} \bar{\lambda}^t x^t, \qquad T \to \infty \tag{28}$$

is a solution of the problem. Unfortunately, it seems that the method will not give any useful results if the convexity assumptions do not hold.

As far as making efficient use of the grid points needed is concerned, the decomposition algorithm seems perhaps as good as possible. Actually, the burden of the work has been shifted to the subproblem, Eq. (27), which must be solved afresh for each iteration using $\bar{u}_i$ from the previous iteration; the over-all efficiency of the procedure depends on how readily it can be solved. In the general case, it is not necessarily substantially easier to solve than the original problem, but in many special cases it is. The fact that it is expressed without inequalities often makes classical extremization techniques practical.

For example, suppose that the original problem is separable: that is, that f and g_i are of the form given by Eqs. (22). Then the problem, Eq. (27), becomes

$$\text{Maximize} \sum_{j} \left[f_j(x_j) - \bar{u}_0 - \sum_{i} \bar{u}_i g_{ij}(x_j) \right] \tag{29}$$

Since there are no constraints on x in this problem, its solution is obtained when each of the terms of the summation is independently maximized. The new x^{T+1} is thus made up of the components $x_j^{T+1} = x_j$ obtained from the solutions of the n problems

$$\text{Maximize} \ f_j(x_j) - \sum_{i} \bar{u}_i g_{ij}(x_j) \tag{30}$$

In most practical cases, these are readily solved by elementary calculus.

The decomposition procedure for nonlinear problems has so far been tried only in an experimental routine written by Shapiro [23] for the IBM 704, designed to solve the "chemical equilibrium" problem of minimizing the expression $\Sigma_j x_j(c_j + \ln x_j / \Sigma_k x_k)$ under linear constraints. While detailed records of computational experience were not kept, the procedure worked satisfactorily, although no better than a special method devised earlier for this problem [24].

9. THE CUTTING-PLANE METHOD

The cutting-plane method of Kelley [25] is a dual of the decomposition method (in a manner which can be made precise, but which is not done here); while the decomposition method was based on the idea that the constraint set could be represented as the set of all convex combinations of a sufficiently dense set of points in it, the cutting-plane method is based on the idea that it can be represented as the intersection of a sufficiently numerous set of half-spaces which contain it. In both procedures we try to do as good a job as possible of deciding what data are needed before calculating them.

It is most convenient to describe the method for a problem having a linear objective function; as mentioned in the Introduction, no generality is lost. We must assume that the nonlinear constraint functions are convex —the procedure will not give reasonable answers otherwise.

The main tool of the procedure is the representation of the constraints by first-order Taylor's series approximations. Let x^t be some n-vector. Expanding the function g_i about x^t, the nonlinear constraint $g_i(x) \leq 0$ will be replaced by the linear constraint

$$g_i(x^t) + \nabla g_i(x^t)\,(x - x^t) \leq 0 \tag{31}$$

Note that the left-hand side of Eq. (31) is never greater than $g_i(x)$, since g_i is concave; so that if x happens to belong to the constraint set—that is, if $g_i(x) \leq 0$ for all i—then x will satisfy every inequality of the form of Eq. (31), for any x^t.

Let now a sequence of points $x^1, \ldots, x^T$ be given. The linear programming problem to be solved as an approximation to the original problem is:

Maximize f(x) subject to

$$g_i(x^t) + \nabla g_i(x^t)(x - x^t) \leq 0 \qquad (i = 1, \ldots, m; \ t = 1, \ldots, T) \tag{32}$$

If the solution $x = \bar{x}$ of this problem should happen to satisfy all the original constraints, then it would be the solution of the original problem, because it would maximize the objective over a constraint set—that defined by Eq. (32)—which is at least as large as the original.

The recursive step of the cutting-plane procedure is this: If $\bar{x}$ does not satisfy all the constraints of the original problem, define $x^{T+1} = \bar{x}$, use x^{T+1} to construct new linear inequalities of the form of Eq. (32), and solve the new linear programming problem.

The convergence of the procedure is not difficult to prove. The only starting condition which must be assumed is that an initial set of points $x^1, \ldots, x^T$ can be chosen so that the objective of the linear programming problem is bounded above. (If any of the family of linear problems thus generated should have no point satisfying its constraints, it would follow that the original problem had the same property, so that satisfaction of the constraints is guaranteed if the original problem is known to have solutions.)

It is noteworthy that, unless the process terminates, the added point x^{T+1} always lies outside the constraint set. Neither does that point satisfy all the constraints constructed from it for the next iteration, since letting $x = x^{T+1}$ in the relation of Eq. (32) gives $g_i(x^{T+1}) \leq 0$, which cannot hold for all i. The point x^{T+1} thus lies on the opposite side from the constraint set of the hyperplane

$$g_i(x^{T+1}) + \nabla g_i(x^{T+1})(x - x^{T+1}) = 0 \qquad (33)$$

for such i that $g_i(x^{T+1}) > 0$. These hyperplanes constitute "cuts," cutting off pieces of the polyhedral constraint set defined by Eq. (32) and producing an improved approximation to the original constraint set in the neighborhood of the point x^{T+1}.

Considerable advantage can be taken of the fact that the linear program, Eq. (32), does not change appreciably from one iteration to the next. The dual simplex method makes it possible to add constraints to a linear problem which has already been solved and efficiently find a solution to the new problem. In this respect the cutting-plane method is a sort of "dual" of the columnar methods, in which rows rather than columns are added to a linear programming problem at each iteration.

In practice one would not add all constraints of the form of Eq. (32) at each iteration. The best scheme would probably be to add a single linear

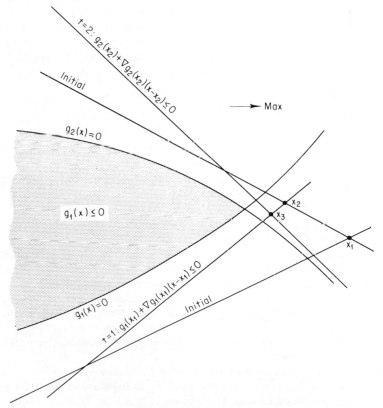

Fig. 3. The cutting-plane method

constraint corresponding to the "most unsatisfied" nonlinear constraint, formed for that i which achieves $\text{Max}_i\ g_i(x^{T+1})$. This step is then exactly analogous to the decomposition procedure step of augmenting its linear programming problem by the single most profitable column. Figure 3 shows two steps in this process.

The following acceleration device [26] has been proposed for the cutting-plane method as applied to a problem having linear constraints: At, say, every other step of the procedure, define a point $\bar{\bar{x}}$ from which a new inequality is to be constructed by

$$\bar{\bar{x}} = \sum_{t=1}^{T} u^t x^t$$

where u^t is the sum of the values of the dual variables associated with the constraints generated from x^t. Whether this device will indeed accelerate the procedure in general is not known, but if the objective is quadratic, then the procedure will terminate; some $\bar{\bar{x}}$ will solve the problem.

Computer routines using the cutting-plane method have been reported by Dornheim [27] and in a simplified version by Griffith and Stewart [28], but they are not available, and experience with them has not been detailed. It appears that the method has given these users satisfaction. While we have no experimental evidence to support our view of this method, its general tidiness leads us to feel that it should constitute an excellent procedure for problems having convex nonlinear constraints.

REFERENCES

1. Wolfe, Philip, Recent Developments in Nonlinear Programming, The RAND Corporation, R-401-PR, May 1962.
2. Frank, Marguerite, and Philip Wolfe, "An Algorithm for Quadratic Programming," Naval Research Logistics Quarterly, Vol. 3, No. 1-2, March-June 1956, pp. 95-110.
3. Beale, E. M. L., "On Quadratic Programming," Naval Research Logistics Quarterly, Vol. 6, 1959, pp. 227-243.
4. Wolfe, Philip, "The Simplex Method for Quadratic Programming," Econometrica, Vol. 27, No. 3, July 1959, pp. 382-398.
5. Kuhn, H. W., and A. W. Tucker, "Nonlinear Programming," Proceedings of the Second Berkeley Symposium on Mathematical Statistics and Probability, University of California Press, 1951, pp. 481-492.
6. Gale, David, The Theory of Linear Economic Models, McGraw Hill, New York, 1960.
7. Brown, R. R., Gradient Methods for the Computer Solution of System Optimization Problems, Massachusetts Institute of Technology, Department of Electrical Engineering, WADC Technical Note 57-159, September 1957.

8. Carroll, C. W., "The Created Response Surface Technique for Optimizing Nonlinear Restrained Systems," Operations Research, Vol. 9, No. 2, March-April 1961, pp. 169-184.

9. Ablow, C. M., and G. Brigham, "An Analog Solution of Programming Problems," Operations Research, Vol. 3, No. 4, November 1955, pp. 388-394.

10. DeLand, E. C., Continuous Programming Methods on an Analog Computer, The RAND Corporation, P-1815, September 29, 1959.

11. Pyne, I. B., "Linear Programming on an Electronic Analogue Computer," A.I.E.E. Transactions Annual—Part I, 1956, pp. 139-143.

12. Arrow, K. J., L. Hurwicz, and H. Uzawa (eds.), "Studies in Linear and Non-Linear Programming," Stanford Mathematical Studies in the Social Sciences, II, Stanford University Press, 1958.

13. Wolfe, Philip, "An Extended Simplex Method," Notices of the Amer. Math. Soc., Vol. 9, No. 4, August 1962, p. 308 (Abstract).

14. Rosen, J. B., "The Gradient Projection Method for Nonlinear Programming—Part I: Linear Constraints," J. Soc. Indust. and Appl. Math., Vol. 8, No. 1, March 1960, pp. 181-217.

15. Zoutendijk, Guus, Methods of Feasible Directions, Elsevier Publishing Company, Amsterdam, 1960.

16. Lemke, C. E., "The Constrained Gradient Method of Linear Programming," J. Soc. Indust. and Appl. Math., Vol. 9, No. 1, March 1961, pp. 1-17.

17. Frisch, Ragnar, "The Multiplex Method for Linear Programming," Universetetets Socialokønomiske Institut (Oslo), Memorandum, October 1955.

18. Witzgall, C., Gradient-Projection Methods for Linear Programming, Princeton University and International Business Machines Corporation, Report No. 2, August 1960.

19. Witzgall, C., "On the Gradient Projection Methods of R. Frisch and J. B. Rosen," [This volume (Abstract)].

20. Rosen, J. B., "The Gradient Projection Method for Nonlinear Programming—Part II: Nonlinear Constraints," J. Soc. Indust. and Appl. Math., Vol. 9, No. 4, December 1961, pp. 514-532.

21. Fiacco, A. V., N. M. Smith, and D. Blackwell, "A More General Method for Nonlinear Programming," paper presented at Seventeenth National Meeting of the Operations Research Society of America, New York, May 20, 1960.

22. Miller, C. E., "The Simplex Method for Local Separable Programming," (This volume).

23. Dantzig, G. B., and M. B. Shapiro, Solving the Chemical Equilibrium Problem Using the Decomposition Principle, The RAND Corporation, P-2056, August 10, 1960.

24. White, W. B., S. M. Johnson, and G. B. Dantzig, Chemical Equilibrium in Complex Mixtures, The RAND Corporation, P-1059, October 8, 1957.

25. Kelley, J. E., Jr., "The Cutting-Plane Method for Solving Convex Programs," J. Soc. Industr. and Appl. Math., Vol. 8, No. 4, December 1960, pp. 703-712.

26. Wolfe, Philip, "Accelerating the Cutting-Plane Method for Nonlinear Programming," J. Soc. Industr. and Appl. Math., Vol. 9, No. 3, September 1961, pp. 481-488.

27. Dornheim, F. R., "Optimization Subject to Nonlinear Constraints Using the Simplex Method and its Application to Gasoline Blending," Sinclair Research Laboratories, Inc. (Harvey, Illinois), paper presented at Optimization Techniques Symposium, New York University, May 18, 1960.

28. Griffith, R. E., and R. A. Stewart, "A Nonlinear Programming Technique for the Optimization of Continuous Processing Systems," Management Science, Vol. 7, No. 4, 1961, pp. 379-392.

ON THE GRADIENT PROJECTION METHODS
OF R. FRISCH AND J. B. ROSEN

C. Witzgall

ABSTRACT

R. Frisch (1958, Multiplex Method) and J. B. Rosen (1959) gave two closely related methods for solving linear and convex programming problems. Both methods use the same tableau technique, but different rules for selecting the pivot.

A few experiments were conducted in the linear case in order to compare these methods with the simplex method. These experiments indicate a superior numerical stability of the simplex method. Compared with Rosen's pivot selection, the one of Frisch payed off by reducing the number of operations and increasing numerical stability.

More or less all algorithms for solving the linear programming problem are known to be modifications of an algorithm for matrix inversion. Thus the simplex method corresponds to the Gauss-Jordan method. The methods of Frisch and Rosen are based on an interesting method for inverting symmetric matrices. However, this method is not a happy one, considered from the numerical point of view, and this seems to account for the relative instability of the projection methods.

The iteration steps of Rosen and Frisch may be interpreted as simplex steps using a tableau which is based on the product $A^T A$ where A denotes the constraint matrix. This interpretation leads into the neighborhood of techniques due to P. Wolfe and G. Zoutendijk.

As far as the author is informed, the termination of the multiplex method of Frisch is still not established, even in case of nondegeneracy. Of course, this is a largely theoretical problem since nontermination is, in any case, highly improbable. In this paper, two sets of pivot selection rules are presented, which allow a termination proof. They may be regarded as a "primal" and a "dual" method.

The Simplex Method for Local Separable Programming

Clair E. Miller†

FUNCTIONS OF A SINGLE VARIABLE

An important problem in mathematical programming is to generalize the simplex method to solve certain nonlinear programming problems [1, 6, 10]. This paper describes such a generalization, to a class of problems known as separable; i.e., ones in which the only nonlinear functions allowed are functions of a single variable. The method has been programmed and has been in productive use for over two years.

The basic idea is to use a representation of polygonal functions in terms of linear equations coupled with logical restrictions and to employ a modified simplex method which enforces the required logical restrictions. These ideas are implicit in the work of many authors, notably Dantzig [2, 3], Charnes and Cooper [1], and Manne and Markowitz [8].

Polygonal Approximation

Suppose a function f of a single variable is replaced by a piecewise linear approximation. Then there are finitely many points $P_i = (a_i, f(a_i))$ $= (a_i, b_i)$ on the graph of $f(x)$ and linear interpolation between adjacent points will approximate f satisfactorily. An example is shown in Fig. 1. This relation between y and x can be described by introducing variables

$$\bar{x}_0, \bar{x}_1, \ldots, \bar{x}_k \quad \text{with} \quad \bar{x}_i \geq 0 \quad i = 0, \ldots, k$$

and requiring that

$$1 = \sum_0^k \bar{x}_i \tag{1}$$

$$x = \sum_0^k a_i \bar{x}_i \tag{2}$$

$$y = \sum_0^k b_i \bar{x}_i \tag{3}$$

---

†This work was done while the author was with Standard Oil of California.

89

No more than two $\bar{x}_i$ can be nonzero and these must be consecutive. (4)

Except for (4), the system of equations would be purely linear. The modified simplex method enforces this requirement.

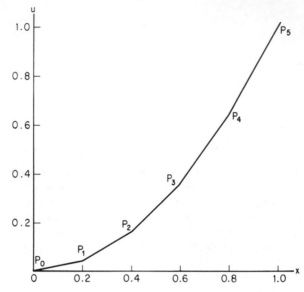

Fig. 1. The approximation to $u = x^2$.

The Algorithm

Data are given as in a linear problem, with the addition that certain sets of variables are designated as "special." There is one set, $S = (\bar{x}_0, \bar{x}_1, \ldots, \bar{x}_k)$, for each nonlinear function $y = f(x)$ (see Fig. 2). The simplex algorithm is modified to inhibit pricing (calculation of the reduced cost coefficients) of the special variables within each set, as follows:

a. If no element of S is in the basis, then all of S will be allowed for pricing. (This can occur only when artificial variables are in the basis.)
b. If precisely one element of S is in the basis, then only the variable (if any) immediately preceding it and the variable (if any) immediately following it within S are allowed for pricing.
c. If two variables from S are in the basis, then no others from S shall be allowed for pricing.

For separable programming the ordinary calculations of the simplex algorithm are carried out except that the new rules are independently applied at each iteration to each of the sets of special variables. These

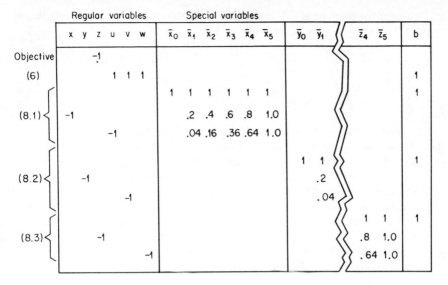

Fig. 2. The constraint matrix for the example problem.

enforce the requirement that within each such set no more than two of the special variables can be nonzero and these two must be adjacent.

An Example

To illustrate, consider the problem of maximizing z, subject to:

$$x^2 + y^2 + z^2 = 1 \qquad (5)$$

Restated, (5) becomes:

$$u + v + w = 1 \qquad (6)$$

$$u = x^2 \qquad (7.1)$$

$$v = y^2 \qquad (7.2)$$

$$w = z^2 \qquad (7.3)$$

Replacing (7.1) by a polygonal approximation gives:

$$1 = \bar{x}_0 + \bar{x}_1 + \cdots + \bar{x}_5$$
$$x = 0\bar{x}_0 + .2\bar{x}_1 + \cdots + 1.0\bar{x}_5$$
$$u = 0\bar{x}_0 + .04\bar{x}_1 + \cdots + 1.0\bar{x}_5 \qquad (8.1)$$

and similar sets of equations, and special variables, for (7.2) and (7.3).

The constraint matrix for the example is shown in Fig. 2. Note that it has three sets of special variables

$$\overline{x}_0, \overline{x}_1, \ldots, \overline{x}_5$$

$$\overline{y}_0, \overline{y}_1, \ldots, \overline{y}_5$$

$$\overline{z}_0, \overline{z}_1, \ldots, \overline{z}_5$$

one for each of the nonlinear equations (7.1), (7.2), and (7.3). Evidently, then, these parabolas have been replaced by polygonal functions (Fig. 1), and these in turn induce a replacement of the original constraint set (the surface of a sphere) by a piece wise linear approximation to it. A sketch of the resulting constraint set is shown in Fig. 3.

This example was computed using a standard linear programming code modified to do separable programming. It terminated Phase I with the initial feasible solution, Q_{16}, shown in Fig. 3. It took eight more iterations in Phase II, stepping along the path indicated in Fig. 3, to reach the optimal solution, the north pole of the sphere.

Optimality and Termination

To have a workable algorithm, it must be shown that the process terminates after a finite number of iterations and that the terminal solution is locally optimal. Since the process presented here is a simplex method, the same reasoning applies as in the proofs of these facts for the ordinary simplex algorithm [4, 5]. This reasoning is sketched below.

At each step the objective function increases (barring degeneracy) and, therefore, a basis cannot reappear, once having been used. Since there are only finitely many bases, the process terminates. Cycling theoretically can occur around degenerate bases but, as in the ordinary simplex method, it hasn't been found to happen. It can be prevented by the use of lexicographic ordering (i.e., the so-called ϵ method of Charnes or Dantzig, Orden and Wolfe).

The terminal solution will be an optimum solution in a local sense. That is, no other feasible solution sufficiently close to it will have a better objective value. If the problem possesses more than one local optimum solution there is no guarantee that the separable programming process will select the best among them. But for a large class of problems, including linear and convex problems, there is only one local optimum, and the separable programming process will find it.

Consider the terminal solution and examine a particular set of special variables $S = (\overline{x}_0, \ldots, \overline{x}_k)$. In view of equations (1) there must be at least one element of S in the basis. Three cases can arise:

Case 1 One (say $\overline{x}_i$) of S is basic. Necessarily $\overline{x}_i = 1$.

Case 2 Two (say $\overline{x}_i, \overline{x}_{i+1}$) of S are basic, and $\overline{x}_i \neq 0$, $\overline{x}_{i+1} \neq 0$.

Case 3 Two $(\overline{x}_i, \overline{x}_{i+1})$ of S are basic but one of them is zero.

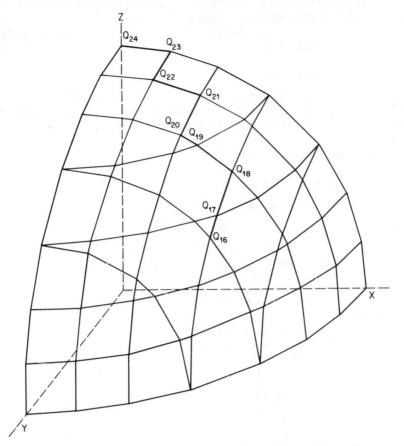

Fig. 3. The approximate sphere of the example problem. Here $Q_{16}, \ldots, Q_{24}$ is the sequence of basic solutions through which the algorithm moved in Phase II. Subscripts are iteration numbers.

If Case 3 doesn't occur, look at the terminal solution again and take any other nearby feasible solution. Express this solution in terms of the variables of the problem using only those special variables which have just been priced. Specifically, if Case 2 occurs ($\bar{x}_i$, $\bar{x}_{i+1}$ basic), express the nearby solution using only $\bar{x}_i$ and $\bar{x}_{i+1}$ —i.e., stay between P_i and P_{i+1} on the graph of $y = f(x)$, Fig. 1. If Case 1 occurs stay between P_{i-1} and P_i or P_i and P_{i+1}, using only $\bar{x}_{i-1}$ and $\bar{x}_i$ or $\bar{x}_i$ and $\bar{x}_{i+1}$. But all of these special variables were already priced at the last simplex iteration and found to have disadvantageous reduced cost coefficients. Hence, evaluating the nearby feasible solution via the reduced objective functional shows it to have a less desirable (at any rate, no better) objective value than the terminal one. So the terminal one is a local optimum.

If Case 3 should occur, the algorithm may have terminated on a solution which is not a local optimum. However, Case 3, with $\bar{x}_i = 0$ or $\bar{x}_{i+1} = 0$, is a degenerate situation and rare. And, as the example in the next section illustrates, such a solution is the limiting case of a truly local optimum one, in an appropriate sense.

An Example of Degeneracy

The following example illustrates how degeneracy among the special variables can cause the algorithm to stop with a nonoptimum solution. It also shows that such a case is truly singular and not of practical computational significance.

Consider the problem:

Maximize y, subject to

$$-x + y + s \qquad\qquad\qquad = 0$$
$$x \qquad\qquad -\tfrac{1}{2}\,\overline{x}_0 - \overline{x}_1 - 3\overline{x}_2 = 0$$
$$y \qquad\qquad\quad - \overline{x}_1 - 2\overline{x}_2 = 0$$
$$\overline{x}_0 + \overline{x}_1 + \ \overline{x}_2 = 1 \qquad\qquad\qquad (9)$$

In this problem there is one set of special variables, $S = (\overline{x}_0, \overline{x}_1, \overline{x}_2)$. It is a two dimensional problem, as sketched in Fig. 4.

The basis $x, y, \overline{x}_0, \overline{x}_1$ is the trouble maker. The canonical representation of the problem relative to the basis is

$$y \qquad\quad + 2s - 3\overline{x}_2 = 1$$
$$x \qquad + \ s - 3\overline{x}_2 = 1$$
$$\overline{x}_0 \quad - 2s + 2\overline{x}_2 = 0$$
$$\overline{x}_1 + 2s - \ \overline{x}_2 = 1 \qquad\qquad\qquad (10)$$

and it is degenerate because $\overline{x}_0$ enters the solution at level 0.

This basis appears to the algorithm to be locally optimal since the only variable with negative cost coefficient, $\overline{x}_2$, is not allowed for pricing. Thus the algorithm terminates erroneously at this solution (the true solution is evidently at $x = 3$, $y = 2$).

The trouble with this basis is that the vertex (1,1) is exactly on the constraining line $y = x$. Had the vertex been below the line the basis wouldn't even have been feasible. Had it been above the line the basis would have been feasible, non-degenerate, and truly a local optimum.

Useful Modeling Devices

The algorithm does not directly take into account the structure of the special variables, equations (1), (2), and (3). This may be used to advantage in several ways. For example, if one replaces (1) by

$$z = \sum_{0}^{k} \overline{x}_i$$

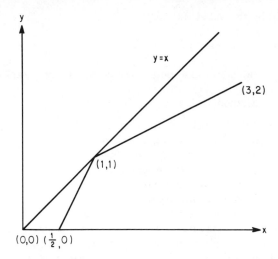

Fig. 4. A degenerate example. The feasible set is the polygonal line
$(\frac{1}{2},0)$, $(1,1)$, $(3,2)$ and the optimal solution is $(3,2)$.

with the points (x_i,y_i) vertices of the graph of $f(x)$, then the constraint being enforced among x, y, and z is

$$y = z\ f(x/z)$$

This is the most general section-wise linear homogeneous function of two variables, x and z, that one can have.

Another device is to use the same set of special variables in a multiple fashion. If, for example, one has two functions

$$y = f(x)$$
$$v = g(x)$$

of the same argument, x, then the same set of special variables will work for both functions. One appends to (1), (2), and (3) the equation

$$v = \sum_0^k d_i\ \bar{x}_i \quad \text{where } d_i = g(x_i).$$

This can be extended to several functions of x.

Many functions of several variables can be separated by appropriate change of variable and thus placed in separable programming format. For example, a quadratic form can always be diagonalized, which separates the form after a linear change of variables. As a special case of this, one can separate a product of two variables. For example, the expression

$$w = uv$$

can be separated by the substitutions

$$w = (x^2 - y^2), \quad u = x + y, \quad v = x - y$$

Clearly this expression can also be separated by taking logarithms.

Limitations of the Method

Several features of the method stand out as limiting its range of application, so that it cannot be called a general-purpose nonlinear programming procedure. Often the constraint set is not convex, so that there may be several extremal or locally optimum solutions. There is, in general, no way to show that the particular solution produced by the algorithm is a global optimum. Ordinarily one has smooth nonlinear functions, and the polygonal functions are merely approximations to them. The resulting polygonal model can in some cases have local optima which are not good approximations to local optima of the underlying smooth model, even though the objective value is nearly optimum. Estimating the extent of such discrepancies is a difficult problem, intimately related to an exhaustive sensitivity analysis of the model. The previously mentioned tricks can increase model size substantially and thus restrict the size of problem which can be computed economically. The number of simplex steps to optimum is increased by the use of many sets of special variables, and is further increased by the use of fine grids in the polygonal approximations. In extreme cases machine time has been four times what one would expect of a purely linear problem with the same size constraint matrix. Within these limits, however, the method has proved to be a dependable and effective technique for coping with many nonlinearities. It has been in productive use for over two years.

GENERALIZATIONS TO MULTI-DIMENSIONAL FUNCTIONS

The ideas just described extend quite readily to functions of several variables

$$y = f(x)$$

where y is real, but x is a variable in m-dimensional space. With some modifications, to be discussed, this extension appears to be a workable method for solving general nonlinear problems, provided that the dimension of x is not large.

It is necessary to introduce the notion of a triangulation, the standard topological tool for defining piecewise linear functions. A triangulation of a region, R, of m-dimensional space is merely a partition of the region into m-dimensional simplexes, the latter being all convex combinations of m+1 points or vertices a_0, a_1, ..., a_m in m-dimensional space. The simplex is said to be spanned by its vertices. This isn't a complete

definition of triangulation, but it will do for present purposes by noting
the following two additional properties:

A real-valued function on R is piecewise linear if it is linear over
every simplex of the triangulation.

Simplexes of lower dimension than m are allowed. In fact every
face of a simplex (a face is a lower dimensional simplex spanned by
any subset of the vertices of the original simplex) is required to belong
to the triangulation.

Returning to the nonlinear programming problem, let $y = f(x)$ be a
real valued function of an m-dimensional variable, x, and suppose one has
a triangulation on the domain of x, with vertices $a_0, a_1, \ldots, a_k$. Then the
relations (1), (2), (3), and (4) define a piecewise linear approximation to
the function with minor changes in definitions. Equation (2) must be interpreted as an m-dimensional vector equation. It is equivalent to m constraint equations, one for each coordinate of x. Condition (4) becomes:

No more than m+1 of $\bar{x}_0, \bar{x}_1, \ldots, \bar{x}_k$ can be nonzero, and these must
belong to vertices which span a simplex in the triangulation.   (11)

This representation of the function $y = f(x)$ gives rise to a natural
generalization of the criterion for selecting variables for pricing.

Let S be a set of special variables and $S_B \subset S$ those which are
basic. Then if $\bar{x}_i$ is in S, but not basic, $\bar{x}_i$ shall be allowed
for pricing if and only if the vertices associated with S_B and
$\bar{x}_i$ span a simplex in the triangulation.   (12)

The algorithm discussed earlier is evidently this m-dimensional algorithm particularized to m = 1.

This statement of the m-dimensional algorithm is deceptively simple.
The difficulty is that a general triangulation is cumbersome to deal with
and gives rise to awkward computer programming problems. It does not
appear to be feasible to program a completely general algorithm, with the
nature of the triangulation unspecified. It does seem feasible to handle
a standard triangulation, though it hasn't been done. A reasonable approach is described in the next section.

Cubical Triangulations

The triangulation of the m-cube described in [7] appears attractive as a
standard triangulation on which to base a computer code. The vertices are
lattice points in m-space (points whose coordinates are integers) in the
domain of definition of the nonlinear function $y = f(x)$. By choosing the unit
of length in each coordinate one can control the fineness of the triangulation.
A sequence of vertices

$$a_0, a_1, \ldots, a_p \tag{13}$$

span a simplex in this triangulation if and only if they are vertices of a unit cube, and they can be ordered so that

$$a_0 \leq a_1 \leq \cdots \leq a_p$$

(the inequality to be interpreted coordinate-wise). This condition can be restated as

$$a_p - I \leq a_0 \leq \cdots \leq a_p \leq a_0 + I \qquad\qquad (14)$$

where $I = (1, 1, \ldots, 1)$.

The criterion (12) requires that all vertices be generated which can be adjoined to a given basic simplex (13), and still get an allowed simplex. This can be done, since a new vertex, to be admissible, must be equal to $a_p - I$ or $a_0 + I$ (if $a_0 + I \neq a_p$), or else must be insertable somewhere into the inequality sequence (14). Two adjacent terms, say a_i and a_{i+1} in this sequence have integer coordinates differing by either 1 or 0. If the number of coordinates which differ by 1 is q, then there are exactly $2^q - 2$ readily generated vertices between a_i and a_{i+1}.

Column Generation

The method for one dimensional problems calls for pre-calculating the columns of the constraint matrix associated with each special variable, $\overline{x}_i$. Since there is one $\overline{x}_i$ for each vertex a_i, this leads to a very large set of columns, most of which are in fact passed over during the computation. For example, a function of 3 variables with each coordinate partitioned into 10 divisions gives rise to $10 \times 10 \times 10 = 1000$ vertices.

This can be avoided by using the revised simplex method and generating each column when it is needed for pricing. This is easy to mechanize, since the only nonzero entries are the coordinates of the vertex, a_i, the function evaluated at a_i, $f(a_i)$, and 1. This requires a subroutine whose arguments are the coordinates of a_i and whose result is the desired column.

Grid Refinement

It is natural that a fine grid, or triangulation, will result in more iterations to reach optimum than a coarse grid. This is borne out by experience in the one dimensional case. Therefore a grid refinement procedure seems in order, in which one iteratively solves the nonlinear problem, each time using a grid which is a refinement of the preceding one and using the old optimal solution as a starting point for the new problem.

The steps involved in this procedure are:

Step 1. Solve the problem initially, using a coarse grid for each nonlinear function.

Step 2. Refine the grid on each nonlinear function.

Step 3. For each nonlinear function, $y = f(x)$, examine the old optimal value, x^0, of x. Find the simplex in the refined grid in which x^0 lies. Record its vertices.

Step 4. Re-solve the problem using the refined grid, and starting the problem with the old optimal basis, as modified by Step 3 for each nonlinear function (i.e., for each set of special variables).

Step 5. If each grid is not satisfactorily fine, return to Step 2.

Two points of caution need to be observed in applying grid refinement. First, it is important that the new grid be a literal refinement of the old; otherwise Step 3 will, in general, generate a simplex of higher dimension than its predecessor, and this will not yield a basis for Step 4. Second, the basis in Step 4,will, in general, turn out to be infeasible. Thus the underlying simplex algorithm must be able to cope with negative solution values. The Orchard-Hays composite algorithm [9] is designed to do this. However, to work efficiently with it, criterion (12) should be modified so that S_B is the set of basic variables whose solution value is nonnegative.

Although this procedure has not been automated, several experiments have been made to simulate it, using the separable codes discussed in Part I. This evidence suggests that an effective method of reducing total machine time is to start at Step 1 with very coarse grids.

Open Mathematical Questions

The problem of degeneracy has not been satisfactorily solved, even though it has been found to be an insignificant operational problem. The problem is that if the algorithm terminates with a solution in which one or more of the basic special variables has value zero, there is no guarantee that the solution is locally optimal. Do recovery procedures exist which can be employed to continue in such circumstances?

Another problem, which is probably more fundamental, stems from the fact that the algorithm addresses itself to an approximate programming problem, rather than the original programming problem. What can one say about the quality of the solution obtained in this way? This latter problem can be put in better perspective by referring to the grid refinement procedure described above. In it, one finds exactly, barring degeneracy, a locally optimal solution $V(j)$, to a programming problem $P(j)$. One then uses $V(j)$ as an aid in finding a solution $V(j+1)$ to $P(j+1)$. What can one say about the sequence $V(0)$, $V(1)$, ..., $V(j)$, ... ? Does it converge at all? If so, is its limit a locally optimal solution to $P(\infty)$, the underlying problem which $P(j)$ approximates? Certainly $P(j)$ converges to $P(\infty)$ in an appropriate sense. More generally one would like to have some way of knowing that when $P(j)$ is a good approximation to $P(\infty)$ then $V(j)$ will be a good approximation to some locally optimum solution to $P(\infty)$.

REFERENCES

1. Charnes, A., and W. W. Cooper, "Nonlinear Power of Adjacent Extreme Point Methods," _Econometrica_, Vol. 25, No. 1, Jan. 1957.
2. Dantzig, G. B., "On the Significance of Solving Linear Programming Problems with some Integer Variables," RAND Report P-1486, Santa Monica, 1959.

3. Dantzig, G. B., S. M. Johnson, and W. B. White, "A Linear Programming Approach to the Chemical Equilibrium Problem," Management Science, Vol. 5, No. 1, Oct. 1958.

4. Garvin, W. W., Introduction to Linear Programming, McGraw-Hill, New York City, 1960.

5. Gass, S. I., Linear Programming, McGraw-Hill, New York City, 1958.

6. Hartley, H. O., "Nonlinear Programming for Separable Objective Functions and Constraints," The RAND Symposium of Mathematical Programming, RAND Corporation Report R-351, Santa Monica, 1960.

7. Kuhn, H. W., "Some Combinatorial Lemmas in Topology," IBM Journal of Research and Development, Vol. 4, No. 5, Nov. 1960, pp. 518-524.

8. Manne, A. S., and H. M. Markowitz, "On the Solution of Discrete Programming Problems," Econometrica, Vol. 25, No. 1, Jan. 1957.

9. Orchard-Hayes, W., "Evolution of Computer Codes for Linear Programming," RAND Corporation Report P-810, Santa Monica, 1956, pp. 22-24.

10. Wolfe, P., "The Simplex Method of Quadratic Programming," Econometrica, Vol. 27, No. 3, July 1959.

MINIMIZATION OF INDEFINITE QUADRATIC FUNCTIONS
WITH LINEAR CONSTRAINTS

Alex Orden

ABSTRACT

In the classical problem of minimization of a quadratic function subject to linear equations it is useful to introduce a basis for the null-space of the constraint matrix. The result provides a computation scheme and necessary and sufficient conditions for a minimum.

Let $\phi = PX + XQX$ be a quadratic function, of a real n-term vector X, where P is a given vector and Q a given symmetric matrix. ϕ is to be minimized under the constraints $AX = B$ where A is a given rectangular matrix and B a given vector.

Let N be a matrix whose columns span the null-space of A. An N matrix can easily be computed as part of a Gauss-Jordan reduction on A.

<u>Necessary and sufficient</u> conditions for existence of a minimum of ϕ are that both of the following hold:

(a)   That the linear system of equations

$$2N^{T}QX = -N^{T}P$$

$$AX = B$$

be solvable for X.

(b)   That the matrix $(N^{T}QN)$ be nonnegative (positive definite or positive semi-definite).

When both conditions hold, any solution of (a) is an X which minimizes ϕ.

Q may be an indefinite matrix. When Q is a nonnegative matrix, condition (b) always holds, i.e., Q nonnegative implies that $(N^{T}QN)$ is nonnegative.

Lagrange multiplier type equations may be used in place of (a). In place of the above we can write:

Necessary and sufficient conditions for existence of a minimum are that both of the following hold:

(a)   That the linear system of equations

$$2QX + A^{T}W = -P$$

$$AX = B$$

where W is a vector of Lagrange multipliers associated with the constraints, be solvable for X and W

(b)   That $(N^{T}QN)$ be nonnegative.

Linear Programming under Uncertainty

Albert Madansky

This paper will describe some attempts at introducing "uncertainty," or, to be more precise, "risk" into the linear programming model. The distinction between "risk" and "uncertainty" is that in a risky situation one knows completely the probability distribution of the random variables, whereas in an uncertain situation one might know the probability distribution except for, say, a parameter. The terminology in this area has grown up out of a paper by Dantzig [3], entitled "Linear Programming under Uncertainty," but what was really meant was "linear programming under risk." In any event, we shall assume that the probability distributions of any random variables which are introduced into the problem are completely known.

Let us take as the standard linear programming problem one given by constraints $Ax \geq b$, $x \geq 0$, and where $c'x$ is to be minimized. Here b is an m-vector, x and c are n_1-vectors, and A is an $m \times n_1$ matrix. The introduction of risk into the problem can occur in either the coefficients of the objective function, or in the constraints—either the right-hand side, b, or the matrix A, or both. These two situations are clearly distinct.

THE STOCHASTIC OBJECTIVE FUNCTION

There has been some work done on the problem of introducing risk into just the objective function. In this problem, the optimum vector x lies in the convex polyhedron defined by the inequalities $Ax \geq b$, $x \geq 0$, and the problem is just one of trying to find a vector in this polyhedron which minimizes an appropriate objective function for the risky situation. The appropriate objective function, as is well know, is obtained as follows: Consider the utility of each possible value of the objective function, that is, the utility of $c'x$ for each possible c. Then take the expected value of the utility of $c'x$ over the distribution of the random vector c as the objective function to be minimized. If the utility function is linear in the objective function, then the problem reduces to one of merely looking at the inner product of the expected value of c with x, and this now becomes a nonstochastic linear programming problem. But whatever the nature of the utility function, the problem has been converted to one which is nonstochastic.

In practice, the solution of this nonstochastic program may be very difficult to obtain, as it depends on the nature of one's utility function. Only one problem with nonlinear utilities has been studied in the literature. This is in a paper by Freund [6], studying a maximization problem in which the utility function was $1 - \exp(-ac'x)$ where the vector c had a multivariate normal distribution. For such a problem, maximizing the expected utility of the objective function reduced to a quadratic programming problem.

STOCHASTIC CONSTRAINTS: THE "FAT" FORMULATION

A problem of quite different nature arises when one introduces risk into either the matrix A or the right-hand side b. In this situation one is confronted with the question of how to carry over the notion of feasibility, inherent in linear programming, to a "linear program" whose matrix and right-hand side are random variables. The various formulations in this area have been directed at different ways of answering this question. The simplest answer is embodied in the so-called "fat" formulation, characterized by the following reasoning: The decision maker has to decide on some vector x of activities before he can observe the values of A and b. After he has made his choice, he is confronted with particular A and b and can see whether or not x has satisfied the constraints. The difficulty, though, is that his prechosen x may not be feasible for the observed A and b. What the "fat" formulation prescribes is that one restrict oneself to the convex set of those x which are feasible no matter what values of A and b will subsequently be observed. That is, one looks at the intersection for all A and b of the polyhedra given by the constraints $Ax \geq b$, $x \geq 0$. The problem for the decision maker is one of finding the x in this set $S = \bigcap_{A,b} \{x \mid x \geq 0, Ax \geq b\}$, the "permanently feasible" set, such that $c'x$ is minimum.

It is easy to characterize an optimal solution for the "fat" formulation [8]. If x belongs to S, and is optimal for any particular programming problem $Ax \geq b$, $x \geq 0$, $c'x = $ min for some possible value of A and of b, then x is also optimal for the "fat" formulation. One difficulty with this formulation is that it may not lead to a decision because this permanently feasible set S may be empty. In problems in which the probability distribution of either A or b is defined over the entire real line, that event is likely. In this case the "fat" formulation is not going to help us even to the extent of presenting a problem which we can try to solve. But this formulation has been taken and is a point of view marked by extreme pessimism, and characterized by the fact that one wants to preserve feasibility no matter what occurs. A variant of this formulation, which may not preserve feasibility, is the modification of the "fat" formulation requiring that one only be $100P\%$ sure of being feasible. Then one would look at the set of nonnegative x's such that the probability that $Ax \geq b$ is P and minimize $c'x$ for x in this set.

THE "SLACK" FORMULATION

A more realistic statement of the problem is what we may call the "slack" formulation. It involves converting the problem to a two-stage problem, which can be described roughly as follows: The decision maker is supposed to choose a nonnegative x, then observe a value of the random matrix A and the random vector b, and finally compare Ax with b. The vector x may or may not be feasible. But whether feasible or not, we are going to allow the decision maker after the fact to make another decision y to compensate for any discrepancies between Ax and b, based on his original decision x and the later-observed A and b, but at a penalty cost.

The linear inventory problem is an example of this kind. Here x is the amount of inventory which the storekeeper must have on hand, b is the later-to-be-observed random demand, A is a nonrandom matrix of relevant technology coefficients, and y is the second-stage decision, embodying two kinds of activities. If the demand exceeds the inventory, the storekeeper must go out on the open market and at a penalty cost buy goods to take care of the excess of demand over supply. If the inventory exceeds the demand, then he will have to scrap the excess at a penalty, reflecting the loss to him due to not having made a better choice of x. This is a more realistic way of looking at the problem than the "fat" solution, in that it keeps the decision maker in business after he has made his choice of x and the random variables have been observed. The constraints for the two-stage problem are given by

$$Ax + By = b$$

(We include, in the n_2-vector y, enough slack so that the inequality constraints $Ax \geq b$ are equalities.) Typically the $m \times n_2$ matrix B is going to be a matrix of zeros and plus or minus ones. We require that x and y be nonnegative.

The objective function for this two-stage problem is constructed as follows. Let f be the nonrandom penalty cost vector for the second-stage decision vector y. For given A, b, and x, we find the best second-stage decision, that is, the y which is optimal for

$$By = b - Ax$$

$$y \geq 0$$

$$f'y = min$$

Now, assuming that the utility of the objective function is linear, the appropriate objective for the two-stage problem is $c'x + E \min_y f'y$.

It is also assumed that for every possible x and (A,b) there exists a y which will compensate for any discrepancy between Ax and b, given that one has made the decision x and observed the particular (A, b). Rather than viewing this as an assumption, it may be taken as a definition of the domain of the vectors x which are admissible for consideration in minimizing this objective function. This "slack" formulation, it should be noted, reduces to the "fat" formulation in case any component of f is infinite—in case it costs so much to compensate for certain types of discrepancies that one does not want to do so and therefore wants to be permanently feasible in the first stage. The above assumption, then, is the counterpart of the assumption in the "fat" formulation that S be nonempty.

Work on the solution of the "slack" formulation of the problem has been restricted to the case where only b is random. The case where A is also random is much harder. One direction of effort has been the search for a <u>certainty equivalent,</u> that is, a nonrandom vector with which one can replace the random vector b so that the solution of the resulting nonrandom problem will also be the solution of the two-stage problem. It is easy to see in simple examples that the expected value of b is not always a certainty equivalent, but there are some situations under which it is. One such circumstance is as follows: Let $C(b,x) = c'x + \min_y f'y$. It is shown in [7] that if $C(b,x)$ has the form

$$C(b,x) = A_1(x) + A_2(b) + A_3(x)b$$

then replacing b by its expected value and solving that nonstochastic problem will yield the solution of the two-stage problem. An example is a function which is quadratic in both x and b. Further, when the components of the vector b are each independent and have uniform distributions over some finite range, then the part of the function $EC(b,x)$ which is essential in the minimization is under fairly wide circumstances going to be of this quadratic nature [1], and the expected value solution will be the solution of this problem.

CHANCE CONSTRAINTS

Another formulation of the problem is as a "chance-constrained" program. One looks at each of the constraining equations of the original problem

$$Ax \geq b$$

$$x \geq 0$$

$$c'x = \min$$

and specifies for each constraint a probability with which one wants this constraint to be achieved—whence the name "chance-constrained." Now, subject to these probabilistic constraints, one wishes to minimize c'x. This is reminiscent of the aforementioned variant of the "fat" formulation, except that one is here explicit about the probabilities of each possible infeasibility.

The difference between the chance-constrained formulation and the "slack" formulation is that in the latter the specific contingency plans of the decision maker for each possible infeasibility are explicitly spelled out, as are the explicit costs for all the possible infeasibilities, whereas in the former these explicit costs of the various types of infeasibility are reflected in the probabilities associated with each of the constraints. If a violation of a particular constraint is going to be costly, in the "slack" formulation one would have to think hard about what the actual costs of the specific contingency plan under infeasibility would be, whereas in the chance-constrained formulation one might say: If violation of this constraint is going to be very costly, I want to be 99% sure of satisfying this constraint.

SOLVING TWO-STAGE PROBLEMS

Aside from the search for certainty equivalents for the two-stage problem, there has been some research on obtaining algorithms for minimizing $EC(b,x)$. This work is contained in [4], based on the following considerations. Part of the two-stage problem is the second-stage problem, the problem that the decision maker has once he has made the initial decision x and observed the random vector b. This problem has the form:

$$By = b - Ax$$

$$y \geq 0$$

$$f'y = min$$

Now for this problem, for given b and x, there is an optimal set of prices, or dual variables, $\bar{\pi}(b,x)$. It turns out that one way of characterizing the solution of the two-stage problem is in terms of the expected optimal price of the second-stage problem.

More specifically, the following three results are what led to the algorithms of [4].

I. Suppose $\bar{x}$ is the optimal first-stage decision, i.e., it minimizes $EC(b,x)$ and satisfied the constraints, and let x_1 be feasible. Then

$$[c' - E\bar{\pi}'(b,x_1)A]\bar{x} \leq [c' - E\bar{\pi}'(b,x_1)]x_1$$

that is, given any other feasible vector x_1, the optimum $\bar{x}$ for the two-stage problem provides a smaller value than does x_1 for the linear form $[c' - E\bar{\pi}'(b,x_1)A]x$.

This gives an inkling into a way of proceeding. One would hope to generate linear forms based on a particular choice of x_1 and an evaluation of the expected optimal price for the second-stage problem given x_1, and then determine whether there exists a vector which makes the above-mentioned linear form smaller than when evaluated at x_1.

II. $EC(b,x)$ is convex in x. In other words, the "slack" formulation of the problem is in reality a recasting of the problem as a convex programming problem. Unfortunately the function $EC(b,x)$, though convex, is not necessarily differentiable everywhere in the interior of the region of definition of x, so one cannot just take derivatives and set them equal to zero in order to find solutions. On the other hand, one can construct the supports to this convex function in terms of the expected optimal prices for the second-stage problem.

III. The plane given by $[c' - E\bar{\pi}'(b,x_1)A]x + E\bar{\pi}'(b,x_1)b$ is a support to $EC(b,x)$ at $x = x_1$. That is, the term $c' - E\bar{\pi}'(b,x_1)A$ behaves as the gradient of this convex function at x_1.

What we have is a combination of two results: one a result about the convexity of $EC(b,x)$ and a characterization of the support planes, and the other a necessary condition for optimality of x. Using these in conjunction, algorithms for minimizing this convex function can be developed. These are given in some detail in [4].

Another direction of effort has been in determining optimizing algorithms for the case in which the vector b takes on only a finite number of possible values. In that case, the problem can be written out in full as the following large linear programming problem:

$$
\begin{aligned}
Ax + By_1 \quad\quad\quad\quad &= b_1 \\
Ax + \quad\quad By_2 \quad\quad\quad &= b_2 \\
\vdots \quad\quad\quad\quad\quad\quad &\quad \vdots \\
Ax + \quad\quad\quad\quad\quad By_N &= b_N \\
c'x + p_1f'y_1 + p_2f'y_2 + \cdots + p_Nf'y_N &= b_N
\end{aligned}
$$

where the p's are now the probabilities of the various b's. In this format, one solves not just for optimal x, but also for the whole set of optimal contingency plans, $y_1, \ldots, y_N$, whereas in the formulation as a convex programming problem one is only interested in determining the optimum first-stage decision. (The reason for this is that the decision maker is not directly interested in obtaining the entire set of contingency plans. The decision in the second stage depends only on the value of b that is observed, as well as on his first-stage decision x, and so the decision maker has a simple task. He doesn't care about all the possible situations that might have arisen. But in this way of setting up the finite problem one obtains all the contingency plans $y_1, \ldots, y_N$, as well as the first-stage optimal decision.) The dual of this large scale program can be seen to be in suitable form for use of the decomposition algorithm [5], so that, though the linear program is a large-scale program, it is now feasible to handle it on a computer.

DUALITY THEOREMS

Another direction of work in this area has been in obtaining duality theorems for the "slack" formulation of the problem. We briefly sketch what has been done in [9]. Let $D = (A,B)$, $e' = (c',f')$, $\xi'(b) = (x',y'(b))$, and let $\mu(b)$ be the distribution function of b. Let $\{\xi(b)\}$ denote a collection of vectors $\xi(b)$, indexed on b, where all the members $\xi(b)$ of a collection

$\{\xi(b)\}$ have the same first n_1 components. The primal problem then becomes:

$D\xi(b) \geq b$

$\xi(b) \geq 0 \qquad$ all b

$\int e'\xi(b) \, d\mu(b) = \min.$

One can then write out the dual problem:

$D'\delta(b) \leq e$

$\delta(b) \geq 0$

$\int b'\delta(b) \, d\mu(b) = \max.$

Consider any particular collection $\{\xi(b)\}$ now as the tabulation of a function ξ of b. Let $\{\delta(b)\}$ be a collection of dual vectors $\delta(b)$, indexed on b, and view any particular collection now also as the tabulation of a function δ of b. Assume that the functions ξ and δ are measurable and square integrable with respect to μ, and that the squared length of b is measurable and integrable with respect to μ. Then the Lagrangian for the problem is

$$\phi(\xi,\delta) = -\int e'\xi(b)d\mu(b) + \int \xi'(b)D'\delta(b)d\mu(b) - \int b'\delta(b)d\mu(b)$$

One then obtains the usual kind of result, that

$$\phi(\xi,\bar{\delta}) \leq \phi(\bar{\xi},\bar{\delta}) \leq \phi(\bar{\xi},\delta)$$

if and only if $\bar{\xi}$ and $\bar{\delta}$ are optimal for the primal and dual problems, respectively. Now these problems are not the original primal and dual problems, but have been restricted to those involving ξ and δ which are measurable and square integrable functions of b and for which the additional assumption is made that, roughly speaking, the distribution of b have finite variance. These certainly seem to be reasonable restrictions to place on any problems which will occur in practice.

RELATED WORK

We will finally describe briefly the work of Tintner and his school [10]. They are not directly concerned with the problem of decision making under risk. Rather, they are interested in such questions of the form: What is the distribution—or at least what are the expected value and variance—of the objective function if one were to "wait-and-see" the value of the random A and b, and then solve that nonrandom problem? Explicit analytic results for this problem would be quite useful for the "slack" formulation, for they might enable one to find an analytic expression of $E \min_{y} f'y$ as a function of x. However, their work has shown that analytic expressions for particular distributions are hard to come by.

REFERENCES

1. Beale, E. M. L., "The Use of Quadratic Programming in Stochastic Linear Programming," RAND Corporation Paper P-2404, August 15, 1961.
2. Charnes, A., and W. W. Cooper, "Chance-constrained Programming," Management Science, Vol. 6, 1959, pp. 73-79.
3. Dantzig, George B., "Linear Programming under Uncertainty," Management Science, Vol. 1, 1955, pp. 197-206.
4. Dantzig, George B., and Albert Madansky, "On the Solution of Two-stage Linear Programs under Uncertainty," Proceedings of the Fourth Berkeley Symposium on Mathematical Statistics and Probability, Vol. I, (J. Neyman, ed.), Berkeley, University of California Press, 1961, pp. 165-176.
5. Dantzig, George B., and Philip Wolfe, "The Decomposition Algorithm for Linear Programs," Econometrica, Vol. 29, 1961, pp. 767-778.
6. Freund, Rudolf J., "The Introduction of Risk into a Programming Model," Econometrica, Vol. 24, 1956, pp. 253-263.
7. Madansky, Albert, "Inequalities for Stochastic Linear Programming Problems," Management Science, Vol. 6, 1960, pp. 197-204.
8. Madansky, Albert, "Methods of Solution of Linear Programs under Uncertainty," Operations Research, Vol. 10, 1962, pp. 463-471.
9. Madansky, Albert, "Dual Variables in Two-stage Linear Programming under Uncertainty," Journal of Mathematical Analysis and Applications, Vol. 6, 1963, pp. 98-108.
10. Tintner, G., "Stochastic Linear Programming with Application to Agricultural Economics," Second Symposium on Linear Programming, National Bureau of Standards, Washington, D. C., Vol. 1, 1955, pp. 197-228.

A PRIMAL-DUAL ALGORITHM FOR CONVEX PROGRAMMING

Robert Wilson

ABSTRACT

This paper develops an algorithm for exact solution of a broad class of practical convex programming problems, including, for example, stochastic linear programming with convex losses, and quadratic programming. The algorithm finds a vector x^* yielding the minimal value of $f(x) = c'x + g(Ax)$ within a bounded set of linear constraints, $x \geq 0$ and $Bx \geq b$, where b and c are vectors, A and B are matrices, and $g(\cdot)$ is a convex, continuously differentiable function of the components of $a \equiv Ax$. Since A might include the identity as a submatrix, $g(\cdot)$ could be a function of x directly.

The Kuhn-Tucker conditions for a solution are analyzed to identify a natural dual problem for which the feasible subspace is a convex polyhedron. A mapping between the dual and primal spaces, used together with iterations of the ordinary simplex method enable one to proceed to the solution. Cycling in the simplex algorithm between two vertices of the dual feasible subspace identifies a nonvertex solution, and in this case a simple parametric technique suffices to yield the solution immediately. The method is illustrated by solving a stochastic linear programming problem.

The algorithm takes its easiest form when $g(\cdot)$ is a separable function of the components of $a \equiv Ax$, due to resulting simplicities in the mapping process. When $g(\cdot) \equiv 0$ the algorithm reduces to the simplex method applied to linear programming.

Extending the analysis, it is shown that the method is applicable also to sequential convex programming problems. Although the numerical task now becomes burdensome, the method is illustrated on a sequential stochastic linear programming problem involving inventories (or backorders) carried over from period to period.

Characterizations by Chance-constrained Programming

G. L. Thompson

W. W. Cooper

A. Charnes

It is useful to think of the models referring to stochastic programming, linear programming under "risk" (it should be, rather than "uncertainty"), chance-constrained programming, etc., as originating in the problem:

$$\text{Max } c^T x \qquad\qquad \text{Min } w^T b$$
$$Ax \leq b \qquad\qquad w^T A \geq c^T$$
$$x \geq 0 \qquad\qquad w \geq 0$$

which has the well-known features of duality. The problems arise, of course, when the vectors b and c, possibly the matrix A also, involve random variations. It is necessary to decide what is to be understood as the problem to be solved before asking how the problem is going to be solved. The direction we have taken is something like the following:

First, let us set down one example of the intended class of problems. Suppose we want to maximize an expected value, e.g.

$$\text{Max } E \, (c^T x)$$

subject to chance constraints. These conditions are that the probability that certain inequalities are satisfied is at least α. This is only a partial prescription. We also require that the variables, the quantities x, arise from some class of decision rules which might depend on the A's, the c's and the b's, where $A = (a_{ij})$, $b^T = (b_1, \ldots b_m)$, $c^T = (c_1, \ldots c_n)$. Thus our chance-constraints and decision rules may be written:

$$P\{Ax \leq b\} \geq \alpha$$
$$x = D(A, \, c, \, b)$$

We are not merely trying to find mixed strategies. We are rather interested in determining decision rules which will tell us—assuming that this is a problem that marches forward in time—what to do at each emerging stage; not what we should do with a certain probability, as in the case of a mixed strategy in game theory, or in the case of a stochastic model of Markov process type, where we determine conditional (transition) probabilities of various actions. To fix the ideas one might keep in mind, say, scheduling the production of heating oil to meet the emerging random demands through the season as well as to meet whatever other constraints are relevant on storage and transportation.

The terminology we use overlaps with that of others. The meanings have gotten mixed up as is to be expected. Two terms arise from the formulation above. The first is "deterministic equivalent"; by this we mean a problem not involving any random variables which when solved will give us optimal decision rules to use. And we talk of the "certainty equivalent" as being this set of optimal decision rules, because having these, we know with certainty what we are to do in any specific case.

How does the so-called linear programming under uncertainty of Dantzig, Madansky, et. al., relate to chance-constrained programming? Much of their work is concerned with the so-called two-stage instance of linear programming under uncertainty. Referring to our chance-constrained formulation, their variables—and here we include their (second stage) penalty variables—are those that have c's attached to them. Then with these, you must restrict to the special case in which the α_i's are all 1 in order to have linear programming under uncertainty. This is true whether it is two-stage or k-stage. Further, the concept of decision rules and their optimal determination is absent in any explicit sense in the published work of this "l.p.u.u." group except in the two stage case, to which we shall return.

We have however been able to get some characterizations of optimal classes of decision rules for general l.p.u.u. by restricting our formulation to $\alpha_i = 1$. For example, in the case of analyticity of the decision rules in the random variables it turns out that the class of linear rules is sufficient to consider. And piecewise analyticity would yield piecewise linear rules. For the general case ($\alpha_i \neq 1$) we have been able to make a certain amount of progress in finding deterministic equivalents. We have looked at this chiefly, but not exclusively, in terms of linear decision rules,

$$x = Db$$

where D is a matrix. If in a dynamic problem, the components of x with larger subscripts represent later times, D may have a triangular or a block triangular structure. But there are cases when D does not have such a structure. Also, if forecasts of some of the random variables are included in the decision rules, a forecast could appear as a random variable which is available with (perhaps) smaller variance at certain times along the pathway than the random variable available at an earlier stage.

In any case, if we look at this class of linear decision rules it is clear that in order to do something of a general nature with deterministic equivalents, we must rely on a class of distributions for which the algebra is sufficiently convenient. Such a class (suggested by Charnes and Ben-Israel) is that of mixtures of normal distributions. This class has the property that a linear combination of random variables which are governed by a (multivariate joint) mixture of normal distributions is again governed by such a mixture, and one can specify the corresponding means and covariances in a fairly reasonable manner. Further, with mixtures of normal distributions it is possible to approximate distributions of fairly arbitrary shapes—U-ness and all that sort of thing can be had. Thus one can build up more general theory through approximation by mixtures of this type.

In this linear case, there is one more point of content. The case of two-stage linear programming under uncertainty has a case in which both α_i = 1 (for all i) and $x = \Gamma y$ where γ does not depend on b. In other words x is a vector of parameters; the decision rule degenerates so that there are no terms involving the random variables b. We call this the zeroth order linear decision rule. For the more general case with $\alpha_i \neq 1$, Ben-Israel and Charnes have given a dual theorem. For that case, the left-hand side in each chance constraint is a number, it isn't a random variable. But the probability of a random variable with a known distribution being greater than or equal to some particular number, of course specifies a fractile and leads immediately out of a chance constraint into a constraint involving the corresponding fractile of the distribution. This result holds also for dependent, not just independent, random variables.

Three types of functionals for chance-constrained models have come up in connection with various problems in the real, or conceptual real, world. One of these (pointed out already) is that where the functional is the expected value. We call this the E type. Another type (the V type) is that in which—as for example, in the work of Markowitz on portfolio selection and investment—something like a variance measure of risk is minimized. This could be written Min E $(c^T x - c^T x_0)^2$. Finally the goal might be to maximize the probability that at least a certain level of the functional is achieved, again subject to chance constraints and the choice of the decision rule from a given class. Call this the P type.

There is still another class of problem which has come into the social science literature through the notion (due to H. A. Simon) of "satisficing" rather than optimizing. But it too can be specified in a certain way in an extremal or optimizing manner.

What do these problems look like for the case in which we have a linear decision rule? It turns out that in this case, when the distributions are mixtures of normal distributions we can get a deterministic equivalent. The results are more general but this level of generality will do. The components of b and c may be correlated. There is one more condition: if the distributions are symmetric, then we require $\alpha_i \geq 1/2$ for all i. If this isn't the case then the deterministic equivalent is not a convex programming problem. But it is interesting that then you really would not consider such a chance-constraint as a policy constraint, or as very much of a requirement since it would not hold at least 50% of the time. When the hypothesis is satisfied (the usual case) the problem is convex and the deterministic constraints will turn out to be at most quadratic. The quadratic character arises from the covariances of the components of the random vectors involved.

Incidentally, we have said "convex" programming problem for each functional type. That is not true directly for the P type. It leads to a model involving programming over a convex set, but the functional is a linear fractional one. We have shown how to reduce this to a model with a linear objective, one extra constraint, and one more variable, so it is true that at most a second transformation converts all three types to convex programming models with at most quadratic constraints as their deterministic equivalents.

For example, let us write down the deterministic equivalent for the V type. It will be:

$$\text{Min } E[c^T Db - c_0^T x_0]^2$$

$$\text{subject to} \quad -a_i^T D\mu_b - v_i \geq -\mu_{b_i}$$

$$\text{and} \quad -K_{\alpha_i}^2 E[b_i - a_i^T Db]^2 + v_i^2 \geq 0 \text{ with } v_i \geq 0$$

Solving this problem we would get D and thus would have the certainty equivalent; that is, we would be able to specify our action since the corresponding x components would be precisely determined as specific events developed which gave particular values to the b.

Similar results hold for the other types of models; the same sort of structures arise. It follows from the above expected value form of the chance constraints that the quadratic character of the equivalent constraints comes essentially from the variances or covariances involved. At the very worst, to deal directly with distributions other than mixtures of normal distributions, it is only necessary to determine quantities such as K^2. These may come from a method of parametric variation or from things like Chebychev's inequality. This would yield values of K^2 which would be higher than necessary in order that these chance-constraints hold.

Let us proceed now to something which is a good deal more special. We've done some work on extension of the critical path problem to one involving uncertainty in the times of completion of each task in the network of required tasks. Here, consider a network with a starting node, a finishing node and various other nodes. A unit amount is sent in which is required to go through the network and come out at the finish node in correspondence to total completion of all the tasks implied by all the links. Recall that in this formulation one searches for the chain of maximal length in the network. Equivalently, maximize $\Sigma_j t_j x_j$, where t_j is the time on the jth link, x_j the amount of flow there subject to the incidence conditions and unidirectional flow,

$$\sum_j \epsilon_{ij} x_j = a_i$$

$$x_j \geq 0$$

This of course is associated with a dual problem:

$$\text{Min} \sum_i u_i a_i \text{ subject to } \sum_i u_i \epsilon_{ij} \geq t_j$$

Here all the a's except two will be zero. One of these is 1 and the other is −1.

If you look for the moment at the deterministic case in this form, and you look for the obvious directed sub-dual method (see Charnes and Cooper, "Mathematical Methods and Industrial Applications of Linear Programming," Volume II), it turns out that it's possible to solve it in one pass through. And the method that you get in this manner turns out to be one which Dijkstra published in Numerische Mathematik, Volume I, 1959. This method seems to be an improvement over previous solution methods. It's rather interesting that his ingenious method which is based purely on graph considerations is identical with one you get from simply a routine examination of the problem and construction of an obvious directed sub-dual algorithm in the dual.

In the dual, Min $\Sigma_i u_i a_i$ subject to $\Sigma_i u_i \epsilon_{ij} \geq t_j$, the u_i may be considered virtual potentials at the nodes. Their optimal values can be interpreted as "early start times" for their following tasks. And it is from this side, too, that we can take this problem up into chance-constrained form, where we replace the deterministic constraints above with the probability that these happen is respectively at least β_j. E.g. the constraints become $P(\Sigma_i u_i \epsilon_{ij} \geq t_j) \geq \beta_j$. Here the t_j are random variables with known distributions, and for simplicity we consider zero order linear decision rules for the u_i's ("two-stage" in the linear programming under uncertainty terminology; note this is not l.p.u.u. since the β_j are not necessarily 1) i.e. we take the u_i's as parameters to be solved for. Now then we can do something like minimize the expected value of the functional, or we can minimize the probability that the time taken for completion is more than a certain amount. Or we can maximize the probability that the time is less than a certain amount for completion. Any one of these criteria would give us a perfectly valid chance-constrained zero order model.

To show the relevance of this to PERT procedure, let us suppose, for example, that the t's are independent with distribution functions F_j. Then the chance-constraints can be inverted immediately into the fractile form,

$$\sum_i u_i \epsilon_{ij} \geq F_j^{-1}(\beta_j)$$

Taking the E form for the functional, it remains as $\Sigma_i u_i a_i$ since the u_i are not random variables.

Now we have a dual problem:

Max $\qquad \sum_j F_j^{-1}(\beta_j) x_j$

subject to $\sum \epsilon_{ij} x_j = a_i$

and $\qquad\qquad x_j \geq 0$

This is of the same form as the original deterministic critical path formulation with the $F_j^{-1}(\beta_j)$ replacing the (fixed) times for task completions.

PERT arises for special discrete (3 point) distributions and with replacement of the random times by their expected value. But this corresponds here to the $\beta_j = 1/2$. You may form your own conclusions as to the protection afforded by this level of β_j in chance constraints.

Aside from the above considerations, this model has other interesting aspects. For example, we have obtained the (Tintner) variety of stochastic programming solution for some cases. When one uses exponential distributions then the distribution of the maximum of two random variables and other necessary distributions turn out to be easy to determine. The integrations involved can be carried out and for some simple examples we can actually get the distribution for the minimum total completion time. Although the mode of individual task times is at zero, the total completion time distribution is very flat and small near zero. Further it is often multi-modal! This is at variance with certain (fallacious) central limit theorem usages.

REFERENCES

1. Ben-Israel, A., "On Some Problems of Mathematical Programming," Ph.D. Thesis in Engineering Science, Northwestern University, Evanston, Ill., June, 1962.
2. _____, and A. Charnes, "Constant Level Inventory Policies and Chance-Constrained Programming Models," Northwestern University, Evanston, Ill., 1961.
3. Charnes, A., and W. W. Cooper, "Chance-Constrained Programming," Management Sci., Vol. 6, No. 1, Oct. 1959.
4. _____, and _____, Management Models and Industrial Applications of Linear Programming, Wiley, New York, 1961.
5. _____, and _____, "Normal Deviates and Chance Constraints," J. Am. Stat. Assoc., Vol. 57, 1962, pp. 134-148.
6. _____, and _____, "Programming with Fractional Functionals, I: Linear Fractional Programming," Naval Res. Log. Quart. (forthcoming, scheduled to appear Dec., 1962.)
7. _____, and _____, "Systems Evaluations and Repricing Theorems," Management Sci. 9 (1962), pp. 33-49.
8. _____, and _____, "The Theory of Search: Optimum Distribution of Search Effort," Management Sci., Vol. 5, No. 1, 1958.
9. _____, _____, and K. Kortanek, "Duality, Haar Programs and Finite Sequence Spaces," Proc. National Acad. Sci., Vol. 48, 1962, pp. 783-786.
10. _____, _____, and _____, "Duality in Semi-Infinite Programs and Some Works of Haar and Caratheodory," Management Sci. 9 (1963), pp. 209-228.
11. _____, _____, and M. H. Miller, "Application of Linear Programming to Financial Budgeting and the Costing of Funds," J. Business Univ. of Chicago, Vol. 32, 1959, pp. 20-46.
12. _____, _____, and G. H. Symonds, "Cost Horizons and Certainty

Equivalents: An Approach to Stochastic Programming of Heating Oil Production," Management Sci., Vol. 4, No. 3, 1958.

13. _____, _____, and G. L. Thompson, "Chance Constrained Studies for Linear Programming Under Uncertainty, 'Part One: Constrained Generalized Medians and Two-Stage Problems with General Linear Structure.' 'Part Two: Linear Decision Rules and General k-Stage Structure.' " Management Sci. (forthcoming).

14. Cooper, W. W., and J. D. Savvas, "Motivational Cost and Transients In Budgeting the Behavior of Cost and Aspirations," ONR Research Rep't 83. Pittsburgh: Carnegie Institute of Technology, GSIA, May, 1961.

15. Dantzig, G. B., "Linear Programming under Uncertainty," Management Sci., Vol. 1, 1955, pp. 197-206.

16. _____, "Recent Advances in Linear Programming," Management Sci., Vol. 2, 1956, pp. 131-144.

17. Holt, C. C., F. Modigliani, J. Muth, and H. A. Simon, Planning Production, Inventory and Work Force, Prentice-Hall, Englewood Cliffs, New Jersey, 1960.

18. Madansky, A., "Inequalities for Stochastic Linear Programming Problems," Management Sci., Vol. 6, 1960, pp. 197-204.

19. March, J. G., and H. A. Simon, Organizations, Wiley, New York, 1958.

20. Markowitz, H. M., Portfolio Selections: Efficient Diversification of Investment, Wiley, New York, 1959.

21. Naslund, B., and A. W. Whinston, "A Model of Multi-Period Investment under Uncertainty," Management Sci., Vol. 8, 1962, pp. 184-200.

22. Simon, H. A., Models of Man, New York, 1957.

23. _____, "Theories of Decision-Making in Economics and Behavioral Science," Am. Economics Rev., Vol. 49, No. 3, 1959.

24. Stedry, A., Budget Control and Cost Behavior, Prentice-Hall, New York, 1960.

25. _____, and A. Charnes, "Exploratory Models in the Theory of Budgetary Control," ONR Research Memo 43, Mimeo, for project Temporal Planning and Management Decisions under Risk and Uncertainty, Northwestern University, Evanston, Ill., Jan. 8, 1962.

26. Symonds, G., "Stochastic Scheduling by the Horizon Method," Management Sci., Vol. 8, 1962, pp. 138-167.

27. Theil, H., "Some Reflections on Static Programming under Uncertainty," Weltwirtschaftliches Archiv., Vol. 87, 1961, and reprinted as Publication No. 5 of The International Center for Management Science (Rotterdam: The Netherlands School of Economics).

28. Tintner, G., "A Note on Stochastic Linear Programming," Econometrica, Vol. 28, 1960, pp. 490-495.

29. _____, "Stochastic Linear Programming with Applications to Agricultural Economics," Second Symposium on Linear Programming, H. A. Antosiewicz, ed., National Bureau of Standards, Washington, D.C., 1955.

30. Vajda, S., "Inequalities in Stochastic Linear Programming," Bull. International Stat. Institute, Vol. 36, 1958, pp. 357–363.
31. Van de Panne, C., and W. Popp, "Minimum-Cost Cattle Feed under Probabilistic Protein Constraints," Management Sci., (forthcoming).
32. Weingartner, H. M., "Mathematical Programming and the Analysis of Capital Budgeting," Ph.D. Thesis, Graduate School of Industrial Administration, Carnegie Institute of Technology, Pittsburgh, Pa., 1961.

PROGRAMMING WITH STANDARD ERRORS IN THE CONSTRAINTS AND THE OBJECTIVE

S. M. Sinha

ABSTRACT

This paper deals with a linear programming problem, where the coefficients of the objective, the constraint inequalities and the available quantities are random variables. The appropriate formulation under the situation is then to consider that our activities should be such that with a certain preassigned high probability, the total quantities required for each item should not exceed the available quantities and at the same time guarantee a maximum objective with a preassigned high probability. With the assumption that at least the means, variances and covariances of these random variables are known, our formulation reduces the stochastic linear programming problem to the case of the following convex programming problem:

$$\text{Max } D'X - (X'BX)^{1/2}$$

subject to $\quad A_i X + (X'B^i X)^{1/2} \le b_i, \ X \ge 0$

where $\quad D, A_i', X$ are $(n \times 1)$

and $\quad B, B^i \quad$ are $(n \times n)$

symmetric positive semi-definite matrices

$(i = 1, 2, \ldots, m)$ $\qquad\qquad\qquad\qquad$ (1)

It has been shown that in a particular case, where only the coefficients of the objective are random variables, the problem can be stated as

$$\text{Max } D'X - (X'BX)^{1/2}$$

subject to $\quad AX \le b, \ X \ge 0$

where $\quad b$ is a $(m \times 1)$

and $\quad A$ is a $(m \times n)$ matrix,

which can be solved by the available algorithms for quadratic programming

It is also noted that if all the correlation coefficients are unity, (1) reduces to a linear programming problem with known coefficients.

INEQUALITIES FOR STOCHASTIC NONLINEAR PROGRAMMING PROBLEMS

O. L. Mangasarian and *J. B. Rosen*

ABSTRACT

The inequalities given by Albert Madansky (Management Science, Vol. 6, 1960, p. 200) have been generalized to a class of nonlinear programming problems via the duality theorems of nonlinear programming. In particular, the constraints considered are of the type $g(x) + h(y) \geq b$ where the components of the vectors g and h are nonlinear concave functions of their arguments and satisfy some further restrictions. The right-hand side b is subject to a random variation with an expected value Eb. It is desired to minimize the expected value of the convex objective function $\varphi(x) + \Psi(y)$ subject to the constraints. If $\gamma(x,b)$ denotes $\min_y [\varphi(x) + \Psi(y)]$ subject to the constraints, then under certain restrictions the following inequalities hold

$$E\gamma(b, \bar{x}(Eb)) \geq \min_x E\gamma(b,x) \geq E \min_x \gamma(b,x) \geq \min_x \gamma(Eb,x),$$

where $\bar{x}(Eb)$ denotes the solution of $\min_x \gamma(Eb,x)$. It is also shown that the function $\min_x \gamma(x,b)$ is a convex, continuous function of b and that the some-times-sharper upper bound to $E \min_x \gamma(b,x)$ given on p. 201 of Madansky also holds if b is defined over a bounded rectangle and has independent elements.

Compact Basis Triangularization for the Simplex Method

George B. Dantzig

Alex Orden was the first to point out that the inverse of the basis in the simplex method serves no function except as a means for obtaining the representation of the vector entering the basis and for determining the new price vector. For this purpose one of the many forms of "substitute inverses" (such as the well known product form of the inverse) would do just as well and in fact may have certain advantages in computation.

Harry Markowitz was interested in developing, for a sparse matrix, a substitute inverse with as few nonzero entries as possible. He suggested several ways to do this approximately. For example, the basis could be reduced to triangular form by successively selecting for pivot position that row and that column whose product of nonzero entries (excluding the pivot) is minimum. He also pointed out that, for bases whose nonzeros appear in a band on a staircase about the diagonal, proper selection of pivots could result in a compact substitute inverse with no more nonzeros than the original basis.

We shall adopt Markowitz's suggestion. However, instead of recording the successive transformations of one basis to the next in product form, we shall show that it is efficient to generate each substitute inverse in turn from its predecessor. The substitute inverse remains compact, of fixed size. Thus "reinversions" are unnecessary (except in so far as they are needed to restore loss of accuracy due to cumulative round-off error).

The procedure which we shall give can be applied to a general m x m basis without special structure. As such, it is probably competitive with the standard product form, for it may have all of its advantages and none of its disadvantages. With certain matrix structures, moreover, it appears to be particularly attractive.

We shall focus our remarks on staircase structures. The reader will find no difficulty in finding an equally efficient way to compact block-angular structures. Letting B_{ij} be a submatrix of the basis, a basis B with staircase structure has, for example, the form:

†This research has been partially supported by the Office of Naval Research under Contract Nonr-222(83) and the National Science Foundation Grant No. G21034 with the University of California. Reproduction in whole or in part is permitted for any purpose of the United States Government.

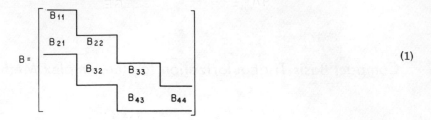

$$(1)$$

In (2), the marks x, *, and ⊗ indicate the staircase pattern of nonzero entries in the basis-matrix B. The P_S is some column of coefficients not in the basis. The asterisks along the diagonal mark the successive pivot positions. It is assumed (and this need not be true) that the basis can be reduced to triangular form by pivoting successively on the lower right-hand element of each submatrix formed by deleting the preceding pivot row and column. Each pivot operation consists in using the assumed nonzero diagonal term to eliminate the column variable from all nonzero terms above the diagonal only. The symbol ⊗ indicates the resulting position of zero coefficients above the diagonal.

$$B = \begin{bmatrix} * & \otimes & \otimes & & & \\ x & * & \otimes & & & \\ x & x & * & \otimes & & \\ x & x & x & * & & \\ & & & & x & * & \otimes \\ & & & & & x & x & * \end{bmatrix} \quad ; \quad P_S = \begin{bmatrix} \\ \\ x \\ x \\ x \\ x \end{bmatrix}$$

(drop)   (enter)

$$(2)$$

Let T be the resulting triangularized matrix; it has the form (3). Note particularly that the pattern of nonzeros in T is precisely the same as the pattern of nonzeros on and below the main diagonal of the original basis B and that P_S^*, the transform of P_S under the same row operations, may have nonzeros in its leading components.

$$T = \begin{bmatrix} * & & & & & \\ x & * & & & & \\ x & x & * & & & \\ x & x & x & * & & \\ & & & & x & * & \\ & & & & x & x & * \end{bmatrix} \quad ; \quad P_S^* = \begin{bmatrix} x \\ x \\ x \\ x \\ x \\ x \end{bmatrix}$$

(drop)   (enter)

$$(3)$$

The sequence of operations on rows by which T is obtained from B is equivalent to multiplying B on the left by a succession of elementary matrices so that

$$T = E_1 E_2 \ldots E_m B \tag{4}$$

Here $E_m = E_6$ represents an elementary matrix corresponding to a pivot in row 6. Thus the first pivot operation is the same as multiplying B on the left by

$$E_6 = \begin{bmatrix} 1 & & & & & \\ & 1 & & & & \\ & & 1 & & & \\ & & & 1 & & \\ & & & & 1 & P_{56} \\ & & & & & 1 \end{bmatrix} \tag{5}$$

where p_{56} is selected so that row 6, when multiplied by p_{56} and added to row 5, will cause the element (5,6) of the matrix to vanish. Since no eliminations are required in column 5, E_5 is an identity matrix. Next, E_4 will be similar to E_6 except with one nonzero entry p_{34} for element (3,4) and E_3 will have at most two nonzero entries above the diagonal p_{13}, p_{23}, corresponding to the factors required to eliminate elements (1,3) and (2,3) from the matrix using row 3. Similarly E_2 will have an entry p_{12}, and E_1 will be an identity matrix. Since each elementary matrix E_i is an identity matrix except for nonzero entries above the diagonal of column i, we may, for purposes of compact recording, simply list side by side the entries in column 1 of E_1, in column 2 of E_2, etc. We shall refer to this typical product form record of the transformations as the E-structure. For our example

$$E\text{-structure} = \begin{bmatrix} 1 \\ \end{bmatrix} \begin{bmatrix} P_{12} \\ 1 \end{bmatrix} \begin{bmatrix} P_{13} \\ P_{23} \\ 1 \end{bmatrix} \begin{bmatrix} P_{34} \\ 1 \end{bmatrix} \begin{bmatrix} \\ 1 \end{bmatrix} \begin{bmatrix} \\ P_{56} \\ 1 \end{bmatrix} \tag{6}$$

Note again that the pattern of nonzeros in the E-structure (excluding the units on the diagonal) is precisely the same as the pattern of nonzeros

above the main diagonal of the original basis B. Thus the statement in
product form of the nonzero coefficients in the transformations E_i necessary to reduce a basis to triangular form T and the record of nonzeros in
T have as compact a representation as the original basis.

We give the formulas for the determination of the set of simplex multipliers (or pricing vector) π and the representation $\overline{P}_S$ of the vector P_S
entering the basis, when E_i and T are known. Let γ be the vector of coefficients of the cost form for the basic variables, then by definition

$$\pi B = \gamma \tag{7}$$

If now we define π^* by the relation

$$\pi^* T = \gamma \tag{8}$$

then, it is easy to see, by (4), that

$$\pi = \pi^* E_1 E_2 \ldots E_m \tag{9}$$

Because T is triangular, π^* can be directly computed from (8) and π from
(9) by applying to π^* the transformations E_1, E_2, ... in turn on the right.

Having obtained π, we can by the usual "pricing out" procedure determine the vector P_S to enter the basis by

$$\pi P_S = \underset{j}{\text{Min }} \pi P_j < 0 \tag{10}$$

By definition, the representation $\overline{P}_S$ of P_S in terms of the basis satisfies

$$B\overline{P}_S = P_S \tag{11}$$

If now we define P_S^* by the relation

$$P_S^* = E_1 E_2 \ldots E_m P_S \tag{12}$$

then, it is again easy to see, by (4) and (11), that

$$T\overline{P}_S = P_S^* \tag{13}$$

Relation (12) allows us to compute P_S^*, and because T is triangular, $\overline{P}_S$
is computed by direct solution of (13).

Given $\overline{P}_S$ and the basic feasible solution, the usual rules are next applied
to determine the vector P_r to drop from the basis and to determine the
basic feasible solution for the next iteration. We shall omit these steps
assuming they are known to the reader.

Our problem now becomes one of "up-dating" our substitute inverse.
This of course could be done by succession of pivot operations above the
diagonal such as we described earlier. But this is not very efficient com-

putationally. We shall show instead an efficient procedure for easily modifying the E-structure and T matrix of one iteration to obtain those of the next.

Let us assume in our example [see (2)] that the vector P_s entering the basis, if entered in its proper position in the staircase array, would be located, say, between either vectors P_4 and P_5 of the basis (or vectors P_3 and P_4), and let us suppose that vector P_1 is to be dropped. Starting with the columns of B and P_s <u>after</u> they have been transformed by the row operations $E_1 E_2 \ldots E_m$, namely with T and P_s^* as shown in (3), our objective is to triangularize the matrix formed by deleting the first column and introducing P_s^*, say, between columns 4 and 5 (actually between columns 3 and 4 would be less work). The row operations that accomplish this are to create zeros in the first three rows of P_s^* column by successively adding first a multiple of row 2 to row 1, next a multiple of row 3 to row 2, and then a multiple of row 4 to row 3. We shall denote these single-row transformations by E_2^1, E_3^2, and E_4^3. For the present we have assumed above that the second, third and fourth components of P_s^* are nonvanishing (this need not be the case). The results of these operations are shown in (14) where * indicates the elements of the previous diagonal and □ those of the new diagonal.

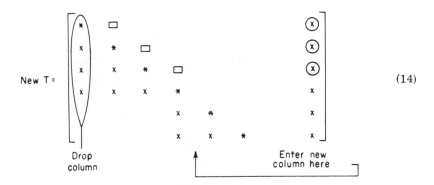

The relationship between the new T and the new B may be written

$$(\text{New } T) = E_4^3 E_3^2 E_2^1 E_1 E_2 E_3 E_4 E_5 E_6 \ (\text{New } B) \tag{15}$$

If, however, the column to be dropped were $j = 4$ (instead of $j = 1$), it would be necessary to eliminate the □ element in column 3 and then the ones in column 2 by additional transformations of the type E_i^{i-1}, say $\overline{E}_3^2$, $\overline{E}_2^1$, in this case

$$(\text{New } T) = \overline{E}_2^1 \overline{E}_3^2 E_4^3 E_3^2 E_2^1 E_1 E_2 E_3 E_4 E_5 E_6 \ (\text{New } B)$$

We have shown that the new T can be obtained by applying to the previous product of the E_i a succession of row operations of the form E_i^{i-1} where, in general, we have denoted by E_i^k an elementary matrix corresponding to adding a multiple of row i to row k. Our objective, however, has not been accomplished until we have shown how to obtain easily the new T directly from the new B by a succession of new pivot operations E_i^*. This is easy to accomplish if we observe the following rules:

I. If E_i and $\overline{E}_i$ are two elementary matrices representing adding a multiple of row i to other rows, then their product $E_i \overline{E}_i$ can be replaced by an elementary matrix of the same type, say, E_i^*. For example

$$
\begin{bmatrix} 1 & & p_{13} \\ & 1 & p_{23} \\ & & 1 \end{bmatrix}
\begin{bmatrix} 1 & & \overline{p}_{13} \\ & 1 & \overline{p}_{23} \\ & & 1 \end{bmatrix}
=
\begin{bmatrix} 1 & & p_{13} + \overline{p}_{13} \\ & 1 & p_{23} + \overline{p}_{23} \\ & & 1 \end{bmatrix}
$$

II. "Near commutativity" of adjacent-indexed matrices E_i^{i-1} and E_{i-1} holds; thus the product $E_i^{i-1} E_{i-1}$ can be replaced by $E_{i-1}\overline{E}_i$. For example

$$
\begin{bmatrix} 1 & & & \\ & 1 & & \\ & & 1 & p_{34} \\ & & & 1 \end{bmatrix}
\begin{bmatrix} 1 & & q_{13} & \\ & 1 & q_{23} & \\ & & 1 & \\ & & & 1 \end{bmatrix}
=
\begin{bmatrix} 1 & & q_{13} & \\ & 1 & q_{23} & \\ & & 1 & \\ & & & 1 \end{bmatrix}
\begin{bmatrix} 1 & & & -q_{13}p_{34} \\ & 1 & & -q_{23}p_{34} \\ & & 1 & p_{34} \\ & & & 1 \end{bmatrix}
$$

III. Nonadjacent-indexed matrices can be commuted; thus

$$E_i^{i-1}E_k = E_k E_i^{i-1} \qquad \text{if } k < i - 1$$

For our example let us denote the new E_i by E_i^*, so that we are interested in obtaining the relation

$$(\text{New } T) = E_1^* E_2^* E_3^* E_4^* E_5^* E_6^* (\text{New } B)$$

by applying the above rules to (15). In this case

$$E_1^* = E_1 \quad \text{(the identity)}$$
$$E_2^* = E_2^1 E_2$$
$$E_3^* = \overline{E}_3 E_3 \qquad \text{where } E_3^2 E_2^* = E_2^* \overline{E}_3$$

Note particularly that the formation of each E_i^*, from a computational point of view, consists essentially of multiplying most of the elements of column $i - 1$ of E_{i-1} by a constant and adding it to the corresponding elements of column i of E_i.

The process described above of reducing to triangular form the matrix formed by dropping a column of T and inserting P_s^* was based on the assumption that certain coefficients of P_s^* were nonzero. If, for example, the second component is zero but the first component is not, it would not be possible to use a row operation E_2' to cause the first component of P_S^* to vanish.

Let us suppose that the position of column P_S in the new basis is k columns from the left (we assume that pivoting is done by starting always with the lower right-hand element of each submatrix).

Let the column being dropped from the basis be $r \leq k$. In the process of computation of P_S^* by (12), we obtain the vector

$$P_S' = E_k E_{k+1} \ldots E_m P_S$$

Now P_S' must have its first nonzero component for some index $h \leq k$ since the new B is nonsingular. We assume for the moment that the kth component is not zero. Accordingly, starting with P_S^*, the elimination of its first nonzero component with index s_1 can be effected by using its second nonzero component with index s_2, etc., until its nonzero component with index $s_t = k$ is used. This corresponds to row operations of the form $E_{s_2}^{s_1}$ followed by $E_{s_3}^{s_2}$, etc. The remaining components with indices k, k+1, ..., m are unaffected by the above operations and hence remain the same as those of P_S^*. Thus the result is the same, as far as columns $P_k, P_{k+1}, \ldots, P_m$ are concerned, as if triangularization had been effected directly using these columns. If $s_1 + 1 - s_2 = \Delta > 0$, it will be necessary to permute cyclically certain of the rows by relabeling rows $s_1, s_1 + 1, \ldots, s_2 - 1$ as rows $s_2 - 1, s_1, s_1 + 1, \ldots, s_2 - 2$. In a similar manner, rows $s_2, s_2 + 1, \ldots, s_3 - 1$ are permuted if $s_2 + 1 - s_3 > 0$, etc. Allowing such permutations, it is no longer necessary to assume above that the kth component of P_S^* (or P_S') was not zero.

It is important to note that such permutations would have been required if direct triangularization of all columns had been effected initially. Moreover, as far as staircase-structured systems are concerned, these permutations would not have affected the below-diagonal-staircase-form of T or the above-diagonal-staircase-form of the E-structure because, if direct eliminations were used, the eliminations and row interchanges would have been confined only to rows where the components of P_S are nonzero.

Let us now turn our attention to the column P_r to be dropped from the basis. Suppose first $r < k$. Deletion of the corresponding column of T followed by the necessary eliminations to restore triangularity discussed earlier will also require permutations if the indicated pivot position along the diagonal has a zero coefficient. For example, a two-cycle permutation will be required in order to lower to the diagonal the nonzero coefficient just above the diagonal. If $r \geq k$, it appears to be necessary first to drop the column corresponding to P_r from T and to retriangularize columns k, k+1, ..., r−1 (omitting r), and, <u>next</u>, to insert the column corresponding to P_S by performing the eliminations described above to P_S^*.

Since, in general, row permutations are required to obtain the triangular arrangement in standard form, it is necessary to replace (4) by

$$T = E_1 E_2 \dots E_m JB \tag{4'}$$

where J represents a permutation matrix. Each new cyclic permutation C introduced in the process of elimination to a new triangular form can be accounted for by appropriately relabeling the row designations of coefficients in E_i and J.

Finally, it is necessary to restate the rules given earlier for up-dating the substitute inverse when elementary matrices of the type E_i^ℓ, where $\ell < i$, appear on the left instead of E_i^{i-1} discussed earlier. In this case the rules are:

II': $E_i^\ell E_\ell = E_\ell \overline{E}_i$ where $\ell < i$ and where, letting $p_{i\ell}$ be the ℓ,i component of E_i^ℓ, the ith column of $\overline{E}_i$ is formed by multiplying by $-p_{\ell i}$ the corresponding coefficients in column ℓ of E_ℓ with the exception of rows ℓ and i. For row ℓ, the coefficient is $p_{\ell i}$, and for row i, the coefficient is unity.

III': $E_k^\ell E_i = E_i E_k^\ell$ if $i < \ell < k$

IV: $\overline{E}_i E_q = E_q \overline{E}_i$ if $\ell < q < i$, where ℓ is the same ℓ as that which generated $\overline{E}_i$ in II'. Note that the commutativity of the matrices holds because $\overline{E}_i$ has a zero coefficient in column i for row q and E_q has a zero coefficient in column q for row i.

The Simplex Method Using Pseudo-basic Variables for Structured Linear Programming Problems

E. M. L. Beale

A procedure is described for solving linear programming problems that consist of separate subproblems with a few linking variables that occur in all (or several) subproblems. This is the simplex method, organized so that the advantages of the special structure of the problem are preserved.

1. INTRODUCTION

Dantzig and Wolfe [2] have described a "decomposition principle" for solving linear programming problems consisting of a set of separate sub-problems except for a few "linking equations" containing variables that occur in all (or several) subproblems. This paper presents a method of solving the dual problem, i.e., one consisting of separate subproblems except for a few linking variables that occur in all (or several) subproblems.

Problems of this sort arise in many contexts. For example, they arise when one is scheduling operations over several time-periods; and also in 2-stage linear programming under uncertainty when the random variables have discrete distributions.

Of course, by the duality theorem, the linking variables problem and the linking equations problem can be transformed into one another. But, although it was inspired by Dantzig and Wolfe's decomposition principle, this work is in fact more closely related to Dantzig's work on block triangularity [1]. Dantzig there proposed the use of the simplex method with an "artificial basis $\bar{B}$" and a "true basis B." The true basis consists of the coefficients of the basic variables in the present trial solution, and the artificial basis differs from this in at most a few columns and is "square block triangular." The inverse of $\bar{B}$ can then be stored compactly, and the work is carried out in terms of $\bar{B}^{-1}$ and a

†Part of this work was done at the symposium on Combinatorial Problems sponsored by the RAND Corporation from July 10 to August 18, 1961. I am grateful for helpful comments from G. B. Dantzig, A. J. Hoffman, W. Orchard-Hays and D. M. Smith. Any views expressed in this paper are those of the author. They should not be interpreted as reflecting the views of The RAND Corporation or the official opinion or policy of any of its governmental or private research sponsors. This paper appeared in print previously as RAND Corporation Paper P-2405, August 15, 1961.

matrix η defining the columns of $\overline{B}$ not in B in terms of the columns of B.

The present work proceeds similarly. But a more specialized problem has been considered, with the result that the lay-out becomes considerably neater. It seems likely that the proposed algorithm will be more efficient for these problems than that derived from the decomposition principle, since this algorithm follows the simplex method, and includes plausible rules for choosing the nonbasic variables to be introduced into the trial solution.

The algorithm is motivated in Section 2, described algebraically in Section 3, and illustrated by an annotated small-scale numerical example in Section 4. Rules for choosing pivotal columns and rows are presented in Section 5. These rules do not affect the theoretical properties of the algorithm, but they may be vital to its practical efficiency. Finally, some general remarks about solving linear programming problems with special structure are offered in Section 6.

For ease of exposition, the various stages of the algorithm are written out in explicit equation form in the first part of the paper, and the numerical example is given in the detached coefficient form. In practice there is no difficulty about using the inverse matrix method for the subproblems. But it may be best to store the coefficients of the linking variables in explicit tableau form, since they are used extensively and are subject to both row and column operations. (They correspond to Dantzig's essential columns of η, which he also visualized as being stored explicitly.) In this respect the algorithm is less compact than that derived from the decomposition principle when the linking coefficients are sparse—since these linking coefficients can conveniently be manipulated through the inverse matrix.

2. MOTIVATION

The essential idea of this method is that the linking variables should be regarded as parameters. It is obvious that if these parameters are given specific numerical values, then it is a straightforward matter to solve the subproblems to optimize the objective function for these parameter values. It then "only" remains to see whether we can do even better by changing the parameters. If these were originally given arbitrary values, then it is almost certain that the solution can be improved by either increasing or decreasing the value of one parameter, keeping the others constant. Because the problem is linear, this situation will persist until some basic variable becomes zero. If one were using the ordinary simplex method, one would then make this variable nonbasic, in place of the parameter. But we cannot do this without spoiling the structure of the problem, so we do not do it. Instead, we make a transformation of parameters, so that if we subsequently change one of the other parameters we do not change this zero-valued basic variable. I call this a "pseudo-basic" variable, since it appears in the tableau as a basic variable but is really a nonbasic variable from the point of view of the rationale of the simplex method.

The resulting process can therefore be regarded as the simplex method, organized in such a way that some nonbasic variables remain on the left-hand sides of the equations so as to avoid spoiling the structure of the problem. They correspond to variables in the artificial basis but not in the true basis in Dantzig's block triangular scheme.

3. ALGEBRAIC DESCRIPTION OF THE ALGORITHM

The problem to be solved can be represented as follows: Find nonnegative vectors θ, $x^{(\ell)}$, $\ell = 1, \ldots, L$, so as to minimize

$$C = c'\theta + \sum_{\ell} c^{(\ell)'}x^{(\ell)}$$

(1)

subject to the constraints

$$T^{(0)}\,\theta \qquad\qquad = b^{(0)}$$
$$T^{(\ell)}\,\theta + A^{(\ell)}\,x^{(\ell)} = b^{(\ell)} \qquad (\ell = 1, \ldots, L)$$

We refer to the components of θ as parameters.

To start the algorithm, we express these constraints in "solved form," so that they read

$$\theta_i = b_{i0} + \sum_{j=1}^{p} t_{ij0}\,\theta_j$$

$$x_{i\ell} = b_{i\ell} + \sum_{j=1}^{p} t_{ij\ell}\,\theta_j + \sum_{k} a_{ik\ell}\,x_{k\ell}$$

$$C = c_0 + \sum_{j=1}^{p} c_j\,\theta_j + \sum_{k}\sum_{\ell} c_{k\ell}\,x_{k\ell}$$

(2)

where the variables on the left-hand sides are all distinct from the variables on the right-hand sides. The θ_i and $x_{i\ell}$ may be artificial variables, in which case the objective function will contain an overriding term representing the sum of the infeasibilities. But this introduces no new principle or complication. When an artificial variable or parameter becomes nonbasic, it may of course be dropped from the problem.

It is natural to start by giving the parameters some plausible values, and solving the subproblems for these parameter values. One can, of course, start with all the parameters equal to zero, in which case one has a genuine basic solution to the problem. But these will often be very unrealistic values, leaving a long way further to go to the optimum. And one may have studied the subproblems separately, with the result that one has a fair idea about what these parameters should be.

Let our plausible values be

$$\theta_j = \alpha_j \qquad (j = 1, \ldots, p)$$

Then we define p new parameters ϕ_j by the equations

$$\theta_j = \alpha_j + \phi_j$$

write these p equations at the top of the tableau, and substitute for θ_j throughout the remaining equations.

Since our "plausible values" of ϕ_j are all zero, this means that the constant terms involved in solving the subproblems for these plausible parameter values are gathered together in the first column of the tableau. But these additional p equations play a central role in the algorithm, and we would have written them in even if our "plausible values" of α_j had all been taken as zero.

After having solved the subproblems for these parameter values, we will have a tableau of the following form:

$$\theta_i = b_{i0} + \sum_{j=1}^{p} t_{ij0} \, \phi_j$$

$$x_{i\ell} = b_{i\ell} + \sum_{j=1}^{p} t_{ij\ell} \, \phi_j + \sum_{k} a_{ik\ell} \, x_{k\ell}$$

$$C = c_0 + \sum_{j=1}^{p} c_j \, \phi_j + \sum_{k} \sum_{\ell} c_{k\ell} \, x_{k\ell} \qquad (3)$$

where all $c_{k\ell} \geq 0$. The coefficients and variables occurring on the right-hand sides of (3) will of course not be numerically equal to those in (2), and the first group of equations (for θ_i) will be p more in number than they were in (2).

The next stage of the algorithm amounts to solving the linear programming problem defined by (3), with the restriction that the nonbasic variables $x_{k\ell}$ must remain equal to zero. This is done by the simplex method using the extended dual tableau.

The extended dual tableau contains the definitions of all variables, including the nonbasic ones, in terms of the nonbasic variables. It therefore includes a permutation matrix amongst its rows. But here the nonbasic variables must be regarded as new transformed parameters, and not identified with the corresponding $x_{i\ell}$, since they are really equal to

$$x_{i\ell} - \sum_{k} a_{ik\ell} \, x_{k\ell}$$

There is also a complication in that this stage starts off from a nonbasic solution. But this is met by first taking each of the original ϕ_j in turn, and either increasing or decreasing it (according to the sign of its co-efficient in the current expression for C) until some basic variable becomes equal to zero. We then make this variable pseudo-basic, introducing an associated parameter—defined by the first $p + 1$ terms of the expression for this pseudo-basic variable—into the nonbasic set. Once each ϕ_j has been processed in this way we always have p pseudo-basic variables (amongst the θ_i and $x_{i\ell}$), each associated with some parameter. There will then be the correct number of genuine basic variables, since p additional variables were added to the left-hand sides of the equations in the transformation from (2) to (3).

Note that a new parameter is introduced into the nonbasic set at each iteration. Nevertheless, the tableau does not grow longer because these parameters are not sign-restricted, and they can be dropped as soon as they cease to be nonbasic. In fact, if one looks only at the tableau and not the names of the nonbasic variables, one is simply doing the simplex method in the extended dual tableau, as pointed out earlier.

Eventually we will obtain a tableau like (3) with all $c_j \geq 0$. This implies that C cannot be further reduced by varying the values of the basic and pseudo-basic variables, keeping the genuine nonbasic variables, i.e., the $x_{k\ell}$, equal to zero. Following the usual procedure in the simplex method, we must then consider whether it would be profitable to increase some nonbasic variable $x_{k\ell}$, keeping the pseudo-basic variables and the other nonbasic variables equal to zero.

So far, each operation has been a very simple one. We have been working exclusively with the first $p + 1$ columns of the tableau, the re-maining columns being simply copied from one tableau to the next—except while we were solving the subproblems for the initial plausible values of the parameters, when we only needed to work with the subproblems in-dividually. But now we have to pay a modest price for this simplification.

When considering the genuine nonbasic variables, we find that the process of computing the effect of a unit increase in such a variable is somewhat more complicated than usual (unless one is using the product form of the inverse, in which case this is already a fairly complicated operation). Then, if any increase is necessary, up to 3 changes of variables may be required. One involves only the subproblem concerned, the second (which may not be needed) involves only the coefficients of one parameter, and the last involves only the constant terms. In a com-puter program these stages may be combined, but for ease of exposition they are here presented separately.

To find the unit effect of increasing some nonbasic variable $x_{k\ell}$ we must find the coefficient $c_{k\ell}^*$ of this variable in the expression for C in terms of the pseudo-basic and nonbasic variables. This must be derived from the tableau represented by (3), where C is expressed in terms of the parameters and nonbasic variables, by substituting for the parameters in terms of the pseudo-basic and nonbasic variables.

Now if the variable $x_{i\ell}$ is pseudo-basic, the expression for it in (3) will be of the form

$$x_{i\ell} = \phi_{(i)} + \sum_k a_{ik\ell} x_{k\ell} \qquad (4)$$

so that the parameter $\phi_{(i)}$ can be represented as

$$\phi_{(i)} = x_{i\ell} - \sum_k a_{ik\ell} x_{k\ell} \qquad (5)$$

and hence

$$c_{k\ell}^* = c_{k\ell} - \sum c_{(i)} a_{ik\ell} \qquad (6)$$

where summation ranges over all i for which $x_{i\ell}$ is pseudo-basic, and $\phi_{(i)}$ is the parameter associated with it.

If, and only if, $c_{k\ell}^* < 0$ can C be reduced by increasing $x_{k\ell}$ and keeping all other nonbasic and pseudo-basic variables equal to zero. If there are several negative $c_{k\ell}^*$, the algorithm, like the original simplex method, does not depend for its theoretical properties on which one is chosen. Discussion of suitable selection rules is therefore deferred until Section 5.

So let us suppose that we have found some nonbasic variable $x_{k\ell}$ such that $c_{k\ell}^* < 0$, and that we wish to increase $x_{k\ell}$. Now it is just possible that there will be no pseudo-basic variable $x_{i\ell}$ in the same subproblem such that $a_{ik\ell} \neq 0$. Then we can perform a regular simplex step, i.e., pivotal operation, within the subproblem. This will increase $x_{k\ell}$ immediately, making it a genuine basic variable, and making some previously genuine basic variable nonbasic.

But the usual situation will be to find some pseudo-basic variable $x_{i\ell}$ in this subproblem such that $a_{ik\ell} \neq 0$. Then we cannot increase $x_{k\ell}$ directly without changing the value of $x_{i\ell}$, which we do not want to do. We therefore have to perform a preliminary pivotal operation within the subproblem to make $x_{k\ell}$ pseudo-basic in place of some existing pseudo-basic variable $x_{i\ell}$ in this subproblem. If there are several such pseudo-basic variables, then again the algorithm theoretically does not depend on which one is chosen, and further discussion is deferred until Section 5.

At this stage it is desirable to study the formulas in detail. We denote the nonbasic variable we ultimately wish to increase by $x_{s\ell}$. The pseudo-basic variable to be made nonbasic is denoted by $x_{r\ell}$, and the other pseudo-basic variables in the same subproblem, if any, are denoted generically by $x_{h\ell}$. Let the parameters associated with the pseudo-basic variables $x_{r\ell}$ and $x_{h\ell}$ be $\phi_{(r)}$ and $\phi_{(h)}$. Let $x_{i\ell}$ denote some other basic variable in the same subproblem, ϕ_j some other parameter, and $x_{k\ell}$ some other nonbasic variable in the same subproblem.

Then the tableau reads, in part,

$$x_{r\ell} = \qquad \phi_{(r)} \qquad\qquad + a_{rs\ell} x_{s\ell} + a_{rk\ell} x_{k\ell}$$
$$x_{h\ell} = \qquad\qquad \phi_{(h)} \qquad\qquad + a_{hs\ell} x_{s\ell} + a_{hk\ell} x_{k\ell}$$

$$x_{i\ell} = b_{i\ell} + t_{ir\ell}\phi_{(r)} + t_{ih\ell}\phi_{(h)} + t_{ij\ell}\phi_j + a_{is\ell}x_{s\ell} + a_{ik\ell}x_{k\ell}$$

$$C = c_0 + c_r\phi_{(r)} + c_h\phi_{(h)} + c_j\phi_j + c_{s\ell}x_{s\ell} + c_{k\ell}x_{k\ell} \tag{7}$$

And we have

$$c^*_{s\ell} = c_{s\ell} - c_r\,a_{rs\ell} - \sum_h c_h\,a_{hs\ell} < 0, \qquad a_{rs\ell} \neq 0 \tag{8}$$

After the pivotal operation this part of the tableau reads

$$x_{s\ell} = \quad - P\phi_{(r)} \qquad\qquad\qquad\qquad + Px_{r\ell} \quad - Pa_{rk\ell}x_{k\ell}$$

$$x_{h\ell} = \quad - Pa_{hs\ell}\phi_{(r)} \quad + \phi_{(h)} \qquad\qquad + Pa_{hs\ell}x_{r\ell} + a'_{hk\ell}x_{k\ell}$$

$$x_{i\ell} = b_{i\ell} + (t_{ir\ell} - Pa_{is\ell})\phi_{(r)} + t_{ih\ell}\phi_{(h)} + t_{ij\ell}\phi_j + Pa_{is\ell}x_{r\ell} + a'_{ik\ell}x_{k\ell}$$

$$C = c_0 + (c_r - Pc_{s\ell})\phi_{(r)} + c_h\phi_{(h)} + c_j\phi_j + Pc_{s\ell}x_{r\ell} + c'_{k\ell}x_{k\ell} \tag{9}$$

where

$$P = 1/a_{rs\ell},$$

$$a'_{hk\ell} = a_{hk\ell} - Pa_{rk\ell}a_{hs\ell},$$

$$a'_{ik\ell} = a_{ik\ell} - Pa_{rk\ell}a_{is\ell},$$

$$c'_{k\ell} = c_{k\ell} - Pa_{rk\ell}c_{s\ell}$$

Now, if there are any other pseudo-basic variables $x_{h\ell}$ in this sub-problem with $a_{hk\ell} \neq 0$, we must "clean up" the coefficients of $\phi_{(r)}$ in the expressions for these variables. Otherwise when we change the value of $\phi_{(r)}$ to change $x_{s\ell}$ we will also change $x_{h\ell}$.
So we write

$$\phi'_{(h)} = - Pa_{hs\ell}\,\phi_{(r)} + \phi_{(h)} \tag{10}$$

and substitute throughout (9) for $\phi_{(h)}$ in terms of $\phi_{(r)}$ and $\phi'_{(h)}$. We can do this for all pseudo-basic variables $x_{h\ell}$ in the subproblem in one operation. It affects only the column of coefficients of $\phi_{(r)}$. We add $Pa_{hs\ell}$ times the column of coefficients of $\phi_{(h)}$, and the tableau then reads

$$x_{s\ell} = \quad - P\phi_{(r)} \qquad\qquad\qquad\qquad + Px_{r\ell} \quad - Pa_{rk\ell}x_{k\ell}$$

$$x_{h\ell} = \qquad\qquad\qquad\qquad \phi'_{(h)} \qquad + Pa_{hs\ell}x_{r\ell} + a'_{hk\ell}x_{k\ell}$$

$$x_{i\ell} = b_{i\ell} + (t_{ir\ell} - Pa_{is\ell} + \sum_h Pa_{hs\ell}t_{ih\ell})\,\phi_{(r)} + t_{ih\ell}\,\phi'_{(h)} + t_{ij\ell}\phi_j + Pa_{is\ell}x_{r\ell} + a'_{ik\ell}x_{k\ell}$$

$$C = c_0 + (c_r - Pc_{s\ell} + \sum_h Pa_{hs\ell}c_h)\,\phi_{(r)} + c_h\,\phi'_{(h)} + c_j\phi_j + Pc_{s\ell}x_{r\ell} + c'_{k\ell}x_{k\ell} \tag{11}$$

Now at last we can increase $x_{s\ell}$, by increasing $\phi_{(r)}$ if $a_{rs\ell}$ (and hence P) is negative, or by decreasing $\phi_{(r)}$ if $a_{rs\ell}$ is positive. [Since the coefficient of $\phi_{(r)}$ in the expression for C in (11) is simply $-Pc^*_{s\ell}$, from (8), this change must be profitable if we calculated $c_{s\ell}^*$ correctly in the first instance.]

We now resume the process of optimizing the problem conditional on keeping all genuine nonbasic variables equal to zero.

The algorithm is now complete, in that we have seen how to improve the trial solution by changing a pseudo-basic variable, or by changing a nonbasic variable. If no such change is profitable then we know we have an optimal solution, just as we would if we had carried out our simplex calculations in the standard way.

Of course it is not essential to find the very best solution with a given set of basic and pseudo-basic variables before examining the possibility of introducing some nonbasic variable. Indeed the following sort of scheme might work out best in practice.

1. After solving the subproblems for the original "plausible values" for the parameters, eliminate each of the original ϕ_j in turn from the nonbasic set. We then have a genuine basic trial solution.

2. If possible, introduce some nonbasic variable from the first subproblem.

3. If possible, introduce some pseudo-basic variable.

4. If possible, introduce some nonbasic variable from the second subproblem.

And so on.

4. A NUMERICAL EXAMPLE

For the benefit of those who, like the present author, prefer numbers to formulas, I now present a minature scale numerical example.
Minimize

$$C = -3\theta_1 - 2\theta_2 - \theta_3 + 2x_{41} + x_{51} + x_{61} + x_{42} + x_{52} + 5_{62},$$

subject to the constraints $\theta_i \geq 0$, $x_{ij} \geq 0$, and

$$x_{11} = 2 - \theta_1 - 2\theta_2 + 2\theta_3 + x_{41} + x_{51} + x_{61}$$
$$x_{21} = 4 - \theta_1 + \theta_2 - \theta_3 + x_{41} + x_{51}$$
$$x_{31} = 2 + \theta_1 + \theta_2 - \theta_3 + x_{51} + 2x_{61}$$
$$x_{12} = 4 + \theta_1 - 2\theta_3 - x_{42} + x_{52}$$
$$x_{22} = -\theta_2 + \theta_3 - x_{42} + x_{52} + 2x_{62}$$
$$x_{32} = 5 - \theta_1 - 3\theta_2 + x_{42} - x_{52} + x_{62}$$

This problem consists of two 3×3 subproblems with three linking variables. In fact the tableau is barely sparse enough to justify using a special method, but the problem serves to illustrate the technique.

Let us suppose that $\theta_1 = \theta_2 = \theta_3 = 1$ are "plausible values" for the parameters. Then we start by writing the tableau in the form

	ϕ_1^0	ϕ_2^0	ϕ_3^0	x_{41}	x_{51}	x_{61}	x_{42}	x_{52}	x_{62}
θ_1	1	1							
θ_2	1		1						
θ_3	1			1					
x_{11}	1	-1	-2	2	1	1	1		
x_{21}	3	-1	1	-1	1	1			
x_{31}	3	1	1	-1		1	2		
x_{12}	3	1		-2				-1	1
x_{22}		-1	1				-1	1	2
x_{32}	1	-1	-3				1	-1	1
C	-6	-3	-2	-1	2	1	1	1	5

Note that all this tableau except the first column has in effect simply been copied from the previous tableau. Similar situations occur throughout the algorithm, but the tableau is nevertheless presented in full at each stage to make it easier to follow.

The parameters ϕ_j have been given superfixes to distinguish them from their successors in the nonbasic set. For practical purposes these super-fixes are just decorations.

The problem of solving the subproblems conditional on keeping the $\phi_i^0 = 0$ is a standard exercise in linear programming. In the example this is already achieved. We therefore proceed to investigate changes in the parameters.

At the moment we do not have a basic trial solution, since we have 8 variables at nonzero levels (plus one accidental zero), and a basic solution should have only 6. So we proceed to increase or decrease each ϕ_i^0 in turn until we obtain a "pseudo-basic" variable with a trial value of zero on the right-hand side of some equation. We do this so as not to increase C at any stage.

Since the coefficient of ϕ_1^0 in the expression for C is negative, we increase ϕ_1^0. Comparing coefficients of ϕ_1^0 with the constant terms in the usual way, we see that this remains possible until $\phi_1^0 = 1$, when both x_{11} and x_{32} become zero. We arbitrarily select x_{11} from these to be the new "pseudo-basic" variable. We then introduce a new parameter ϕ_1^1, defined by the expression for x_{11} without the genuine nonbasic variables, and substitute for ϕ_1^0 throughout. We then have the tableau

	ϕ_1^1	ϕ_2^0	ϕ_3^0	x_{41}	x_{51}	x_{61}	x_{42}	x_{52}	x_{62}
ϕ_1^0	1	-1	-2	2					
θ_1	2	-1	-2	2					
θ_2	1	1							
θ_3	1		1						
$*x_{11}$		1			1	1	1		
x_{21}	2	1	3	-3	1	1			
x_{31}	4	-1	1	1		1	2		
x_{12}	4	-1	-2				-1	1	
x_{22}		-1	1				-1	1	2
x_{32}	1	-1	-2				1	-1	1
C	-9	3	4	-7	2	1	1	1	5

An asterisk has been placed against x_{11} to indicate that it is a pseudo-basic variable. This tableau illustrates the purpose of the transformation of parameters. In the present trial solution $x_{11} = 0$, and we want to be sure that it will not immediately become negative when we vary some other parameter.

We now consider the parameter ϕ_2^0. This has a positive coefficient in the current expression for C, so we decrease it. We can do this until x_{21} becomes zero, and hence we introduce the new parameter ϕ_2^1 defined by the expression for x_{21} without the genuine nonbasic variables, and substitute for ϕ_2^0 throughout. We then have the tableau

	ϕ_1^1	ϕ_2^1	ϕ_3^0	x_{41}	x_{51}	x_{61}	x_{42}	x_{52}	x_{62}
ϕ_2^0	$-2/3$	$-1/3$	$1/3$	1					
θ_1	$10/3$	$-1/3$	$-2/3$						
θ_2	$1/3$	$-1/3$	$1/3$	1					
θ_3	1			1					
*x_{11}		1			1	1	1		
*x_{21}			1		1	1			
x_{31}	$14/3$	$-2/3$	$-1/3$				1	2	
x_{12}	$16/3$	$-1/3$	$-2/3$	-2				-1	1
x_{22}	$2/3$	$1/3$	$-1/3$					-1	1	2
x_{32}	$2/3$	$4/3$	$-1/3$	-3				1	-1	1
C	$-35/3$	$5/3$	$4/3$	-3	2	1	1	1	1	5

We now increase ϕ_3^0 until x_{32} becomes zero, introduce the new parameter ϕ_3^1 defined by the expression for x_{32} without the genuine nonbasic variables, and substitute for ϕ_3^0 throughout. We then have the tableau

	ϕ_1^1	ϕ_2^1	ϕ_3^1	x_{41}	x_{51}	x_{61}	x_{42}	x_{52}	x_{62}
ϕ_3^0	$2/9$	$4/9$	$-1/9$	$-1/3$					
θ_1	$10/3$	$-1/3$	$-2/3$						
θ_2	$5/9$	$1/9$	$2/9$	$-1/3$					
θ_3	$11/9$	$4/9$	$-1/9$	$-1/3$					
*x_{11}		1			1	1	1		
*x_{21}			1		1	1			
x_{31}	$14/3$	$-2/3$	$-1/3$				1	2	
x_{12}	$44/9$	$-11/9$	$-4/9$	$2/3$				-1	1
x_{22}	$2/3$	$1/3$	$-1/3$					-1	1	2
*x_{32}				1				1	-1	1
C	$-37/3$	$1/3$	$5/3$	1	2	1	1	1	1	5

We now consider whether any nonbasic variable from the first subproblem can usefully be increased. To illustrate the process of computing the $c_{k\ell}^*$, we express C completely in terms of the pseudo-basic and nonbasic variables, though in practice only the coefficients of x_{41}, x_{51} and x_{61} would be calculated at this point. We have

$$C = -\frac{37}{3} \qquad\qquad + \qquad 2x_{41} + x_{51} + x_{61} + x_{42} + x_{52} + 5x_{62}$$

$$+ \frac{1}{3}x_{11} \qquad\qquad - \frac{1}{3}(+\ x_{41} + x_{51} + x_{61})$$

$$+ \frac{5}{3}x_{21} \qquad\qquad - \frac{5}{3}(+\ x_{41} + x_{51})$$

$$+ x_{32} \qquad\qquad -(x_{42} - x_{52} + x_{62})$$

$$= -\frac{37}{3} + \frac{1}{3}x_{11} + \frac{5}{3}x_{21} + x_{32} \qquad - x_{51} + \frac{2}{3}x_{61} + 2x_{52} + 4x_{62}$$

So it is profitable to increase x_{51}. But there are 2 pseudo-basic variables in this subproblem, and we cannot make x_{51} basic immediately. We therefore pivot between x_{51} and x_{21}, to make x_{51} pseudo-basic. This produces the following tableau.

		ϕ_1^1	ϕ_2^1	ϕ_3^1	x_{41}	x_{21}	x_{61}	x_{42}	x_{52}	x_{62}
θ_1	10/3	-1/3	-2/3							
θ_2	5/9	1/9	2/9	-1/3						
θ_3	11/9	4/9	-1/9	-1/3						
$*x_{11}$		1	-1			1	1			
$*x_{51}$			-1		-1	1				
x_{31}	14/3	-2/3	-4/3		-1	1	2			
x_{12}	44/9	-11/9	-4/9	2/3				-1	1	
x_{22}	2/3	1/3	-1/3					-1	1	2
$*x_{32}$					1			1	-1	1
C	-37/3	1/3	2/3	1	1	1	1	1	1	5

We now put

$$\phi_1^2 = \phi_1^1 - \phi_2^1$$

This affects only the column of coefficients of ϕ_2^1, and we have the tableau

		ϕ_1^2	ϕ_2^1	ϕ_3^1	x_{41}	x_{21}	x_{61}	x_{42}	x_{52}	x_{62}
θ_1	10/3	-1/3	-1							
θ_2	5/9	1/9	1/3	-1/3						
θ_3	11/9	4/9	1/3	-1/3						
$*x_{11}$		1				1	1			
$*x_{51}$			-1		-1	1				
x_{31}	14/3	-2/3	-2		-1	1	2			
x_{12}	44/9	-11/9	-5/3	2/3				-1	1	
x_{22}	2/3	1/3						-1	1	2
$*x_{32}$					1			1	-1	1
C	-37/3	1/3	1	1	1	1	1	1	1	5

We are at last in a position to increase x_{51}, by decreasing ϕ_2^1. We can continue to do this until θ_2 vanishes. Since the new pseudo-basic variable is a parameter, and not a variable in a subproblem, we could make it the new parameter. But the notation is more uniform if we can give it a new name ϕ_2^2. We then have the tableau

	ϕ_1^2	ϕ_2^2	ϕ_3^1	x_{41}	x_{21}	x_{61}	x_{42}	x_{52}	x_{62}
ϕ_2^1	$-5/3$	$-1/3$	3	1					
θ_1	5		-3	-1					
$*\theta_2$			1						
θ_3	$2/3$	$1/3$	1						
$*x_{11}$			1		1	1			
x_{51}	$5/3$	$1/3$	-3	$-1/3$	-1	1			
x_{31}	8		-6	-2	-1	1	2		
x_{12}	$23/3$	$-2/3$	-5	-1			-1	1	
x_{22}	$2/3$	$1/3$					-1	1	2
$*x_{32}$			1				1	-1	1
C	-14		3	2	1	1	1	1	5

Since the coefficients of the parameters in the expression for C are all nonnegative, we cannot usefully increase any pseudo-basic variable. We therefore look at the nonbasic variables in the second subproblem. We find that their coefficients in the expression for C in terms of the pseudo-basic and nonbasic variables are given by

$$x_{42} + x_{52} + 5x_{62}$$
$$- 2 \ (+ \ x_{42} - x_{52} + x_{62})$$
$$= \quad -x_{42} + 3x_{52} + 3x_{62}$$

So we can profitably increase x_{42}. But we must first make x_{42} pseudo-basic in place of x_{32}. This produces the following tableau.

	ϕ_1^2	ϕ_2^2	ϕ_3^1	x_{41}	x_{21}	x_{61}	x_{32}	x_{52}	x_{62}
θ_1	5		-3	-1					
$*\theta_2$			1						
θ_3	$2/3$	$1/3$	1						
$*x_{11}$			1		1	1			
x_{51}	$5/3$	$1/3$	-3	-1	-1	1			
x_{31}	8		-6	-2	-1	1	2		
x_{12}	$23/3$	$-2/3$	-5				1		1
x_{22}	$2/3$	$1/3$		1			-1		3
$*x_{42}$				-1			1	1	-1
C	-14		3	1	1	1	1	2	4

Since there is no other pseudo-basic variable in the second sub-problem, we can immediately proceed to increase x_{42}, by decreasing

ϕ_3^1. We can do this until x_{22} becomes equal to zero. Then we introduce the new parameter ϕ_3^2, and have the tableau

	ϕ_1^2	ϕ_2^2	ϕ_3^2	x_{41}	x_{21}	x_{61}	x_{32}	x_{52}	x_{62}
ϕ_3^1	$-2/3$	$-1/3$	1						
θ_1	$17/3$	$1/3$	-3	-1					
*θ_2			1						
θ_3	$2/3$	$1/3$	1						
*x_{11}		1			1	1			
x_{51}	$7/3$	$2/3$	-3	-1	-1	1			
x_{31}	$28/3$	$2/3$	-6	-2	-1	1	2		
x_{12}	$23/3$	$-2/3$	-5					1	1
*x_{22}				1			-1		3
x_{42}	$2/3$	$1/3$		-1			1	1	-1
C	$-44/3$	$-1/3$	3	1	1	1	1	2	4

We now find that we can profitably increase ϕ_1^2, and hence the pseudo-basic variable x_{11}. We can do this until x_{12} becomes equal to zero. So we introduce the new parameter ϕ_1^3, and write

	ϕ_1^3	ϕ_2^2	ϕ_3^2	x_{41}	x_{21}	x_{61}	x_{32}	x_{52}	x_{62}
ϕ_1^2	$23/3$	$-3/2$	$15/2$						
θ_1	$19/2$	$-1/2$	$-11/2$	-1					
*θ_2			1						
θ_3	$9/2$	$-1/2$	$-3/2$						
x_{11}	$23/2$	$-3/2$	$-15/2$		1	1			
x_{51}	10	-1	-8	-1	-1	1			
x_{31}	17	-1	-11	-2	-1	1	2		
*x_{12}			1					1	1
*x_{22}				1			-1		3
x_{42}	$9/2$	$-1/2$	$-5/2$	-1			1	1	-1
C	$-37/2$	$1/2$	$11/2$	1	1	1	1	2	4

We now find that no pseudo-basic or nonbasic variable can profitably be increased. In fact we have

$$C = -\frac{37}{2} \qquad\qquad + x_{41} + x_{21} + x_{61} + x_{32} + 2x_{52} + 4x_{62}$$
$$+ \frac{1}{2}x_{12} \qquad\qquad -\frac{1}{2}(x_{32} \qquad + x_{62})$$
$$+ \frac{11}{2}\theta_2$$
$$+ x_{22} \qquad\qquad -(-x_{32} \qquad + 3x_{62})$$
$$= -\frac{37}{2} + \frac{1}{2}x_{12} + \frac{11}{2}\theta_2 + x_{22} + x_{41} + x_{21} + x_{61} + \frac{3}{2}x_{32} + 2x_{52} + \frac{1}{2}x_{62}$$

So we have the optimum solution, given by

$$\theta_1 = \frac{19}{2}, \quad \theta_2 = 0, \quad \theta_3 = \frac{9}{2}$$

$$x_{11} = \frac{23}{2}, \; x_{21} = 0, \; x_{31} = 17, \; x_{41} = 0, \; x_{51} = 10, \; x_{61} = 0$$

$$x_{12} = 0, \quad x_{22} = 0, \quad x_{32} = 0, \quad x_{42} = \frac{9}{2}, \; x_{52} = 0, \quad x_{62} = 0$$

$$C = -\frac{37}{2}$$

5. RULES FOR CHOOSING PIVOTAL COLUMNS AND ROWS

A fair amount of attention has recently been given to the problem of choosing the pivotal column in the simplex method. This is particularly important in large problems, to which the algorithm presented here may have to be applied. It is therefore of interest to consider whether any effective special rule for this can be devised, based on the special structure of the problem. It turns out that there is one important special case where there is an obviously best choice of nonbasic variable to be increased. And this special case suggests a plausible rule that can be applied generally.

We consider the situation where

(1) there is only one pseudo-basic variable $x_{r\ell}$ in the subproblem concerned,

(2) the coefficient $c_{(r)}$ of the associated parameter $\phi_{(r)}$ in the expression for C is nonnegative, so $x_{r\ell}$ itself cannot usefully be increased, and

(3) all the $c_{k\ell}$ are nonnegative, so that we have an optimum tableau for the subproblem given the parameter values.

Now it is likely that the next new pseudo-basic variable will not be in this subproblem, in which case the $c_{k\ell}^*$ for this subproblem will simply be the corresponding $c_{k\ell}$. So we want to keep the $c_{k\ell}$ all nonnegative when we make $x_{r\ell}$ nonbasic. This means that we should use the dual simplex method to choose the pivotal column, i.e., we should choose the nonbasic variable $x_{s\ell}$ such that $a_{rs\ell} > 0$, and

$$\frac{c_{s\ell}}{a_{rs\ell}} = \min_{a_{rk\ell} > 0} \left(\frac{c_{k\ell}}{a_{rk\ell}} \right) \tag{12}$$

We now show that in this case the rule is equivalent to the following rule:

Choose the nonbasic variable $x_{s\ell}$ such that $c_{s\ell}^* < 0$, and

$$\frac{c_{s\ell}}{c_{s\ell}^*} = \max_{c_{k\ell}^* < 0} \left(\frac{c_{k\ell}}{c_{k\ell}^*} \right) \tag{13}$$

To prove this, let $\alpha_k = c_{k\ell}/a_{rk\ell}$. Then (12) says that we should pick the smallest positive α_k. But (13) tells us to maximize

$$\frac{c_{k\ell}}{c_{k\ell}^*} = \frac{c_{k\ell}}{c_{k\ell} - c_{(r)}\, a_{rk\ell}} = \frac{1}{1 - c_{(r)}/\alpha_k}$$

from amongst those columns for which $c_{k\ell}^* < 0$, i.e., for which $0 < \alpha_k < c_{(r)}$. The maximum (i.e., least negative) value of (13) is therefore obtained by taking the smallest positive α_k. So (13) always picks the same column as (12), if any such nonbasic variable can profitably be increased at all.

Formula (13) is advocated for general use on the following grounds:

(1) It is easy to apply, even using the product form of inverse for the subproblems, since it involves only pricing out one row, the $c_{k\ell}$ row, in addition to the $c_{k\ell}^*$ which are essential in any case.

(2) It gives the best answer in the only situation where there is an obvious best answer.

(3) It is nondimensional.

(4) It has the advantage over other similar rules that it will give precedence to a column in which $c_{k\ell}$ and $c_{k\ell}^*$ are both negative. This seems desirable because a column with a negative $c_{k\ell}$ is unsatisfactory in any circumstances. Insignificantly negative values of $c_{k\ell}^*$ must of course be rejected. This can perhaps best be achieved by modifying (13) to read

$$\frac{c_{s\ell}}{c_{s\ell}^*} = \max_{c_{k\ell}^* < 0}\left(\frac{c_{k\ell} + \epsilon}{c_{k\ell}^*}\right) \tag{13'}$$

for some small positive ϵ. The rule is then no longer strictly nondimensional; but the ϵ also serves the useful purpose of selecting large negative values of $c_{k\ell}^*$ when there are no pseudo-basic variables in the subproblem, in which case $c_{k\ell} = c_{k\ell}^*$ for all k.

Having chosen the pivotal column, we must have a rule for choosing the pivotal row when the subproblem contains more than one pseudo-basic variable. Our special case unfortunately throws no light on this problem, since there is then only one possible pivotal row. But the following procedure seems sensible:

Choose the pivotal row, i.e., pseudo basic variable $x_{r\ell}$ to be made nonbasic, from among the pseudo-basic variables in the subproblem so as to maximize $c_{(r)}\,|a_{rs\ell}|$, where $\phi_{(r)}$ is the parameter associated with $x_{r\ell}$, and $a_{rs\ell}$ is chosen to have the same sign as $c_{s\ell}$ if possible.

The merits of this rule are:

(1) It is easy to apply.

(2) It is nondimensional.

(3) It favors large pivots (i.e., large values of $|a_{rs\ell}|$), and also large values of $c_{(r)}$, the latter implying that the pseudo-basic variable being made nonbasic was a very unprofitable one to introduce at a positive level.

(4) In the new expression for C in terms of the parameters and nonbasic variables, the coefficient of the new nonbasic variable—given by (11) as $c_{s\ell}/a_{rs\ell}$—is made positive if possible. (This is always possible if $c_{s\ell} > 0$. If $c_{s\ell} < 0$ it might not be.)

6. THE IMPORTANCE OF SPECIAL STRUCTURE

Many people, and in particular George Dantzig, have stressed the importance of developing special methods for exploiting special matrix structure in linear programming problems. In Ref. 1, Dantzig suggests that the general simplex method may not be practical for systems containing many more than 100 equations. We are now talking about solving systems about ten times this size, but this only increases the importance of special methods, since really large problems are almost bound to have structure that can be taken advantage of.

It seems likely that these special methods will have to be based on the general philosophy first illustrated in the revised simplex method—that one should work with a compact formulation of the problem containing enough information to enable one to compute fairly easily, the quantities one needs, rather than carry around all the quantities that one might conceivably need in a more or less explicit form. I hope I have succeeded in presenting the present algorithm as a natural and straightforward application of this philosophy.

REFERENCES

1. Dantzig, G. B., "Upper Bounds Secondary Constraints and Block Triangularity in Linear Programming," Econometrica, Vol. 23, (1955), pp. 174-183.
2. Dantzig, G. B., and P. Wolfe, "Decomposition Principle for Linear Programs," Operations Research, Vol. 8, (1960), pp. 101-111.

Dual and Parametric Methods in Decomposition

Jean M. Abadie
A. C. Williams

1. INTRODUCTION

The decomposition algorithm of Dantzig and Wolfe for the treatment of large linear programs [1], [2], may be briefly described as follows: (i) the number of rows in a linear program is reduced at the expense of introducing (in general) a very large number of unknowns; then, (ii) the simplex algorithm is modified by the introduction of a "generalized pricing operation" so as to render the new problem (the "extremal problem") amenable to practical solution in spite of the large number of unknowns. The algorithm is basically a primal method. We show here that by introducing a different vector selection method, we are able to formulate an algorithm which is still a decomposition algorithm, but which is basically a dual method. In addition, this vector selection method also allows certain parametric linear programs to be solved by decomposition.

These techniques can easily be incorporated into any general decomposition computer code, thus making possible important post-optimal parametric studies, as well as allowing flexibility of choice in the method of solution of the nonparametric problem. In this latter connection, we remark that dual feasible solutions are sometimes more easily come by than are primal feasible solutions.

2. DUAL DECOMPOSITION FORMULATION

We consider the linear programming problem

$$Ax = a \tag{1.a}$$

$$Bx = b \tag{1.b}$$

$$x \geq 0 \tag{1.c}$$

$$\min fx \tag{1.d}$$

where A is an $m_1 \times n$ matrix, B is an $m_2 \times n$ matrix, a and b are respectively m_1 and m_2 dimensional column vectors, f is an n dimensional row vector, and x is the n dimensional column vector of unknowns.

In order to treat (1) by decomposition, we let $\xi^1, \ldots, \xi^P$ be all the basic (or extreme) solutions to $Bx = b$, $x \geq 0$, and we let $\eta^1, \ldots, \eta^Q$ be a complete set of generators for the solutions to $Bx = 0$, $x \geq 0$. If we now introduce the unknowns λ_p, $p = 1, \ldots, P$; μ_q, $q = 1, \ldots, Q$ then the linear program of (1) is equivalent to

$$\sum_{p=1}^{P} (A\xi^p)\,\lambda_p + \sum_{q=1}^{Q} (A\eta^q)\mu_q = a \tag{2.a}$$

$$\sum_{p=1}^{P} \lambda_p = 1 \tag{2.b}$$

$$\lambda_p \geq 0,\, \mu_q \geq 0 \tag{2.c}$$

$$\min \sum_{p=1}^{P} (f\xi^p)\,\lambda_p + \sum_{q=1}^{Q} (f\eta^q)\mu_q \tag{2.d}$$

in the sense that if (λ_p^0, μ_q^0) is optimal for (2), then

$$x^0 = \sum_{p=1}^{P} \xi^p \lambda_p^0 + \sum_{q=1}^{Q} \eta^q \mu_q^0 \tag{2.e}$$

is optimal for (1), and further; if x^0 is optimal for (1), then for some (λ_p^0, μ_q^0), optimal for (2), x^0 can be written in the form (2.e). The replacement of the linear program (1) by the linear program (2) is thus step (i) of the Dantzig-Wolfe method. Instead of step (ii), we intend to accomplish the same result by modifying Lemke's <u>dual</u> simplex method [3].

In connection with a remark made in the introduction, we may observe that if z^0 is the minimum value for fx subject to $Bx = b$, $x \geq 0$, then the vector $(0, \ldots, 0, z^0)$ is immediately a <u>dual feasible</u> solution for (2). Note, however, that the presence of a zero column in B could easily cause fx to fail to have such a minimum. Of course, in any case, if fx has no minimum on $Bx = b$, $x \geq 0$, some kind of "Phase I" must be used.

In order to solve the linear program (2) by the dual simplex method, we assume that we have, at each iteration: (i) a basic solution (λ, μ), i.e. a basic solution to the constraints (2.a) and (2.b), [but which may not satisfy (2.c)], such that the corresponding dual solution $(\pi, \rho) = (\pi^1, \ldots, \pi^m, \rho)$ is feasible, and (ii) an inverse matrix, i.e. the inverse of the matrix whose columns are the columns corresponding to the various λ_p, μ_q of the given basic solution. This matrix has dimension $(m_1 + 1) \times (m_1 + 1)$. Let the ith row of the inverse be denoted by $(u_i, w_i) = (u_i^1, \ldots, u_i^m, w_i)$.

Let us review briefly and without proof the steps required for linear programming with the dual simplex method. Let it be required to solve

$$Ax = a, \quad x \geq 0, \quad \min fx$$

As above, we assume at each iteration, (i) that we have a basic solution to $Ax = a$, (but $x \geq 0$ may not be satisfied) such that the corresponding dual solution π is feasible, i.e. $\pi A \leq f$; and (ii) that we have an inverse matrix with rows denoted by u_i. The current basic solution x is then given by $\alpha = Ua$. Now, if every component of the basic solution $x = \alpha$ is nonnegative (i.e. the current primal solution is feasible) then the current primal solution is optimal. But if there is some component, say $x_r = \alpha_r$, which is negative, then the transform of the row r may be used as a "pivot row." The selection of the column to enter the basis is as follows. Let the columns of A be written $a^1, \ldots, a^m$. Call a column a^j <u>admissible</u> if $u_r a^j < 0$. If there are no admissible columns, there is no solution to the constraints $Ax = a$, $x \geq 0$. Suppose then, that the admissible set of columns is not empty. Then an admissible column a^j, for which the ratio

$$\frac{\pi \cdot a^j - f^j}{u_r a^j} \tag{3}$$

is a minimum over all admissible columns, is selected for the basis. This vector is then introduced into the basis; a new inverse, a new primal, and a new dual solution are computed. The next iteration then commences.

Turning now to the linear program of the form given by (2), we see that difficulties will arise in the selection of the admissible vector for which the ratio (3) is a minimum over all admissible vectors. This is so because in the decomposition method the columns of the linear program (2) are not explicit, and further, they are in general so very numerous as to make their explicit calculation out of the question. Now the decomposition method for linear programming is a modification of the simplex method whereby linear programs of the type (2) may be solved without having all the columns calculated explicitly. In fact, in the simplex method the only difficulty encountered by not having explicit columns is that of selecting the vector to enter the basis. The Dantzig-Wolfe decomposition method, then, gives an algorithm in terms of a linear "subproblem" whereby the selection can be made. This process may be described as a generalized pricing operation.

The situation here is similar. The only difficulty in the present dual decomposition algorithm is encountered in the selection of a vector for the basis, and we overcome this difficulty by developing a selection algorithm which does not require the vectors to be explicit.

Let us see what has to be done. Suppose the pivot row r has been selected. Then the ratio (3) for columns of the type $A\xi^p$ is given by

$$\nu = \frac{(\pi A - f)\xi^p + \rho}{u_r A\xi^p + w_r} \tag{4}$$

and for columns of the type $A\eta^q$ that ratio is given by

$$\nu = \frac{(\pi A - f)\eta^q}{u_r A\eta^q} \tag{5}$$

The problem which we are considering is thus reduced to the problem of finding that ξ^p or η^q from among the ξ, η for which the denominators of (4) and (5) are negative and for which the ratio (4) or (5) is a minimum over such ξ, η. We note also that the numerators of these ratios are nonpositive, since (π, ρ) is feasible.

The determination of the correct vector ξ or η according to the above criterion is the "subproblem" which has to be solved at each iteration using the current values of the dual variables in (4) and (5). In Section 4 of this paper we give an algorithm, in terms of linear programming, for the solution of this nonlinear program. Of course, once this generalized vector selection step has been taken, the calculation continues exactly as in the dual simplex method.

Before spelling out the selection algorithm, however, we shall show that certain parametric linear programming problems also reduce to this case.

3. PARAMETRIC LINEAR PROGRAMMING

We consider two parametric linear programming (PLP) problems to be solved by the decomposition method.

The first of these is that of finding the optimal solution $x^0(\theta)$ as a function of the parameter θ for the parametric linear program

$$Ax = a + \theta \bar{a}, \qquad Bx = b, \qquad x \geq 0, \qquad \min fx$$

Again, we consider the linear program (2), where in (2.a) we replace a by $a + \theta \bar{a}$.

We assume that an optimal basic solution (λ^0, μ^0) for $\theta = \underline{\theta}$ (initially $\underline{\theta} = 0$) has been found, and that as a by-product of the calculation we have also found an optimal dual solution (π, ρ) and the basis inverse. We now wish to compute an optimal solution for all $\theta > \underline{\theta}$ for which such solutions exist.

The steps required for this type of PLP problem with the simplex method will now be reviewed. Suppose we have a basic optimal solution for

$$Ax = a + \theta \bar{a}, \qquad x \geq 0, \qquad \min fx$$

for some $\theta = \underline{\theta}$. Let the rows of the inverse U of the basis be denoted by u_i. Let π be the optimal dual solution and let $\alpha = Ua$, and $\bar{\alpha} = U\bar{a}$. Now if every element of the vector $\bar{\alpha}$ is nonnegative, we have that $x^0(\theta) = \alpha + \theta \bar{\alpha}$ for all $\theta \geq \underline{\theta}$. But if there are some elements of $\bar{\alpha}$ which are negative, we define

$$\bar{\theta} \equiv \frac{\alpha_r}{-\bar{\alpha}_r} \equiv \min_{\bar{\alpha}_i < 0} \frac{\alpha_i}{-\bar{\alpha}_i}$$

Then $x^0(\theta) = \alpha + \theta\bar{\alpha}$ for $\underline{\theta} \leq \theta \leq \bar{\theta}$. In this case a change of basis is required in order to compute $x^0(\theta)$ for $\theta > \bar{\theta}$. Row r is chosen as the pivot row, and as before we consider the admissible columns a^j, i.e., those columns for which $u_r a^j < 0$. If there are no admissible columns, there are no solutions to the constraints for $\theta > \bar{\theta}$. If there are any admissible columns, then we choose that admissible column which minimizes the ratio given by (3).

Clearly, then, the parametric linear program problem by decomposition, i.e., for a program of the type (2), is similarly reduced to the problem of selecting a vector for which the ratio (4) or (5) is a minimum, subject to the constraint that the denominator be negative. The algorithm of Section 4 is again applicable.

The second parametric linear programming problem is

$$Ax = a, \qquad Bx = b, \qquad x \geq 0, \qquad \min (f + \theta\bar{f})x$$

which we reformulate again in the form (2). We assume that an optimal solution (λ^0, μ^0) is available for $\theta = 0$, also an optimal dual solution (π, ρ) and the basis inverse. Let $(\bar{\pi}, \bar{\rho})$ be the U-transform of the vector whose elements are the elements of $(\bar{f}_\xi P, \bar{f}_\eta q)$ corresponding to the basis elements (λ_p^0, μ_q^0). Now the vector to enter the basis [so as to compute $x^0(\theta)$ for $\theta > 0$] is that vector for which

$$\frac{(\pi A - f)\ \xi + \rho}{(\bar{\pi} A - \bar{f})\ \xi + \rho} \qquad \text{or} \qquad \frac{(\pi A - f)\eta}{(\bar{\pi} A - \bar{f})\eta}$$

is a minimum over the set of all such vectors for which the denominator is negative. (If the denominator is nonnegative for all ξ^p and all η^q, then the current solution is optimal for all $\theta \geq \underline{\theta}$.) The problem is again reduced to the previous ones.

4. THE GENERALIZED VECTOR SELECTION ALGORITHM

In the preceding sections we reformulated linear programming problems by decomposition, and considered the task of solving the resulting extremal linear program by the dual method, or of finding optimal solutions as a function of a linear parameter either in the cost row or in the inhomogeneous part of the extremal constraints. We showed that each of these problems is reduced to a succession of problems of the following type.

Let $\xi^1, \xi^2, \ldots, \xi^P$ be all the basic solutions to $Bx = b$, $x \geq 0$. Let $\eta^1, \ldots, \eta^Q$ be a complete set of generators for the solutions to $Bx = 0$, $x \geq 0$. Assume that the solution set is not empty. Let c and d be given vectors (they stand respectively for $\pi A - f$ and $u_r A$ of 4 and 5 above), and let ρ and w be given numbers. Assume that for each basic solution

$$c\xi^p + \rho \leq 0 \qquad p = 1, \ldots, P$$

and that for each generator

$$c\eta^q \leq 0 \qquad q = 1, \ldots, Q$$

Define an <u>admissible basic solution</u> as a basic solution which satisfies
$d\xi + w < 0$ and an <u>admissible generator</u> as a generator which satisfies
$d\eta < 0$. Define the <u>admissible set</u> S as the union of the set of admissible
basic solutions and the set of admissible generators. Call the members of
the admissible set the <u>admissible vectors</u>. On the admissible set we define
the real valued function

$$\nu(\xi) = \frac{c\xi + \rho}{d\xi + w} \qquad \xi \in S$$

$$\nu(\eta) = \frac{c\eta}{d\eta} \qquad \eta \in S$$

For any $v \in S$ we may call $\nu(v)$ the <u>value</u> of v. Note that $\nu(v) \geq 0$ for
all $v \in S$.

Problem

It is required to find an admissible vector for which the value is a minimum over the set of admissible vectors, or else to determine that the admissible set is empty.

We now give an algorithm in terms of a succession of linear programs
for the solution of this problem. The algorithm is independent of the
method used for the solution of the individual linear programs, subject
only to the following condition. Whatever method is used must find an optimal <u>basic</u> solution (in case the optimal is not unique), or in the case of
the objective function not bounded, a solution to Bx = 0, x ≥ 0 from some
<u>finite set of generators</u>. The simplex method has these properties, but the
decomposition method does not have the first property. These assumptions
may obviously be relaxed for specific algorithms.

When the simplex method is used, however, certain modifications of the
algorithm are possible. These modifications allow the calculations to be
set out in a "tableau" format and, in addition, appear to reduce the amount
of calculation required.

Very briefly, the general algorithm consists of constructing a sequence
$\{v^t\}$ of admissible vectors such that the sequence $\{\nu(v^t)\}$ of their values is
monotonic strictly decreasing. Since the v^t are drawn from a finite set,
termination is thereby assured. We then show that the terminal vector is
the vector sought. If for some t the value $\nu(v^t) = 0$ is attained, the calculation is terminated forthwith, since there can be no admissible vector with
value less then zero.

The Algorithm

(The numbers in parentheses refer to proofs which appear directly following the description of the algorithm.)

Step 1. Consider the linear program $Bx = b$, $x \geq 0$, min $dx + w$.

Case 1. We find an optimal basic solution ξ. Then every generator satisfies $d\eta \geq 0$, i.e. there is no admissible generator.

Subcase A. For ξ an optimal basic solution, we have $d\xi + w \geq 0$. Then there is no admissible basic solution, i.e. the admissible set is empty.

Subcase B. For ξ an optimal basic solution, we have $d\xi + w < 0$. Then take $v^1 = \xi$, and put

$$\nu_1 = \nu(v^1) = \frac{cv^1 + \rho}{dv^1 + w}$$

If $\nu_1 = 0$, v^1 is optimal. If $\nu_1 > 0$, go to step 3.

Case 2. We find that there is no vector which minimizes $dx + w$, i.e., we find a vector which satisfies $\eta \geq 0$, $B\eta = 0$, $d\eta < 0$. Set $v^1 = \eta$ and put

$$\nu_1 = \nu(v^1) = \frac{cv^1}{dv^1}$$

If $\nu_1 = 0$, v^1 is optimal. If $\nu_1 > 0$, go to Step 2.

Step 2. Consider the linear program $Bx = b$, $x \geq 0$, min $\nu_t(dx + w) - (cx + \rho)$.

Case 1. We find a vector $\eta \geq 0$ such that $B\eta = 0$, $\nu_t d\eta - c\eta < 0$. Then η is admissible (1). Set $v^{t+1} = \eta$ and define

$$\nu_{t+1} = \nu(v^{t+1}) = \frac{cv^{t+1}}{dv^{t+1}}$$

Then $\nu_{t+1} < \nu_t$ (2). If $\nu_{t+1} = 0$, v^{t+1} is optimal. If $\nu_{t+1} > 0$, return to step 2.

Case 2. We find an optimal basic solution ξ. Then the value of the admissible generator v^t (the last admissible vector computed) has a value which is minimum over the set of admissible generators (3).

Subcase A. For ξ an optimal basic solution,

$$\nu_t(d\xi + w) - (c\xi + \rho) \geq 0$$

is satisfied. Then the admissible vector v^t is optimal (4).

Subcase B. For ξ an optimal basic solution,

$$\nu_t(d\xi + w) - (c\xi + \rho) < 0$$

is satisfied. Then ξ is an admissible basic solution (5). Set $v^{t+1} = \xi$ and put

$$\nu_{t+1} = \nu(v^{t+1}) = \frac{cv^{t+1} + \rho}{dv^{t+1} + w}$$

Then $\nu_{t+1} < \nu_t$ (6). If $\nu_{t+1} = 0$, v^{t+1} is optimal. If $\nu_{t+1} > 0$, go to Step 3.

Step 3. Consider the linear program $Bx = b$, $x \geq 0$, min $\nu_t(dx + w)$ $- (cx + \rho)$.

This problem now always has a minimal vector (7). Let ξ be an optimal basic solution. Then, since v^t (the last admissible vector calculated) is feasible, we have

$$\nu_t(d\xi + w) - (c\xi + \rho) \leq \nu_t(dv^t + w) - (cv^t + \rho)$$

But by definition of ν_t the right-hand side of this inequality is zero.

Case 1. $\nu_t(d\xi + w) - (c\xi + \rho) < 0$. Then ξ is an admissible basic solution (5). Set $v^{t+1} = \xi$ and put

$$\nu_{t+1} = \nu(v^{t+1}) = \frac{cv^{t+1} + \rho}{dv^{t+1} + w}$$

Then $\nu_{t+1} < \nu_t$ (6). If $\nu_{t+1} = 0$, v^{t+1} is optimal. If $\nu_{t+1} > 0$, return to Step 3.

Case 2. $\nu_t(d\xi + w) - (c\xi + \rho) = 0$. Then the admissible basic solution v^t is optimal (8).

(1)   Since $c\eta \leq 0$ for every generator and since $\nu_t > 0$, the result $d\eta < 0$ follows immediately.

(2)   From $\nu_t d\eta - c\eta < 0$ and $d\eta < 0$ we have

$$\nu_t > \frac{c\eta}{d\eta} \equiv \frac{cv^{t+1}}{dv^{t+1}} = \nu_{t+1}$$

(3)   Since $Bx = b$, $x \geq 0$, min $\nu_t(dx + w) - (cx + \rho)$ has a minimum solution, we have that every generator η satisfies

$$\nu_t d\eta - c\eta \geq 0$$

Therefore every admissible generator η' satisfies

$$\nu_t \leq \frac{c\eta'}{d\eta'} = \nu(\eta')$$

(4)   Every basic solution ξ satisfies

$$\nu_t(d\xi + w) - (c\xi + \rho) \geq 0$$

since that condition is satisfied by an optimal basic solution. Therefore, for every admissible basic solution ξ', we have

$$\nu_t \leq \frac{c\xi' + \rho}{d\xi' + w} = \nu(\xi') \qquad \xi' \in S$$

Thus the value ν_t of the admissible vector v^t is minimal over the set of admissible basic vectors as well as over the set of admissible generators.

(5) Since $c\xi + \rho \leq 0$ for all basic solutions and since $\nu_t > 0$, the result $d\xi + w < 0$ follows immediately.

(6) From $\nu_t(d\xi + w) - (c\xi + \rho) < 0$ and $d\xi + w < 0$ we have

$$\nu_t > \frac{c\xi + \rho}{d\xi + w} \equiv \frac{cv^{t+1} + \rho}{dv^{t+1} + w} = \nu_{t+1}$$

(7) Suppose there were no minimum vector for this linear program. Then there is a generator η such that

$$\nu_t d\eta - c\eta < 0 \tag{7}$$

But then $d\eta < (1/\nu_t)\, c\eta \leq 0$, i.e., such a generator is admissible.

Now if Step 3 was entered from Step 1, Case 1, Subcase B, there can be no admissible generators, so there is a contradiction.

If step 3 was entered from Step 2, Case 2, Subcase B, or from 3, then we know that $Bx = b$, $x \geq 0$, $\min \nu_{t-1}(dx + w) - (cs + w)$ (where $\nu_{t-1} > \nu_t$) has a minimum vector—i.e., every generator must satisfy

$$\nu_{t-1} d\eta - c\eta \geq 0$$

But (7), $d\eta < 0$, $\nu_t < \nu_{t-1}$ yield

$$\nu_{t-1} d\eta - c\eta < 0$$

which is again a contradiction.

(8) Precisely the argument of (3) shows that ν_t is minimal over the set of admissible generators. Then precisely the argument of (4) shows that v^t is optimal.

Discussion

The problem of optimizing a given function subject to constraints is often solved in two parts. In the first part it is determined whether or not there are any solutions to the constraints, and if there are, such a solution is produced. In the second part, then, new solutions are successively calculated, each with a more nearly optimal value than the preceding one. In the above algorithm Step 1 is such a first part—its purpose being to determine whether or not there are any admissible vectors and, if there are, to produce one. Steps 2 and 3 are then the second part operation, in that at each step a new admissible vector with value less than the preceding one is calculated.

The algorithm requires that on each step either we optimize or we produce the generator which shows that there is no minimum. Actually, however, once any admissible vector has been found (not necessarily a minimum as required by Step 1), the operations of Steps 2 and 3 may be commenced immediately, and once these operations are commenced there is no need to run the indicated linear programs to optimal—in fact, if the simplex method is used, it is the usual case that only a single simplex iteration need be done to reduce the value of ν.

The underlying principle is this. At any point in the algorithm we may replace the current admissible vector by an admissible vector whose value is not greater, provided that at the same time the current value ν_t is also replaced by the value of the new admissible vector. We note in this connection that in Step 2 the monotonicity of $\{\nu_t\}$ does not depend on what the previous admissible vector was, but depends only on the number ν_t in the current objective function. In Step 3, there can be no admissible generator with value not greater than that of the current admissible vector. Thus the replacement can only be by an admissible basic solution. But here the monotonicity of $\{\nu\}$ depends only on the feasibility of the previous admissible vector, and the number ν_t.

Therefore, when the simplex method is used, the algorithm may be modified as follows. After each simplex iteration if we obtain a new admissible basic vector with value not greater than the previous value (as we must in Step 3, and as we may in Step 2), the new vector and the new value are used immediately in the next simplex iteration. Clearly, any method for resolving degeneracy for the simplex method can be used here. Finally, we remark that the necessary calculations are conveniently done by forming rows for c and d, adjoining them to the B matrix, and carrying out transformations on them along with the other rows of B.

REFERENCES

1. Dantzig, G. B., and P. Wolfe, "A Decomposition Principle for Linear Programs," RAND Report P-1544, Nov. 10, 1958, revised Nov. 6, 1959.
2. Dantzig, G. B., and P. Wolfe, "The Decomposition Algorithm for Linear Programs," Econometrica, Vol. 29, No. 4, Oct. 1961, pp. 767-778.
3. Gass, S. I., Linear Programming, McGraw-Hill, 1958, p. 125 ff.

Convex Partition Programming

J. B. Rosen

1. INTRODUCTION

There are a number of important types of mathematical programming problems which lead naturally to a block diagonal structure for the constraint coefficient matrix. One kind of problem which may have this structure is a multiple plant or refinery model where each plant or refinery is represented by a different block, the blocks being coupled by raw material allocation and product distribution. Another type of problem leading to a block diagonal structure is a dynamic model with storage, where each block represents a single time period with storage between successive time periods as the coupling between blocks. A large block diagonal structure may also arise from a stochastic programming problem where the constraint right-hand side vector is specified as a random vector selected from a finite set with known probabilities [4].

In all of these cases the complete problem can be represented as a number of smaller problems tied together by coupling equations, coupling variables or both. The first proposal specifically taking advantage of this structure for linear problems was the decomposition principle of Dantzig and Wolfe [3].

The partition programming method for the solution of convex problems with a block diagonal structure [8] is applicable to the nonlinear problem when the blocks are coupled by a set of coupling variables, denoted by an s-dimensional vector y. This structure is shown in Fig. 1, where a problem with ℓ blocks is illustrated. A formal statement of the complete problem is given by (2.1) in the next section. In this paper we will consider the multiblock problem with the structure shown in Fig. 1, which we will call the dual form. The right-hand side vector for each block, $b_i(y)$, $i = 1, \ldots, \ell$ is assumed to be a convex vector function of the vector y. For the special case where the $b_i(y)$ are linear in y we have a completely linear multiblock problem. For this linear case the corresponding primal problem is a multiblock problem with coupling constraints in the form normally considered for the decomposition algorithm. The solution of such linear multiblock problems by partition programming in both the primal and dual form has previously been presented [9] and will be described in a separate paper. A similar approach for the linear problem in the dual form has been developed independently by Beale [2].

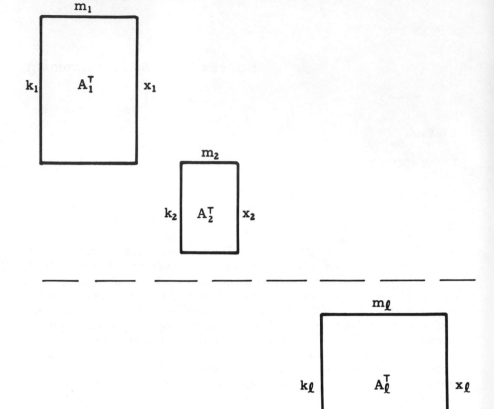

Fig. 1. Complete problem, ℓ-blocks.

The partition programming algorithm is based largely on the fact that for any fixed value of y, the complete problem (2.1) reduces to a set of ℓ relatively small <u>linear</u> subproblems, each of which can be solved <u>independently</u> of the others. These ℓ subproblems (called Problem I) are

$$\Psi_i(y) = \min_{x_i} \{c_i^T x_i \mid A_i^T x_i \geq b_i(y)\}, \qquad i = 1, \ldots, \ell \tag{1.1}$$

Furthermore, it is shown by Theorem 1 that

$$\Psi(y) = \min_{x_i} \left\{ \sum_{i=1}^{\ell} c_i^T x_i \mid A_i^T x_i \geq b_i(y), \qquad i = 1, \ldots, \ell \right\} = \sum_{i=1}^{\ell} \Psi_i(y) \tag{1.2}$$

is a convex function of y. A global minimum of the complete problem (2.1) is therefore given by the minimum of the convex function $\Psi(y)$. For a specific feasible value $y = y_0$, the optimal solution of each of the linear subproblems (1.1) gives a vector x_{i0}, the value $\Psi_i(y_0)$, and a nonsingular basis $\underline{A}_i^T$ and corresponding vector $\underline{b}_i(y)$ such that $\underline{A}_i^T x_{i0} = \underline{b}_i(y_0)$ and $\underline{A}_i^{-1} c_i \geq 0$. We can now reduce the complete problem to one in the y-space only by (temporarily) requiring that each vector x_i be given by $\underline{A}_i^T x_i = \underline{b}_i(y)$, $i = 1, \ldots, \ell$. We can then explicitly formulate an s-dimensional convex problem in the y-space, which we call Problem II. Problem II has a convex objective function and linear constraints and can be solved by the gradient projection method for which an efficient computer program is available [10].

It is shown by Theorem 2 that we can recognize the Kuhn-Tucker conditions for the complete problem optimum in terms of the optimum Problem I and II solutions. If $\Psi(y_0)$ is not a minimum, then Problem II will either give a new feasible value of $y = y_1$ with $\Psi(y_1) < \Psi(y_0)$, or will show how to make a basis change in one or more of the subproblems (1.1) so that such a value y_1 can be found. The iteration procedure is then continued by solving Problem I with the new value $y = y_1$. The solution of Problem II in each iteration is a convergent (but not necessarily finite) procedure, and it is shown in Theorem 3 that only a finite number of iterations are required. The justification for the linearization of constraints in Problem II is given by Theorem 4.

In Section 4, the gradient projection algorithm is summarized. It is also shown there that the general convex programming problem (minimize a convex function in a convex region) can be put in the form (2.1) by introducing appropriate linear slack variables. The way in which linear equalities can be handled is also described there. The partition programming algorithm is described in detail for the multiblock convex problem in the Appendix.

The partition programming algorithm has been coded for the IBM 7090 computer and used successfully to solve a number of linear and nonlinear problems, including a nonlinear multi-refinery model. This computational experience is described elsewhere [11]. Two aspects of this algorithm should be emphasized. First, that the size of the subproblems remains the same throughout the iterative solution, and in fact that it is never necessary to solve a single problem with more than m variables, where $m = \max\{m_i, s\}$. Second, that since a feasible solution is obtained at each cycle the optimization may be terminated before the global minimum has been reached, and still give an improved feasible vector.

With certain obvious exceptions we use capital Roman letters for matrices, lower case Roman letters for vectors and Greek letters for scalars. A subscript normally denotes the corresponding block, except on y where it denotes a specific vector.

2. OPTIMALITY CONDITIONS FOR COMPLETE PROBLEM

A general convex problem will now be stated in the form suitable for optimization by the partition programming algorithm. The problem is shown in Fig. 1 and consists of ℓ linear submatrices A_i^T and corresponding vectors x_i, $i = 1, \ldots, \ell$, with a block diagonal structure. These submatrices are coupled through the single coupling vector y, in the following sense: the right hand side of each constraint is a convex function of the vector y. The constraints for the complete problem may therefore depend in a nonlinear way on y, but for any fixed value of y each submatrix is linear and independent. The objective function to be minimized is a linear function of all the vectors x_i, and the minimum is to be obtained over all vectors x_i, y, which satisfy the constraints. The complete ℓ-block problem may therefore be stated as follows:

$$\min_{x_i, y} \left\{ \sum_{i=1}^{\ell} c_i^T x_i \,\middle|\, A_i^T x_i \geq b_i(y), \qquad i = 1, \ldots, \ell \right\} \qquad (2.1)$$

where the $b_i(y)$ are differentiable convex vector functions of the s-dimensional vector y. Each A_i is a constant matrix with dimensions $(m_i \times k_i)$. Each c_i is a constant m_i-dimensional vector, and the superscript (T) denotes the transpose. A vector inequality means that the inequality applies to every component of the vector. These vectors and matrices have the appropriate dimensions shown in Fig. 1.

The assumption that $b_i(y)$ is a convex function of y means that each component of the vector $b_i(y)$ is a convex function of y. This includes the special cases where some or all components of b_i are constant and where some or all components of b_i depend linearly on y. For the completely linear case we have

$$b_i(y) = b_i - D_i^T y, \qquad i = 1, \ldots, \ell \qquad (2.2)$$

where the D_i^T are constant matrices with the dimensions $(k_i \times s)$. It is also assumed that the minimum given by (2.1) is bounded. The problem is stated in the form of inequalities so that there will be at least as many inequalities (including nonnegativity) as variables in each block, $k_i \geq m_i$, $i = 1, \ldots, \ell$. For a completely linear problem this is the natural structure for the dual problem. The partition programming optimization algorithm to be described in this section is based on this dual structure.

As a matter of convenience certain additional assumptions will be made about the system of inequalities or constraints in (2.1). Any nonnegativity requirements on the components of the x_i or y vectors are assumed to be included as part of the corresponding matrix A_i^T and $b_i(y)$ vector. Note that for constraints which involve only x_i variables the corresponding right hand side is constant, and for constraints in only the y variables the corresponding rows of the A_i^T matrix are zero. Finally, two feasibility assumptions are made. First, that there exist feasible points (x_i, y) which are interior to all nonlinear constraints, that is, points (x_i, y) which satisfy $A_i^T x_i \geq b_i(y)$, $i = 1, \ldots, \ell$, with a strict inequality for every nonlinear component of the $b_i(y)$. This assumption insures the satisfaction of the Kuhn-Tucker constraint qualification [3]. Second, that those constraints which are completely linear (linear in y as well as the x_i) determine a bounded region. This can always be accomplished by imposing suitable upper and lower bounds on each component of the vectors y and x_i. A vector y for which there exist vectors x_i, $i = 1, \ldots, \ell$, such that $A_i^T x_i \geq b_i(y)$, $i = 1, \ldots, \ell$, will be called a feasible vector y. It is also assumed that a feasible vector $y = y_0$ is known. Provided it exists, such a vector y_0 can be found by a "feasibility solution" which reduces to zero a penalty on each constraint violation.

An important structural aspect of the problem in this dual form should be emphasized, since it is basic to the partition programming algorithm. For any fixed value of y, the complete problem (2.1) reduces to a set of ℓ relatively small linear subproblems, each of which can be solved independently of the others. These ℓ subproblems are given by (1.1). The objective function $\Psi(y)$ for the complete problem considered as a function of y is given by (1.2), so that the original problem (2.1) is now equivalent to the minimization problem $\min_y \Psi(y)$, where y is chosen from the set of all values which satisfy $A_i^T x_i \geq b_i(y)$, $i = 1, \ldots, \ell$, for some vectors x_i. We will now prove a theorem from which it will follow directly that $\Psi(y)$ is a convex function of y.

Theorem 1

Let b(y) be a convex vector function of the vector y. Then

$$\varphi(y) = \min_x \left\{ c^T x \mid A^T x \geq b(y) \right\} \tag{2.3}$$

is a convex function of y. Furthermore, the region of definition of $\varphi(y)$ is convex.

Proof

We consider two feasible values y_1 and y_2 of the vector y. Since they are feasible, there exist vectors x_1 and x_2 such that

$$\varphi(y_1) = \min_x \left\{ c^T x \mid A^T x \geq b(y_1) \right\} = c^T x_1$$

$$\varphi(y_2) = \min_x \left\{ c^T x \mid A^T x \geq b(y_2) \right\} = c^T x_2 \tag{2.4}$$

For any scalar λ, $0 \leq \lambda \leq 1$, we define $\overline{y} \equiv \lambda y_1 + (1 - \lambda)y_2$, and $\overline{b} \equiv \lambda b(y_1) + (1 - \lambda)b(y_2)$. Since b(y) is convex, $b(\overline{y}) \leq \overline{b}$ and it follows that in the x-space the convex feasible region $A^T x \geq b(\overline{y})$ is not smaller than the region $A^T x \geq \overline{b}$. Hence

$$\min_x \left\{ c^T x \mid A^T x \geq b(\overline{y}) \right\} \leq \min_x \left\{ c^T x \mid A^T x \geq \overline{b} \right\}$$

Now

$$\varphi(\overline{y}) = \min_{x} \{c^T x \mid A^T x \geq b(\overline{y})\}$$

$$\leq \min_{x} \{c^T x \mid A^T x \geq \overline{b}\}$$

$$\leq c^T (\lambda x_1 + (1 - \lambda)x_2)$$

$$= \lambda \varphi(y_1) + (1 - \lambda)\varphi(y_2),$$

which proves the convexity of $\varphi(y)$. The second inequality follows from the fact that $\lambda x_1 + (1 - \lambda)x_2$ is a feasible solution of $A^T x \geq \overline{b}$. This can be seen directly from (2.4).

To show that the region of definition of $\varphi(y)$ is convex we show that if y_1 and y_2 are feasible, then $\overline{y} = \lambda y_1 + (1 - \lambda)y_2$, $0 \leq \lambda \leq 1$, is also feasible. Since y_1 and y_2 are feasible, there exist vectors x_1 and x_2 such that $A^T x_1 \geq b(y_1)$ and $A^T x_2 \geq b(y_2)$. Then for $\overline{x} \equiv \lambda x_1 + (1 - \lambda)x_2$, we have $A^T \overline{x} \geq \overline{b} \geq b(\overline{y})$, Q.E.D.

This theorem applies directly to the function $\Psi_i(y)$ defined by (1.1) for the ℓ subproblems, so that each of the functions $\Psi_i(y)$, $i = 1, \ldots, \ell$ is convex. The sum of convex functions is also convex, so that $\Psi(y)$ as given by (1.2) is convex. An alternate proof of Theorem 1 can also be given based on a known result [1, 6] that φ is a convex function of the right-hand side vector b.

The original multiblock problem (2.1) has been restated as $\min_{y} \Psi(y)$ over the relatively small number of variables in the y vector. Since $\Psi(y)$ is convex, it is only necessary to find a minimum of $\Psi(y)$ to solve the original problem, since any minimum is also a global minimum. This remark is, unfortunately, deceptively simple, since even the evaluation of $\Psi(y)$ over a coarse grid of, say, 10 points in each dimension of the s-dimensional y-space would require 10^S linear programming solutions of each of the ℓ subproblems (1.1). Furthermore, appropriate constraints in the y-space are required to insure that only feasible values of y are considered.

A practical way in which we can use the convexity of $\Psi(y)$ to solve the complete problem is based on the following remarks. For a specified value, say $y = y_0$, the solution of the kth subproblem (1.1) gives not only the corresponding vector $x_{k,0}$ and function $\Psi_k(y_0)$ but also the partial derivatives $\partial \Psi_k(y_0)/\partial y_j$, $j = 1, \ldots, s$, where they exist. These derivatives are readily obtained from the subproblem optimal shadow prices and the partial derivatives $\partial b/\partial y_j$. They are valid in the y-space region containing y_0 for which the optimal basis at y_0 remains optimal. Furthermore, as long as the same basis is maintained the vector x_i is given as an explicit function of y, so that all the constraints can be represented explicitly in the y-space. With this information a minimization over y in a region containing y_0 can be carried out. For each such y-space minimization, only a single linear programming solution of each of the ℓ subproblems is now required. As will be shown in the next section, this sequence of minimizations gives the desired global minimum, where

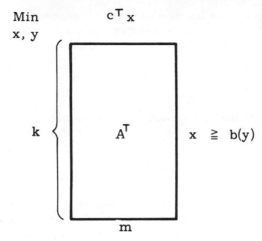

$$\underset{x,\,y}{\text{Min}} \quad c^T x$$

$$k \left\{ \quad A^T \quad \right. \qquad x \ \geq \ b(y)$$

$$m$$

Fig. 2. Single block convex problem.

the Kuhn–Tucker conditions [5] for the complete problem are satisfied.

Since the complete problem is solved by solving a sequence of sub-problems it is essential that we be able to determine from the subproblem solutions when the Kuhn–Tucker conditions for the complete problem are satisfied. In order to simplify the discussion we consider only a single x-block, so that $\ell = 1$. The multiblock case is discussed at the end of this section. We therefore consider a single block problem in x and y (see Fig. 2).

$$\min_{x,y} \left\{ c^T x \mid A^T x \geq b(y) \right\} \tag{2.5}$$

Corresponding to this is the convex function $\varphi(y)$ given by (2.3). We consider a value $y = y_0$ and let x_0 be the corresponding solution of the following linear equation.

Problem I

$$\min_x \left\{ c^T x \mid A^T x \geq b(y_0) \right\} = c^T x_0 = \varphi(y_0) \tag{2.6}$$

We will now obtain necessary and sufficient conditions that the point (x_0, y_0) is a minimum point for the complete problem (2.5). These conditions will be given in terms of quantities obtained from the solution of two subproblems: Problem I above, and Problem II below.

The Kuhn–Tucker conditions that x_0 gives a minimum for Problem I are that $A^T x_0 \geq b(y_0)$, and that there exists a vector $r \geq 0$, such that

$$r^T [A^T x_0 - b(y_0)] = 0$$

$$Ar = c \tag{2.7}$$

Furthermore, by a basic theorem of linear programming there is an $(m \times m)$ nonsingular matrix $\underline{A}$, whose columns are selected from the columns of A, such that all the nonzero components of r are included in the m-vector

$$\underline{r} = \underline{A}^{-1} c \geq 0 \tag{2.8}$$

We let $\underline{b}(y)$ denote the m components of b(y) which correspond to the rows of $\underline{A}^T$. The corresponding rows of $A^T x_0 \geq b(y_0)$ are satisfied as equalities, so that

$$\underline{A}^T x_0 = \underline{b}(y_0) \tag{2.9}$$

We also denote the columns of A which are not in $\underline{A}$ by the matrix B, and the corresponding components of b(y) by e(y). This partition of the complete problem (2.5) is shown in Fig. 3, where it is assumed for purposes of illustration that $\underline{A}^T$ consists of the last m rows of A^T. We also define the $m \times (k-m)$ matrix

$$Q \equiv \underline{A}^{-1} B \tag{2.10}$$

and the $(s \times k)$ matrix of partial derivatives (negative Jacobian)

$$D(y) \equiv -\left(\frac{\partial b_j}{\partial y_i}\right), \qquad i = 1, \ldots, s, \; j = 1, \ldots, k \tag{2.11}$$

The matrix D(y) is also partitioned into two parts, a $(s \times m)$ matrix $\underline{D}(y)$ corresponding to $\underline{b}(y)$ and a $s \times (k-m)$ matrix E(y) corresponding to e(y).

In terms of these quantities we formulate the second problem.

Problem II

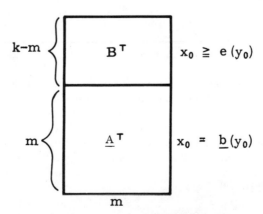

Fig. 3. Problem I optimal basis.

$$\min_{y} \{\underline{r}^T \underline{b}\,(y) \mid (y - y_0)^T [E(y_0) - \underline{D}\,(y_0)Q] \geq e(y_0) - Q^T \underline{b}\,(y_0)\} \qquad (2.12)$$

This gives the complete problem (2.5) in terms of the y variables only, by making the assumption that the m active constraints given by (2.9) determine the dependence of x on y,

$$x = (\underline{A}^{-1})^T \underline{b}\,(y) \qquad (2.13)$$

The nonlinear constraints of (2.5) have also been linearized about the point $y = y_0$. The objective function of Problem II is seen to be equal to $c^T x$ by using (2.8) and (2.13). It follows directly from the convexity of $\underline{b}\,(y)$ and the nonnegativity of $\underline{r}$, that $\underline{r}^T \underline{b}\,(y)$ is a convex function of y. Problem II consists therefore of the minimization of a convex function subject to linear constraints.

The Kuhn-Tucker conditions for Problem II at $y = y_0$ are that y_0 is feasible, that is

$$Q^T \underline{b}\,(y_0) - e(y_0) \geq 0 \qquad (2.14)$$

and that a vector $v \geq 0$ exists such that

$$v^T [Q^T \underline{b}\,(y_0) - e(y_0)] = 0 \qquad (2.15)$$

$$[E(y_0) - \underline{D}\,(y_0)Q] v = -\underline{D}\,(y_0)\, \underline{r} \qquad (2.16)$$

The last relation follows from the fact that $-\underline{D}\,(y_0)\, \underline{r}$ is the gradient of $\underline{r}^T \underline{b}\,(y)$ at $y = y_0$.

In terms of the partition of the original matrix A into $\underline{A}$ and B, the optimality conditions for the complete problem (2.5) at (x_0, y_0) are the feasibility requirements

$$\underline{A}^T x_0 - \underline{b}\,(y_0) = 0 \qquad (2.17)$$

$$B^T x_0 - e\,(y_0) \geq 0 \qquad (2.18)$$

and that nonnegative vectors u and v exist, such that

$$v^T [B^T x_0 - e(y_0)] = 0 \qquad (2.19)$$

$$\underline{A}u + Bv = c \qquad (2.20)$$

$$\underline{D}\,(y_0)u + E(y_0)v = 0 \qquad (2.21)$$

The relation between the subproblem optimal solutions and the complete problem optimal is given by Theorem 2.

Theorem 2

Let x_0, as given by (2.6), be the optimal solution to Problem I corresponding to y_0. Then necessary and sufficient conditions that (x_0, y_0) be the optimum of the complete problem are that y_0 is the optimal solution to Problem II and that the vector u, given by

$$u = \underline{r} - Qv, \qquad\qquad\qquad (2.22)$$

is nonnegative, where v is the shadow price vector at the Problem II optimum.

Proof

We first prove sufficiency by showing that (2.17) through (2.21) follow from the optimality of x_0 and the relations (2.15), (2.16), (2.22) and $u \geq 0$. Since x_0 is the optimal solution to Problem I the relation (2.9) holds as well as $A^T x_0 \geq b(y_0)$. The feasibility requirements (2.17) and (2.18) follow directly. The relation (2.19) is shown to be equivalent to (2.15) by using (2.9) and (2.10). From (2.22) we have

$$\underline{A}u + \underline{A}Qv = \underline{A}\ \underline{r}$$

This, together with (2.8) and (2.10) gives (2.20). Also from (2.22) we have

$$\underline{D}(y_0)u + \underline{D}(y_0)Qv - \underline{D}(y_0)\,\underline{r} = 0$$

This, together with (2.16) gives (2.21). The vector v is nonnegative since it is the optimal shadow price vector for Problem II. This completes the sufficiency proof.

To show necessity we assume (2.17) through (2.21) for nonnegative vectors u and v, and show that y_0 is the optimal solution of Problem II and that (2.22) holds. The two relations (2.14) and (2.15) for Problem II follow directly from (2.18) and (2.19), respectively, by the use of (2.9) and (2.10). The relation (2.16) is obtained by multiplying (2.20) by $-D(y_0)\,\underline{A}^{-1}$, adding to (2.21), and using (2.8) and (2.10). Finally (2.22) is obtained by multiplying (2.20) by $\underline{A}^{-1}$, and using (2.8) and (2.10). Q.E.D.

Corollary

A sufficient condition that (x_0, y_0) is optimal for the complete problem is that y_0 is an interior (unconstrained) minimum for Problem II.

Proof

The Problem II shadow price vector v is zero if y_0 is an interior minimum, since there are no active constraints at the minimum. By (2.8) we have $\underline{r} \geq 0$. Therefore by (2.22), $u \geq 0$, and (x_0, y_0) is the complete problem minimum. Q.E.D.

The theorem is basic to the solution of the complete problem by the partition programming algorithm in the following way. The linear Problem I is first solved by any dual method for $y = y_0$. Either a dual simplex method or the gradient projection method is suitable. The optimal vector x_0, the optimal basis $\underline{A}$, its inverse $\underline{A}^{-1}$ and corresponding shadow price vector $\underline{r}$ are then available. The partial derivative matrix $D(y_0)$, its partitions $\underline{D}(y_0)$ and $E(y_0)$ and the matrix Q as given by (2.10) are also computed. With these quantities we obtain the linear constraints and convex objective function for Problem II as given by (2.12). This problem is solved by means of the linear constraint version of gradient projection for which an efficient computational program is available [10]. The optimal value $y = y_1$ and corresponding shadow price vector v are obtained by gradient projection as described in Theorem 5 in Section 4. If $y_1 = y_0$, and u as given by (2.22) is nonnegative, the point (x_0, y_0) is the desired optimal solution of the complete problem by Theorem 2. On the other hand, with an arbitrary starting value y_0, it will generally be the case that these conditions will not be satisfied, so that (x_0, y_0) is not the complete problem optimal. In that case we will show that a new value of y can be found which decreases $\Psi(y)$. This is discussed in the next section.

In order to keep the presentation above from becoming too unwieldy we have considered the case with only a single block of inequalities, that is with $\ell = 1$. In general, of course, we will wish to solve multiblock problems, so that it is essential that we be able to recognize the optimum for the complete multiblock problem in terms of each of the ℓ Problem I solutions and the single Problem II solution. It can be shown that Theorem 2 can be generalized to the multiblock case, ensuring that the partition programming algorithm is valid for the general problem. In the multiblock case the form of Problem I for each block is given by (1.1), for a fixed value of y. The way in which Problem II is defined for the multiblock case is described in Section 4. It is shown there how the information available from each of the ℓ Problem I optimal solutions is used to form a single Problem II in the s-dimensional y-space. The number of constraints in Problem II will depend on the number of blocks and the number of constraints in each block, but the number of variables in Problem II is always the same as the number of y variables in the complete problem. Since computational time is determined primarily by the problem dimensionality (gradient projection being a dual algorithm), the time required to solve Problem II depends primarily on s and only in a secondary way on the number of blocks.

3. ITERATIVE SOLUTION

We will describe the iterative solution of Problems I and II by which the complete problem is solved. For simplicity we again consider the case $\ell = 1$, with only a single x-block as given by (2.5) and shown in Fig. 2. The actual multiblock algorithm is given in the next section, and it can be shown that the results given here are also valid for the multiblock problem (2.1).

An important aspect of the iterative procedure is the possibility of alternate optimal bases in Problem I. There may be alternate optimal bases corresponding to a point (x_0, y_0) when $A^T x_0 \geq b(y_0)$, with at least $m+1$ of these inequalities satisfied as equalities. If there exists more than one nonsingular $(m \times m)$ matrix $\underline{A}^T$ with rows selected from the set of equalities, such that $\underline{A}^{-1} c \geq 0$, then each such matrix corresponds to an alternate optimal basis. The particular optimal basis which is selected in Problem I will depend on the solution method and the choice of initial basis or starting value of x. There are, of course, only a finite number of possible alternate optimal bases.

We can now summarize the iterative solution procedure in terms of a typical cycle, the jth cycle. At the start of the jth cycle we have a feasible vector y_j, and corresponding value $\varphi(y_j)$ of the convex function $\varphi(y)$ as given by (2.3). The corresponding linear Problem I is solved, giving the vector x_j, optimal basis $\underline{A}$, and shadow price vector $\underline{r} \geq 0$. The corresponding Problem II, with a convex objective function and linear constraints, is formulated and its global minimum obtained. This gives a feasible and optimal vector y_{j+1}, the value of the objective function $\varphi(y_{j+1})$, and the corresponding Problem II shadow price vector v. Note that the solution of the convex Problem II is not necessarily a finite procedure. The feasibility of y_{j+1} follows from the fact that it satisfies $Q^T \underline{b}(y_{j+1}) - e(y_{j+1}) \geq 0$, as shown by Theorem 4. If $y_{j+1} = y_j$ and u as given by (2.22) is nonnegative, we have the desired optimal solution to the complete problem. If $y_{j+1} = y_j$ and u has at least one negative component, we formulate and solve Problem II for each alternate Problem I basis corresponding to y_j. If $\varphi(y_{j+1}) < \varphi(y_j)$, we go on to the next cycle with $y = y_{j+1}$.

Theorem 3

This iterative procedure will find the complete problem minimum in a finite number of cycles.

Proof

It follows from (2.3) that the desired convex function $\varphi(y)$ is given by $\varphi(y) = \underline{b}^T(y) \underline{A}^{-1}c$, where $\underline{A}$ is some Problem I optimal basis, whose choice depends on y. Each Problem II corresponds to a minimization over the feasible y-space for a particular selection of such an optimal basis. For each such selection the minimum over the feasible y-space is obtained. If we consider the jth cycle, we start with y_j and obtain the optimal vector $x_j = (\underline{A}^{-1})^T \underline{b}(y_j)$ which satisfies $B^T x_j \geq e(y_j)$, or using (2.10), $e(y_j) - Q^T \underline{b}(y_j) \leq 0$, so that y_j is feasible for Problem II. It follows that the optimal vector y_{j+1}, for Problem II, satisfies $\varphi(y_{j+1}) \leq \varphi(y_j)$. The desired function $\varphi(y)$, in the neighborhood of y_j, is given by at least one of the alternate Problem I optimal bases. Trying each of these in turn, we will find a basis for which either the complete problem optimum conditions are satisfied [in which case $\varphi(y_j)$ is the complete problem minimum], or a value y_{j+1} will be found such that $\varphi(y_{j+1}) < \varphi(y_j)$. In this latter case, the basis which gives y_{j+1} must be different from the basis chosen in any previous cycle. This is a consequence of the fact that each function $\varphi(y_i)$, $i = 0, \ldots, j$ is the minimum for the optimal basis selected in that cycle, and $\varphi(y_{j+1}) < \varphi(y_i)$, $i = 0, \ldots, j$. Since there are only a finite number of possible Problem I bases, the number of cycles is finite. Q.E.D.

Two points related to this iterative solution should be emphasized. The first is that even when alternate optimal bases exist it is only necessary to solve Problem II for a relatively small number of these bases (often only one or two) in order to obtain a decrease in the objective function. A specific selection procedure is used to choose an alternate optimal basis and modify the inverse $\underline{A}^{-1}$ by a single change of basis to get the desired new basis inverse. The selection is based on the most negative component of the vector u, and is described in the partition programming algorithm in the next section. The second point is that for a nonlinear vector b(y) the Problem II will usually also be nonlinear and must be solved by a convergent (but in general not finite) procedure. The gradient projection method is very well suited to this purpose and is used in the way described in the next section. Any other method suitable for minimizing a convex function subject to linear constraints could also be used.

The justification for the constraint linearization in Problem II is based on the following theorem which shows that if y_0 is not the optimal solution to the linearized Problem II, then a new feasible vector y can be found such that $\varphi(y) < \varphi(y_0)$. We again consider the single x-block problem given by (2.5), the convex function $\varphi(y)$ given by (2.3) and Problems I and II given by (2.6) and (2.12).

Theorem 4

Let the optimal vector y_1 for Problem II be such that

$$\underline{r}^T \underline{b}(y_1) < \underline{r}^T \underline{b}(y_0) \tag{3.1}$$

Then if

$$h(y) \equiv Q^T \underline{b}(y) - e(y) \tag{3.2}$$

is convex, we have

$$\varphi(y_1) \leq \underline{r}^T \underline{b}(y_1) < \underline{r}^T \underline{b}(y_0) = \varphi(y_0) \tag{3.3}$$

For h(y) not necessarily convex, let θ_m be the scalar solution of the one-dimensional maximization

$$\theta_m = \max \{ \theta \mid h(y_0 + \theta(y_1 - y_0)) \geq 0, \ 0 \leq \theta \leq 1 \} \tag{3.4}$$

Then for $\theta_m > 0$, and $\overline{y} = y_0 + \theta_m(y_1 - y_0)$ we have $\varphi(\overline{y}) < \varphi(y_0)$.

Proof

It follows from (2.10) and (3.2) that a vector y and the corresponding value of $x = (A^{-1})^T \underline{b}\,(y)$ are feasible for the complete problem (2.5) if, and only if, $h(y) \geq 0$. Since $x_0 = (\underline{A}^{-1})^T \underline{b}\,(y_0)$ is the optimal vector for Problem I with $y = y_0$, we have $h(y_0) \geq 0$, and $\underline{r}^T \underline{b}\,(y_0) = \varphi(y_0)$. For $h(y)$ convex

$$h(y) \geq h(y_0) + (y - y_0)^T [E(y_0) - \underline{D}\,(y_0)Q] \tag{3.5}$$

since by (2.11) and (3.2), the Jacobian of $h(y)$ at y_0 is $[E(y_0) - \underline{D}\,(y_0)Q]$. Since y_1 is feasible for Problem II, we have that the right-hand side of (3.5) is nonnegative. Therefore, $h(y_1) \geq 0$. It follows that $x_1 = (A^{-1})^T \underline{b}\,(y_1)$ and y_1 are feasible for the complete problem, with $c^T x_1 = \underline{r}^T \underline{b}\,(y_1)$. The minimum solution $\varphi(y_1)$ for $y = y_1$ must therefore satisfy $\varphi(y_1) \leq \underline{r}^T \underline{b}\,(y_1)$, which gives (3.3).

From (3.4) we have $h(\overline{y}) \geq 0$, for $\overline{y} = y_0 + \theta_m(y_1 - y_0)$. The corresponding value of $c^T x$ is $\underline{r}^T \underline{b}\,(\overline{y})$, so that $\varphi(\overline{y}) \leq \underline{r}^T \underline{b}\,(\overline{y})$. Since $\underline{r}^T \underline{b}\,(y)$ is convex

$$r^T b(y) \leq \underline{r}^T \underline{b}\,(y_0) + \theta_m [\underline{r}^{\,T} \underline{b}\,(y_1) - \underline{r}^T \underline{b}\,(y_0)] < \underline{r}^T \underline{b}\,(y_0) \tag{3.6}$$

for $\theta_m > 0$. Then, $\varphi(\overline{y}) \leq \underline{r}^T \underline{b}\,(\overline{y}) < \underline{r}^T \underline{b}\,(y_0) = \varphi(y_0)$. Q.E.D.

For a completely linear problem, where $b(y)$ is linear, it should be noted that the Problem II constraints are identical to those for the complete problem. It follows that for the linear problem we always have $\varphi(y_1) = \underline{r}^T \underline{b}\,(y_1) < \varphi(y_0)$, whenever $\underline{r}^T \underline{b}\,(y_1) < \underline{r}^T \underline{b}\,(y_0)$.

On the basis of Theorem 4, we observe that all points (x_j, y_j) obtained during the iterative procedure are feasible. Thus the procedure may be terminated at any cycle with a new feasible point which gives a lower value of the objective function than the starting point.

4. COMPUTATIONAL ALGORITHM

The computational program for partition programming uses the gradient projection (GP) method to solve both the completely linear Problem I and the linear constraint, convex function, Problem II. We will summarize the use of GP to solve a linear constraint problem by considering

$$\min_X \{ \varphi(x) \mid A^T x \geq b \} \tag{4.1}$$

where $\varphi(x)$ is a differentiable convex function of the m-dimensional vector x with the gradient $g(x)$, A is an m by k matrix and b is a k-dimensional vector.

Theorem 5

Let x_0 satisfy $A^T x_0 \geq b$. If x_0 satisfies the Kuhn-Tucker conditions for the problem (3.1) then GP will demonstrate this fact by finding a k-dimensional vector $r \geq 0$, such that $Ar = g(x_0)$ and $r^T[Ax_0 - b] = 0$. The q, $q \leq m$, non-zero components of r are given by the vector

$$\underline{r} = \underline{A}^{-*} g(x_0) \geq 0 \tag{4.2}$$

where the k by q matrix $\underline{A}$ consists of a set of q linearly independent columns of A which are selected by GP, and $\underline{A}^{-*} \equiv (\underline{A}^T\underline{A})^{-1}\underline{A}$. Furthermore, the matrix $\underline{A}$ is such that $x_0 = (\underline{A}^{-*})^T\underline{b}$ where $\underline{b}$ consists of the q components of b corresponding to the selected columns of A (or rows of A^T).

If the point x_0 does not satisfy the Kuhn-Tucker conditions then GP will find another feasible point which satisfies these conditions, along with the corresponding matrix $\underline{A}$, its pseudoinverse $\underline{A}^{-*}$ and the nonnegative vector $\underline{r}$.

The proof that GP will recognize the optimum (first paragraph of theorem) has been given by Mangasarian [7]. The convergence to the optimum (second paragraph of theorem) has been proved in Part I of the GP paper [10].

The way in which the GP optimization of appropriate subproblems is used to achieve an iterative solution of the complete multiblock problem (2.1) is given in the Appendix to this paper. It is assumed that an initial feasible vector y_0 is known.

We now show how the general convex problem of minimizing a convex function subject to convex constraints can be put in the form (2.1). We consider the convex problem in the form

$$\min_{y} \left\{ \Psi(y) \mid \lambda_i(y) \leq 0, i = 1, \ldots, q \right\} \tag{4.3}$$

We introduce $q + 1$ slack variables x_i, $i = 1, \ldots, q + 1$. Then an equivalent problem in the form (2.1) is given by

$$\min \left\{ x_{q+1} \left| \begin{array}{l} -x_i \geq \lambda_i(y), i = 1, \ldots, q \\ x_i \geq 0, i = 1, \ldots, q \\ x_{q+1} \geq \Psi(y) \end{array} \right. \right\} \tag{4.4}$$

If there are linear equalities in the x_i and y, they can also be handled without difficulty. If such equalities occur in the ith block they are handled by always including in the Problem I optimal basis $\underline{A}_i^T$ those rows of A_i which correspond to the equality constraints.

Acknowledgment.

I would like to acknowledge the valuable comments and suggestions of my colleague Dr. O. L. Mangasarian and of Professor G. B. Dantzig, University of California at Berkeley.

APPENDIX

Partition Programming Algorithm

1. An optimal solution to each of the ℓ linear subproblems (1.1) with $y = y_0$, is obtained using GP or an LP algorithm. This gives $\Psi_i(y_0)$, the optimal vector x_{i0} and basis $\underline{A}_i$ for each subproblem, $i = 1, \ldots, \ell$. The basis $\underline{A}_i$ consists of m_i linearly independent columns selected by GP from the original matrix A_i. The corresponding optimal shadow price vector is given by

$$\underline{r}_i = \underline{A}^{-1} c_i \geq 0$$

The columns of A_i which are not in $\underline{A}_i$ are denoted by B_i. The m_i components of $b_i(y)$ which correspond to the optimal basis $\underline{A}_i$ will be denoted by a vector $\underline{b}_i(y)$ and the remaining $(k_i - m_i)$ components by a vector $e_i(y)$. The complete problem objective function is then given by

$$\Psi(y_0) = \sum_{i=1}^{\ell} \Psi_i(y_0).$$

2. A convex problem in the y variables with linearized constraints is now formed, as follows. For each block, the matrices $D_i(y_0)$, $i = 1, \ldots, \ell$, are calculated as given by (2.11) for the single block case. Each matrix $D_i(y_0)$ is partitioned into $\underline{D}_i(y_0)$ and $E_i(y_0)$ corresponding to the vectors $\underline{b}_i(y_0)$ and $e(y_0)$. A matrix Q_i is also obtained for each block according to

$$Q_i = \underline{A}_i^{-1} B_i$$

We now have the convex <u>Problem II</u>, with s variables and $\Sigma_{i=1}^{\ell} (k_i - m_i)$ linear constraints

$$\min_{y} \left\{ \underline{\Psi}(y) \mid (y - y_0)^T [E_i(y_0) - \underline{D}_i(y_0)Q_i] \geq -h_i(y_0), \, i = 1, \ldots, \ell \right\}$$

where $\underline{\Psi}(y) \equiv \Sigma_{i=1}^{\ell} \underline{r}_i \underline{b}_i(y)$, and $h_i(y) \equiv Q_i^T \underline{b}_i(y) - e_i(y)$, $i = 1, \ldots, \ell$.

3. Problem II is solved by GP, as summarized in Theorem 5 giving an optimal vector $y = y_1$, and the corresponding value of the objective function $\underline{\Psi}(y_1)$. Since y_0 is feasible for Problem II and

$$\Psi(y_0) = \sum_{i=1}^{\ell} c_i^T x_{i0} = \sum_{i=1}^{\ell} c_i^T \left(\underline{A}_i^{-1}\right)^T \underline{b}_i(y_0) = \underline{\Psi}(y_0),$$

we have

$$\Psi(y_0) = \underline{\Psi}(y_0) \geq \underline{\Psi}(y_1). \tag{A1}$$

The solution also gives the shadow price vector $v \geq 0$, with no more than s positive components. We let v_i be the vector whose $(k_i - m_i)$ components are the components of v corresponding to the ith submatrix A_i. We define

$$u_i = \underline{r}_i - Q_i v_i, \qquad i = 1, \ldots, \ell$$

4. There are four possibilities:

a. $y_1 = y_0$ and $u_i \geq 0$, $i = 1, \ldots, \ell$. By Theorem 2 the complete problem optimal vector is $(x_{10}, x_{20}, \ldots, x_{\ell 0}, y_0)$ and $\underline{\Psi}(y_0)$ is the desired minimum value of the objective function. The shadow prices for the complete problem (one for each constraint) are given according to the submatrix in which the constraint occurs. For the ith submatrix, the vector u_i gives the shadow prices for the m_i constraints corresponding to $\underline{A}_i^T$. The vector v_i gives the shadow prices for the remaining $(k_i - m_i)$ constraints.

b. $y_1 = y_0$ and at least one negative component of u_i for at least one submatrix. For each submatrix we choose the most negative component of u_i, if any. The corresponding row of $\underline{A}_i^T$ is replaced with a row of B_i^T for which the corresponding component of v_i is positive. This gives a new nonsingular basis $\underline{A}_i^T$. There will be at least one such selection from B_i^T for which $\underline{A}_i c_i \geq \overline{0}$, that is, $\underline{A}_i^T$ is an optimal basis for the ith submatrix Problem I. Using this basis we form a new Problem II and continue the iteration with (3) above.

c. $\underline{\Psi}(y_1) < \underline{\Psi}(y_0)$ and $h_i(y_1) \geq 0$, $i = 1, \ldots, \ell$. We have $\Psi(y_1) \leq \underline{\Psi}(y_1)$, so that $\Psi(y_1) < \Psi(y_0)$ by (A1). This will always be the case for the completely linear problem where $b_i(y)$ is given by (2.2). We continue the iteration with (2) above with y_1 replacing y_0.

d. $\underline{\Psi}(y_1) < \underline{\Psi}(y_0)$ and at least one of the inequalities $h_i(y_1) \geq 0$, $i = 1, \ldots, \ell$, not satisfied. Let

$$\theta_m = \max \left\{ \theta \mid h_i(y_0 + \theta(y_0 - y_1)) \geq 0, \qquad i = 1, \ldots, \ell \right\}$$

For $\theta_m > 0$, and $\overline{y} = y_0 + \theta_m(y_1 - y_0)$ we have $\Psi(\overline{y}) < \Psi(y_0)$ by Theorem 4. We continue the iteration with (2) above with $\overline{y}$ replacing y_0. If $\theta_m = 0$, we must have at least one component, say $h_{ij}(y)$ the jth component of the vector $h_i(y)$, such that $h_{ij}(y_0) = 0$, and $h_{ij}(y_1) < 0$. The corresponding row of B_i^T is exchanged with an appropriate row of $\underline{A}_i^T$ to give a new optimal basis $\underline{A}_i^T$. Using this new basis we form a new Problem II, and continue the iteration with (3) above.

This takes into account the possible alternatives during a cycle. A typical cycle starts with a feasible vector y_0, and ends with a feasible vector y_1 with $\Psi(y_1) < \Psi(y_0)$ as given by 4c, or a feasible vector $\overline{y}$ with $\Psi(\overline{y}) < \Psi(y_0)$ as given by 4d. As shown in Theorem 3, after a finite number of such cycles the conditions of 4a will be satisfied and the complete problem optimum has been obtained.

REFERENCES

1. Beale, E. M. L., "On Minimizing a Convex Function Subject to Linear Inequalities," J. Roy. Stat. Soc., Vol. 17, Series B, 1955, pp. 173-184.

2. ————, "The Simplex Method Using Pseudo-basic Variables for Structured Linear Programming Problems," this volume.

3. Dantzig, G. B., and P. Wolfe, "Decomposition Principle for Linear Programs," Operations Research, Vol. 8, 1960, pp. 101-111. Also see "The Decomposition Algorithm for Linear Programs," Econometrica, Vol. 29, 1961, pp. 767-778.

4. ————, and A. Madansky, "On the Solution of Two-stage Linear Programs under Uncertainty," Proc. Fourth Berkeley Symposium on Math. Stat. and Prob., Univ. of Calif., 1960, pp. 165-176.

5. Kuhn, H. W., and A. W. Tucker, "Nonlinear Programming," Proc. Second Berkeley Symposium on Math. Stat. and Prob., Univ. of Calif., 1950, pp. 481-492.

6. Madansky, A., "Inequalities for Stochastic Linear Programming Problems," Management Science, Vol. 6, 1960, pp. 197-204.

7. Mangasarian, O. L., "Equivalence in Nonlinear Programming," Shell Development Co., P-1070. Submitted to Naval Research Logistics Quarterly.

8. Rosen, J. B., "Partition Programming," Notices Amer. Math Soc., Vol. 7, 1960, pp. 718-719, Abstract No. 572-22.

9. ————, "Primal and Dual Aspects of Partition Programming, presented at ORSA-TIMS Natl. Meeting, San Francisco, Calif., Nov. 8, 1961.

10. ————, "The Gradient Projection Method for Nonlinear Programming," Parts I and II, J. Soc. Ind. Appl. Math, Vol. 8, 1960, pp. 181-217, and Vol. 9, 1961, pp. 514-532. Program available, SHARE #1399

11. ————, and J. C. Ornea, "Solution of Nonlinear Programming Problems by Partitioning," Shell Development Co., P-1115, June, 1962. Submitted to Management Science.

Experiments in Linear Programming

Philip Wolfe

Leola Cutler

INTRODUCTION

There are many ways to solve linear programming problems. The earliest of these, Dantzig's "simplex method" [2], is the most widely used, and no equally effective alternative is available. Many variations of the original simplex method have been proposed in the last few years. Computational experience seems to us the only way to properly compare the computational efficiencies of these variations; their behavior depends so strongly on features of the process which cannot be known in advance that a priori estimates of their effectiveness inspire little confidence. The purpose of the work reported here has been to compare some of the outstanding variations with each other in their work on actual linear programming problems, and to set some bench marks against which other procedures may be measured.

Under the title of "SCEMP"—Standardized Computational Experiments in Mathematical Programming—this work originated in 1960 at a meeting of the Linear Programming Committee of the SHARE organization, when it was suggested that some of the flexible linear programming routines then forthcoming might serve the task of evaluating the alternative procedures that had been discussed there. The Committee maintains a file of test problems from which those used here were selected; they are described in detail in the next section. A set of statistic-collecting routines, modelled on an all-in-core, FORTRAN-coded linear programming routine for the IBM 704 and 7090 [12], was coded and served as the basis for the computer routines used in the present tests. (The routines and the output of the tests have been retained and can be made available, but the routines are not recommended for general purposes.)

The nature of the output of these routines has been given in detail elsewhere [13]. Briefly, it consists in the following quantities for each simplex method iteration: the amount of infeasibility; the current value of the objective; the pivot row and column; the determinant of the basis; the number of product-form transformation entries; the number of arithmetic operations performed in each of several major subdivisions of

†This research was sponsored by U.S. Air Force Project RAND. It does not necessarily reflect the views or opinions of the Air Force.

177

an iteration; and the number of nonzero elements in certain arrays of interest. (The terms used here are defined in Sections 3 and 8.) At the end of a problem the complete solutions are given as well as the "errors"—the extent to which the final solution fails of being both primal and dual feasible. All solutions obtained have been checked with those obtained by other routines on the same problems, and the statistic-collecting features have been checked in detail for most of the runs by hand calculation of a small problem [10].

The experimental data are organized by "runs," each of which consists in the solution of an entire set of test problems by means of a routine embodying a particular algorithm variation. Of the 47 runs done so far in the SCEMP project, 29 furnish the data used in this report; the others bear on matters not discussed here. Two kinds of data pertaining to a run have been used in this report: we consider the number of simplex method iterations, or changes of basis, required to reach a certain end—either the first feasible solution or the optimal solution of the problem—in Sections 4-7; and we discuss the total number of arithmetic operations required in Sections 8 and 9. The Appendix lists the raw data from which the figures presented in the sequel have been calculated.

Since the point of most of these experiments has been to compare alternative methods, the following general format has been used for the results. The appropriate data (e.g., number of iterations) for a particular run are chosen as a <u>base</u>. In order to compare another run with the base, the corresponding datum obtained in the comparison run for each of the test problems is divided by the corresponding datum for the base run; the resulting ratio is the proportion in which the measure has been reduced by use of the compared procedure. For example, suppose that Algorithm I took 20 iterations to solve problem 1D and 30 to solve problem 2A; and that Algorithm II took 14 and 24 iterations, respectively. Choosing Algorithm I as the base, the comparative results would be given as in Table 1-1.

Table 1-1

ALGORITHM II COMPARED WITH ALGORITHM I

Problem	1D	2A	avg.	c.v.
Alg. II	.70	.80	.75	.07

Note that usually the average of the ratios is given, as well as their coefficient of variation (the standard deviation divided by the average). The problems will be listed in order of their numbers of constraints. The ratios all have equal weights in the averaging, but the average could be viewed as an average of the data of the compared run weighted by the reciprocals of the corresponding data of the base run. For this reason, the average is a somewhat fairer measure when the data of the base are larger than those of the compared run. Owing to the arithmetic of averaging, if II were

chosen as the base and I as the compared run, the resulting average would
be greater than the reciprocal of that of 1-1.

Some gaps appear in the tables that follow. The largest problem cannot
be run on the routines using the standard form of the simplex method, and
two other problems were omitted from some "feasible solution" runs because they had starting feasible solutions.

A good deal of special terminology is used in describing the computations. Special terms are usually defined in context at their first appearance, which is signaled by underlining. Most of them are introduced
in Sections 3 and 8. While the terms "method" and "procedure" are used
interchangeably in a very general way, we use the term algorithm to refer
to any particular version of the simplex method which chooses the pivot
column and the pivot row in a particular manner, regardless of the way in
which the data used in making the choice are obtained. Thus Sections 3 to 7
study only algorithms and the data—principally iteration counts—associated
with them, while the remaining sections study, in part, different methods
of performing the same algorithm.

We are indebted to many people for assistance with SCEMP. Marvin
Shapiro and Richard Clasen at RAND did a substantial part of the computer
programming. Many members of the SHARE Linear Programming Project,
notably David M. Smith and L. Wheaton Smith, offered valuable advice.
Much of the computing labor was defrayed through generous donations of
time by C-E-I-R, Inc., Esso Research and Engineering Co., Phillips
Petroleum Co., Shell Oil Co., Socony-Mobil Oil Co., and Standard Oil Co.
of California.

2. THE PROBLEMS

The linear programming problems on which our experiments were conducted were drawn from the file of thirteen problems maintained by the
Test Problems and Experiments Committee of the SHARE Linear Programming Project. The problems, submitted by various members of the
Committee in 1959 and 1960, were all used as production problems in their
businesses; the majority arose in oil refining studies. None were especially constructed for test purposes, or thought "pathological." The
original problems are available through the Committee.

Four of the problems were not used here. Problem 1C is too small, 4A
is too large, and 3A and 3B had awkward input features. Thus our work
was done with the nine problems of Table 2-1.

Throughout this report the problems are listed in the order of their
numbers of constraints. In Table 2-1, the "name" identifies a problem in
the Committee's files. All the problems are formulated as problems of
minimizing a linear objective function under linear equality constraints.
The objective functions are entered as rows of data, as are the constraints;
some problems have several alternative objective functions, so that there
are always one or more "additional rows." In our runs the highest
numbered objective row was used and the remainder ignored.

Table 2-1

THE TEST PROBLEMS

Name	1D	2A	1E	1A	5A	1G	1F	2B	1B
Number of constraints: M	27	30	31	33	34	48	66	96	117
Number of additional rows: K	1	2	8	1	1	1	1	3	1
Number of variables	45	103	106	64	78	102	135	162	253
Number of entries	252	811	855	245	391	462	644	897	1210

The "number of variables" includes all the variables of the problem but no "artificial" variables. The "number of entries" is the number of nonzero quantities appearing among the constraints and objectives. Some further data regarding starting bases for the problems are given in Section 4.

3. TERMINOLOGY

In order to describe the algorithms studied, we develop here some of the terminology connected with the simplex method. It is not intended to discuss the procedure itself, which is done in many standard works [5, 6]. The discussion in this section is entirely in terms of the standard form of the simplex method; the other forms are dealt with in Section 8.

Let a linear programming problem have N variables $x_1, \ldots, x_N$ and M equation constraints. At any stage in the simplex method solution there is defined a <u>basis</u>, which is a set of M <u>basic variables</u>, say $x_{j_1}, \ldots, x_{j_M}$; let the remaining variables be $x_{j_{M+1}}, \ldots, x_{j_N}$. The current <u>tableau</u> is the set of coefficients of the linear equations

$$x_{j_1} + a_{11} x_{j_{M+1}} + \cdots + a_{1, N-M} \; x_{j_N} = b_1$$
$$\vdots \qquad\qquad\qquad\qquad\qquad \vdots$$
$$x_{j_M} + a_{M1} x_{j_{M+1}} + \cdots + a_{M, N-M} \; x_{j_N} = b_M$$

which are uniquely defined by the current basis and the requirement that this set be equivalent to the linear equations defining the original problem. We say that the basic variable x_{j_i} <u>occupies position i</u> in the basis for $i = 1, \ldots, M$.

It is further supposed that the objective function to be minimized is expressed at this time in terms of the nonbasic variables as

$$c_1 x_{j_{M+1}} + \cdots + c_{N-M} x_{j_N} + z_0$$

the coefficients c_j are the <u>reduced costs</u>. (The quantities a_{ij} and c_j defined here commonly carry a superior bar to indicate that they change in each iteration; we omit the bar.) The <u>basic solution</u> of the equations above is obtained by setting all nonbasic variables to zero, giving the basic variables the values $x_{j_1} = b_1$, etc., and the objective the value z_0.

In a single <u>iteration</u> of the simplex method a <u>pivot column</u> J (where j_{M+J} is the index of a nonbasic variable) and a <u>pivot row</u> I of the tableau are chosen, and the roles of the basic variable occupying position I and the nonbasic variable associated with column J are interchanged, new data of the form of the equations above being obtained by <u>pivoting</u> on the entry a_{IJ} of the tableau. The value of the objective changes by the amount $c_J b_I / a_{IJ}$.

Some M variables must be chosen as the <u>starting basis</u> for the procedure. If not all these variables belong to those of the original problem, the remainder are <u>artificial</u>. Each instance of a basic variable whose current value is negative, or of an artificial variable whose value is not zero, is an <u>infeasibility</u>. A basic solution having no infeasibilities is <u>feasible</u>. When it is necessary to adjoin artificial variables in order to have a starting basis, we always adjoin for each a column of coefficients of the form $[0, \ldots, 1, \ldots, 0]$ to the original problem, the single "1" of the column lying in a row corresponding to an otherwise unoccupied position of the basis. When there are infeasibilities, a separate objective function involving them is defined, and it is required that this <u>infeasibility</u> objective be minimized. The process of minimizing that objective is <u>Phase One</u>; the subsequent minimization of the proper objective, once a feasible solution is obtained, is <u>Phase Two</u>.

In the sequel we refer to the <u>ordinary</u> simplex method, by which we mean the simplex method as most commonly presented, except that we extend the usual procedure for the choice of pivot row to that of the "composite algorithm" [3].

In Phase Two the procedure is quite ordinary. A pivot column J is chosen so that c_J is minimal (if all are nonnegative, the current solution is optimal). Then the pivot row I is chosen so that after pivoting the current solution will still be nonnegative: I is the i which minimizes b_i / a_{iJ} for all $a_{iJ} > 0$. If $b_I = 0$—degeneracy—should happen, then I is chosen as the i maximizing a_{iJ} among all i for which $b_i = 0$. (This rule is not known to prevent "cycling," but is very effective in practice [15].)

In Phase One the objective is defined as the sum of the infeasibilities: $\Sigma \{x_j \mid x_j < 0 \text{ or } x_j \text{ artificial}\}$. The reduced cost for the nonbasic variable j is then $\Sigma \{a_{ij} \mid b_i < 0\} - \Sigma \{a_{ij} \mid b_i > 0 \text{ and position i artificial}\}$. The pivot column J is chosen for minimal reduced cost, and the pivot row I so that no variable nonnegative in the current solution becomes negative after pivoting: I is the i which achieves the smaller of the two ratios $\text{Min}_i \{b_i / a_{iJ} \mid b_i, a_{iJ} > 0\}$, $\text{Max}_i \{b_i / a_{iJ} \mid b_i, a_{iJ} < 0\}$. A somewhat more complicated rule is needed for degeneracy. In the absence of negative b_i, the pivot-row rule operates just as in Phase Two.

4. STARTING BASES

The basis with which a problem is started naturally has a great influence on the number of iterations required to solve it. In practice one often attempts to guess a starting basis which will be as nearly feasible and optimal as possible; a sophisticated routine will make good use of such a guess even if the basis is incomplete, infeasible, or singular. The three methods studied here do not, of course, make any use of special information about the problem; they assume complete ignorance, and may be used with any problem.

N basis: When no starting basis is specified, a full set of M artificial variables is adjoined to the problem and constitutes the starting basis.

S basis: By singleton we mean a variable having only one nonzero entry, and that positive, in the equations of the initial tableau. An S basis is a starting basis consisting of a maximal set of singletons, with artificial variables used as necessary for the unfilled positions. (The computational cost of pivoting on singletons is almost nothing, and feasibility is improved if all the original right-hand sides are nonnegative.)

F basis: A full basis was produced by this procedure: first, an S basis was chosen; subsequently, each column of the tableau was examined, and pivoted into the basis if it had a nonzero entry corresponding to any unfilled position. The only basis positions left unfilled by this procedure are those corresponding to redundant constraints. Naturally, the resulting basis is not likely to be primal or dual feasible. Other procedures for obtaining a full basis have been tried but not yet fully evaluated; they do not seem to offer much advantage over the above.

Table 4-1 describes the bases resulting from the use of procedures S and F. All the data are proportions, the number of variables in a given category being divided by the number of constraints in the problem. The last two lines constitute the proportion of infeasibilities in the starting basis. Note, however, that artificial variables initially at zero level tend to become nonzero before they are eliminated, so that for an S basis the total number of artificials is the better measure of infeasibility.

Table 4-1

STARTING BASIS CHARACTERISTICS

Problem	1D	2A	1E	1A	5A	1G	1F	2B	1B
			(S basis)						
Singletons used	.19	.87	.19	.30	1.00	.90	.65	.86	.29
Positive artificials	.81	.00	.19	.70	.00	.10	.35	.05	.60
Zero artificials	.00	.13	.61	.00	.00	.00	.00	.08	.11
			(F basis)						
Negative variables	.41	.00	.42	.30	.00	.23	.26	.10	.46

Note that the proportion of infeasibilities in the F basis runs a little more than half the proportion in the S basis. We view this as accounting for the advantage, to be seen below, of the F basis over the S basis.

We are mainly interested in the number of simplex method iterations required to obtain the first feasible solution after the starting basis has been constructed. (In Section 9 the effect of the work required to produce the starting basis, as included in the total work to solve the problem, is considered.) Bases N and S have been used with two algorithms: the ordinary procedure and the "ratio pricing" procedure, described in Section 6. The results are summarized in Table 4-2. The first line compares basis S (run 21) with basis N (run 5, used as the base), for the ordinary algorithm; the second line compares basis S (run 6) with basis N (run 8, used as base) for the ratio pricing algorithm. The ratios thus represent the proportion in which the number of iterations in Phase One is decreased by using an S basis rather than an N basis.

Table 4-2

S BASIS COMPARED TO N BASIS FOR TWO ALGORITHMS

Problem	1D	2A	1E	1A	5A	1G	1F	2B	1B	avg.
Ordinary alg.	.89	.00	.69	.61	.00		.51	.42	.83	.50
Ratio pricing	.86	.01	.85	.82	.00	.40	.58	.83		.54

Evidently use of an S basis entails, on the average, a saving of about 48% in the number of iterations required for Phase One.

Comparison of bases S and F has been made in each of three algorithms, with the number of iterations for basis S taken as the base data: the ordinary algorithm (runs 21 and 39, respectively); the sequential procedure (runs 31 and 36); and the least-infeasibility procedure (runs 33 and 37). The last two procedures are discussed in Section 6. Table 4-3 summarizes these, omitting problems 2A and 5A because their starting S and F bases are feasible.

Table 4-3

F BASIS COMPARED TO S BASIS

Problem	1D	1E	1A	1G	1F	2B	1B	avg.
Ordinary alg.	.32	.71	.48	1.62	.05	.69	.53	.63
Sequential	.37	1.00	.37	2.43	.11	1.07	.55	.84
Least infeas.	.33	.94	.35	2.27	.09	.93	.78	.81

The over-all average of these proportions is 0.76, predicting a saving of 24% in use of an F basis rather than an S basis.

We conclude that in the absence of other knowledge of the problem, an F basis should be used. Some linear programming routines [1] make it possible to use a mixed procedure, entering a known partial basis and subsequently completing It in an arbitrary manner.

We may try to predict the number of iterations Phase One requires using the ordinary algorithm. Each entry in Table 4-4 is obtained by averaging, for all problems, the number of iterations taken using the basis N, S, or F divided by one of three possible measures of problem difficulty—the number, M, of constraints, the number of nonsingletons, or the number of infeasibilities in an F basis. Thus, for example, the number of iterations required using an S basis is expected to be 0.78 M. The coefficients of variation are given in parentheses. It is disappointing that the number of constraints is a better basis for prediction than the more informative measures.

Table 4-4

PHASE ONE ITERATIONS VERSUS MEASURES OF
PROBLEM DIFFICULTY

		Measure		
	M	Number of nonsingletons		Number of negatives in F basis
Starting Basis	N 1.69 (.3)			
	S .78 (.8)	2.13	(.9)	
	F .56 (.6)	2.07	(1.1)	2.12 (.8)

5. THE FEASIBLE SOLUTION

In general Phase One, the task of obtaining a first feasible solution, is accomplished by employing the simplex method to minimize some measure of the infeasibility of a solution. The five procedures studied here employ four different measures of infeasibility. In all of them the measure constitutes an objective function whose reduced costs are calculated so that the choice of pivot column can be made by the ordinary rule. In all but the "extended composite" algorithm the ordinary rule of pivot row selection is used.

The ordinary procedure is described in Section 3.

The extended composite procedure [14] differs from the ordinary in choice of pivot row. After the pivot column has been chosen in the ordinary way, the pivot row is selected so that the sum of infeasibilities after pivoting will be minimized; variables are allowed to change sign freely. Thus I is defined by $\theta_0 = b_I/a_{IJ}$, where θ_0 minimizes $\Sigma_i \{|b_i - \theta a_{iJ}| \mid b_i - \theta a_{iJ}$ is infeasible $\}$.

In the sequential procedure, the infeasibility is corrected one component at a time, in order. At any iteration, let i_0 be the least i for which some b_i is infeasible, and x_r the corresponding variable. The objective for minimization is defined as x_r if position i_0 is artificial and b_{i_0} is positive, or as $-x_r$ if b_{i_0} is negative. (The reduced cost for column j will then be just $a_{i_0 j}$ or $-a_{i_0 j}$.) During the procedure, row i_0 will be made feasible, feasibility on the previous rows being preserved.

The least-infeasibility procedure is like the sequential, except that at each iteration the index i_0 is taken so that x_r is minimal among all infeasible variables; the index may increase or decrease.

The fudge procedure, but not its name, is due to Gass [5, pp. 120-125]. A problem having negative solution values is augmented by a single artificial variable and subjected to a transformation yielding nonnegative solutions for the augmented problem. Specifically, the tableau is augmented by a column containing the entry -1 in each row having $b_i < 0$ and zeros elsewhere; and the desired tableau is obtained by pivoting on the Ith entry of the added column, where $b_I = \min_i b_i$. Subsequently the sum of all the artificial variables is minimized using the ordinary algorithm; when it has been reduced to zero, a feasible solution is at hand. (Of course other means of getting feasible could be used once the negativity has been removed.)

Table 5-1 lists the runs done using these five procedures, indicated at the left. The starting basis used is listed at the top.

Table 5-1

FEASIBLE SOLUTION RUNS

	N	S	F
Ordinary algorithm	5	21	39
Extended composite algorithm	(5)	(21)	38
Sequential algorithm		31	36
Least-infeasibility algorithm		33	37
Fudge procedure	(5)	(21)	32

Runs indicated in parentheses were not done, since the same results would have been obtained as in the run whose number is given.

Tables 5-2 and 5-3 give the results for these procedures, for bases S and F, relative to the ordinary procedure. The last line of each table is the proportion of infeasibilities in the starting basis for each problem. The amount of infeasibility does not seem to affect the relative efficiencies of these methods much, although it does affect the total work done, as the data for runs 21, 31, and 37 in the Appendix, or those of Table 4-4, show.

The results pretty well establish the ordinary procedure as superior in getting feasible. Its objective is responsible, since the minimization algorithm is the same in all the runs. It seems that by moving in a direc-

Table 5-2

PHASE ONE, S BASIS, RELATIVE TO ORDINARY ALGORITHM

Problem	1D	1E	1A	1G	1F	2B	1B	avg.
Sequential	.96	.94	1.52	1.00	.98	.97	1.04	1.06
Least-infeasibility	1.08	1.03	1.36	1.05	1.24	1.12	.94	1.12
Proportion infeas.	.81	.19	.70	.10	.35	.05	.60	

Table 5-3

PHASE ONE, F BASIS, RELATIVE TO ORDINARY ALGORITHM

Problem	1D	1E	1A	1G	1F	2B	1B	avg.
Extended composite	1.00	1.08	1.42	.65	1.00	1.04	1.01	1.03
Sequential	1.12	1.33	1.17	1.50	2.00	1.51	1.08	1.39
Least-infeas.	1.12	1.37	1.00	1.47	2.00	1.51	1.39	1.41
Fudge	1.25	1.08	1.25	1.00	2.00	1.34	1.01	1.27
Proportion infeas.	.41	.42	.30	.23	.26	.10	.46	

tion tending to minimize the sum of all the infeasibilities we give more chance to a number of infeasibilities to leave, while the sequential and least-feasible procedures, concentrating on a single variable at a time, are too single-minded. Since several negative infeasibilities can be removed in one iteration, while only one artificial variable can, it is reasonable that the difference is more decisive for F bases than for S bases.

The extended composite procedure is somewhat disappointing. It might work better if, at the expense of considerably more calculation, the pivot column were chosen by the same criterion as is the pivot row.

6. THE OPTIMAL SOLUTION

Of greatest interest to the ordinary user is the amount of work required to solve a complete problem. In this section six algorithms are compared in the number of iterations required to obtain an optimal solution. All but one of these are designed to handle artificial variables; for them, the ordinary Phase One objective—the sum of all infeasibilities—is used; this was found most efficient in Section 5. Unless otherwise noted, each procedure uses the same method for minimizing its objective in Phase One as it does in Phase Two, only the definition of the objective changing between the phases. Similarly, each procedure (except the "symmetric") uses the ordinary choice of pivot row. They differ primarily in the manner of choosing the pivot column.

The ordinary procedure was described in Section 3.

The positive-normalized procedures (PN1 and PN2) can be viewed as representative of those proposals which aim at eliminating the effects of bad scaling of the problem data by dividing the reduced costs, used in choosing the pivot column, by some combination of the coefficients a_{ij}. The first of the two considered here, proposed by Dickson and Frederick [4], uses the formula $d_j = c_j^2/(c_j^2 + \Sigma_i a_{ij}^{+2})$, where a_{ij}^+ is the "positive part" of a_{ij}, choosing the pivot column as that j for which d_j is maximal for $c_j < 0$. The procedure PN2 is essentially this, using instead the formula $d_j = c_j^2/\Sigma_i a_{ij}^{+2}$, which gives the same result.

The PN1 procedure employs the slightly simpler formula $d_j = c_j/\Sigma_i a_{ij}^+$, with the pivot column chosen for minimal d_j.

The greatest-change procedure was described long ago, but has been little used. That column is chosen which, after pivoting, will give the greatest decrease in the value of the objective; it is the j which minimizes the expression $c_j \min_i \{b_i/a_{ij} \mid a_{ij} > 0\}$ for the change of the objective.

The ratio-pricing procedure was suggested informally by Markowitz some time ago. It differs from the ordinary procedure only in Phase One. Letting w_j be the reduced cost for the infeasibility objective then, and c_j be the reduced cost for the proper objective, the pivot column j is chosen so as to maximize c_j/w_j for $w_j < 0$; we obtain the largest possible improvement in the proper objective per unit change of infeasibility. It may be viewed as an application of parametric linear programming [5]: defining ϕ^* at each iteration as the largest ϕ such that $c_j + \phi w_j \geq 0$ for all $w_j < 0$, the pivot column is chosen so as to increase ϕ^*. Evidently when ϕ^* becomes sufficiently large we have all $w_j \geq 0$, and Phase One is ended. It turns out that almost all c_j are then nonnegative, too, so that Phase Two is quite short. The aim of the procedure is to obtain a first feasible solution which is nearly optimal; the data of the Appendix for run 6 show that it does this well.

The symmetric procedure of Talacko [9] is employed only with a full basis; it may take either "primal" or "dual" simplex method steps. For one iteration: Among those columns with negative reduced costs, and those rows whose basic variables are nonnegative, a potential pivot is determined using the greatest-change procedure as described above; and among columns with positive reduced costs and rows with negative variables, a potential pivot is determined using the dual of the greatest-change procedure (for which the greatest increase of the objective is sought). That pivot is used for which the magnitude of the objective change is greater. If a step of the first kind is taken, all nonnegative basic variables stay nonnegative; if of the second kind, all nonnegative reduced costs stay nonnegative. The procedure does not always terminate in a solution of the problem [11, p. 10]; but it did for the test problems.

Table 6-1 compares all these, taking the ordinary procedure as the base (run 21).

Table 6-1

ALGORITHMS AND BASES COMPARED WITH ORDINARY, S BASIS

Problem	1D	2A	1E	1A	5A	1G	1F	2B	1B	avg.	c.v.
				Singleton basis							
PN1— run 10	.76	.80	.96	1.00	.73	.66	.84	.82		.82	.1
PN2—run 14	.83	.82	.98	.93	.76	.73	.66	.90		.83	.1
Greatest-change run 15	.70	1.10	1.23	.76	.86	.65	.73	1.21		.91	.2
Ratio-pricing run 6	.59	1.62	1.42	.81	.95	.82	.55	1.35		1.01	.4
				Full basis							
Ordinary run 39	.63	1.24	.92	.52	1.00	1.21	.45	.76	.76	.83	.3
Symmetric run 40	.43	.82	1.53	.45	.84	.74	.49	.73		.75	.4
Greatest-change run 41	.39	.82	.68	.55	.84	.94	.38	.90	.27	.64	.4

(Note: If problem 1B is eliminated from 39 and 41, the averages are .84, .69.)

Of the runs with singleton basis, the positive-normalized procedures are outstanding, and over-all the greatest-change procedure with full basis is best. Unfortunately the positive-normalized procedures have not yet been tried with full bases; they might perform even better. Incidentally, the data of the Appendix show that, with the natural exception of ratio-pricing, the differences among the procedures are reflected in Phase One in about the same way as in the entire process.

The data of Table 6-1 allow the symmetric and greatest-change procedures to be compared directly with the ordinary procedure with full basis. Using run 39 as base, the averages and coefficients of variation obtained are: symmetric algorithm, .92, .3; greatest-change algorithm, .78, .3. The relative efficiencies of these procedures are not changed much by calculating them from the different base run.

It is of considerable interest to find some means of predicting the work needed for a problem about which little is known. In Table 4-4 it was found that the number M of constraints was the best guide of those studied to the number of iterations for Phase One; we shall use it also in connection with the total iterations required. Table 6-2 thus lists the number of iterations required to solve each of the problems using the ordinary algorithm divided by M. It would appear that rule of "2M iterations" from folklore is fairly good when a singleton basis is used.

Table 6-2

ITERATIONS/CONSTRAINTS FOR ORDINARY, S BASIS (RUN 21)

Problem	1D	2A	1E	1A	5A	1G	1F	2B	1B	avg.	c.v.
	2.00	1.67	1.71	1.27	1.09	1.29	1.83	1.18	3.33	1.71	.4

The corresponding data for the algorithms of Table 6-1 can be found by multiplying the entries of Table 6-2 by those of Table 6-1. The averages thus obtained appear in Table 6-3.

Table 6-3

SUMMARY OF ITERATIONS/CONSTRAINTS

Algorithm	Run	Average	C.V.
	Singleton basis		
Ordinary	21	1.71	.4
PN1	10	1.24	.2
PN2	14	1.24	.2
Greatest-change	15	1.36	.3
Ratio pricing	6	1.50	.4
	Full basis		
Ordinary	39	1.39	.4
Symmetric	40	1.13	.5
Greatest-change	41	.98	.2

A more detailed examination of the data seems to show that the dependence of the number of iterations on M could be better expressed by a formula of the form $a\,M^b$, where b is slightly less than one, but this is not clear. Using a singleton basis an estimate of between M and 3M iterations will almost always be correct.

7. SUBOPTIMIZATION

Versions of suboptimization have been used for some time in linear programming routines bothered by small core size, but the advantages of a version of it for routines for which core size is no particular handicap were first exploited by D. M. Smith [9]. As used here, the course of the solution of a problem consists of a number of passes, at the beginning of each of which some number L of nonbasic columns is selected as a set of candidates for pivoting (those having the L minimal reduced costs are chosen). During the pass no other nonbasic columns are considered; simplex method iterations are performed using the selected columns until the objective has been minimized on that subset. (A basic column which becomes nonbasic during the pass is not futher considered.)

The number L of candidates is an important parameter; values of 2, 3, 5, and 8 were used here. During a pass, any of the various means of selecting a pivot column discussed previously might be used in minimizing the objective on the candidates. Three were tried here: the ordinary procedure of minimal reduced cost; the greatest-change procedure; and the procedure PN1.

Both the number of iterations and the number of passes required to solve a problem are of interest. In the table below, the numbers required are all compared with the number of iterations used by the ordinary simplex method (run 21), which would be the number of passes for any of the algorithms for L = 1. Only the averages and coefficients of variation are given for these runs; the individual data fluctuate considerably less than in most of our experiments. An interesting feature of the raw data not reflected in the averages is that the greatest-change procedure commonly requires fewer iterations under suboptimization than does the ordinary procedure without it, which is generally not the case for the other methods.

Table 7-1

SUBOPTIMIZATION RUNS COMPARED TO ORDINARY ALGORITHM

Run	Algorithm	L	Iterations average	c.v.	Passes average	c.v.
22	ordinary	2	1.15	.2	.72	.2
27	"	3	1.28	.2	.60	.2
28	"	5	1.26	.2	.45	.2
29	"	8	1.31	.3	.37	.4
23	greatest-change	2	1.07	.2	.72	.2
24	"	3	1.08	.2	.59	.2
25	"	5	1.08	.3	.45	.3
26	"	8	1.13	.3	.40	.3
42	PN1	2	1.15	.1	.72	.2
43	"	3	1.22	.2	.58	.2

The term "pass" arises from the fact that it is only necessary to consult the data for the entire problem once during a pass; the data which have to be retained for the subsequent suboptimization are much fewer. This fact makes it particularly valuable in product form routines and those which use tapes extensively. (The three main forms of the simplex method are discussed in Section 8.) The significance of the statistics above depends on the form of routine used. In the product form, the total work done depends largely on the number of passes; in the standard form, on the number of iterations; and the explicit form is intermediate. Thus suboptimization is of value in the product form even for all-in-core routines, but not in the standard form. Three production linear programming routines now use it in the manner described. They are all product form routines, one using the ordinary algorithm with $L = 2$ [1], another the greatest-change algorithm with $L = 2$ [9], and the third has options for either algorithm and any L up to 5 [7].

8. OPERATIONS AND FORMS

So far we have been concerned only with the number of iterations required to solve a problem. A better guide to the computational efficiency of a procedure is the number of floating-point arithmetic operations performed—the work which must be done no matter how the algorithm is implemented. While logic and bookkeeping time are usually appreciable, and vary between different algorithms and different forms of the simplex method, it is precisely in such nonarithmetic work that computers and programming systems differ the most. Having programmed each of the procedures studied here as economically as we could from the standpoint of arithmetic, we feel that the results on arithmetic work come close to a machine independent measure of efficiency.

Although it would be possible to count separately each elementary operation, it turns out that there are only three combinations of elementary floating-point operations used significantly often in each of the major subdivisions of an iteration: addition and multiplication; division and subtraction; and addition alone. Each of the following three groups is thus called one operation:

1 floating add and 1 floating multiply	(17.4)
1 floating divide and 1 floating add	(19.4)
3 floating adds	(19.2)

The average number of 7090 cycles taken by each combination is given in parentheses. While some error is made in considering all these equivalent, it is very small, because the first combination accounts for almost all of the calculations. In all cases (except for a portion of the reverse-transformation calculation in the product form) an operation is counted only when both operands are nonzero.

There are many ways of calculating the data required for the steps of the simplex method. In all of them the data used in the ordinary procedure are obtained, but in different ways. The three main forms of the method are described below in outline; the details may be found in the literature [5, 6]. In considering the number of operations performed in one iteration in any form it is convenient to have a priori estimates in terms of M (the number of constraints), N (the current number of variables), and M + K (the total number of rows of data). In the formulas below, factors of proportionality θ between zero and one reflect the fact that operations involving zero data are not counted; the quantities of order smaller than M^2 are disregarded.

The standard form is done just as the ordinary procedure is described in section 3. Pivoting in the tableau is most of the work [requiring $\theta_1(M + K)(N - M)$ operations].

Both forms of the "revised simplex method" calculate needed items of the tableau by multiplying parts of the original matrix A by parts of the inverse, the inverse of the (M + K)-order matrix consisting of the basic columns of A. The reduced costs are obtained by multiplying A by the prices, that row of the inverse corresponding to the objective row of A $[\theta_2(M + K)(N - M)$ operations]; the selected pivot column of the tableau is obtained by multiplying the appropriate column of A by the inverse (the number of operations required for this and the remaining steps differs for the two forms); the pivot row is selected as usual; and pivoting is done both in the inverse and the current solution.

In the explicit form, or the "revised simplex method with explicit form of the inverse," the inverse is a square M + K-order matrix, all of which is pivoted in at each iteration. Pivoting requires $\theta_4(M + K)^2$ operations, and the prior multiplication for the pivot column requires $\theta_3(M + K)^2$ operations.

In the product form, or the "revised simplex method with product form of the inverse," the inverse is maintained as a sequence of transformations, each of which, having at most M + K nonzero entries, constitutes the nontrivial portion of the pivot column of the tableau as of some previous iteration. Applied appropriately, these transformations accomplish the work of matrix multiplication required by the revised simplex method. In a pivot step these data are not altered but are augmented by one more transformation. Their total number is generally somewhat less than $(M + K)^2$, and most, but not all, of them are used once in obtaining the prices $[\theta_5(M + K)^2$ operations] and the pivot column $[\theta_6(M + K)^2$ operations]. The number of accumulated transformations is periodically reduced by "reinversions," the reconstruction of a product-form inverse from A in a minimal sequence of pivots. The routines used here reinvert automatically at those points they determine will minimize the total operation count for the calculation.

In summary, the formulas of Table 8-1 indicate the dependence of the number of operations per iteration on problem size.

It is beyond the scope of this study to discuss the factors θ of these formulas in detail. They will be used instead as guides to the scaling of our operation counts. Since for our problems N is closely proportional

Table 8-1

NUMBER OF OPERATIONS PER ITERATION

Standard form $\qquad$ $\theta_1 (M + K) (N - M)$

Explicit form $\qquad$ $\theta_2 (M + K) (N - M) + \theta_3 (M + K)^2 + \theta_4 (M + K)^2$

Product form $\qquad$ $\theta_2 (M + K) (N - M) + \theta_5 (M + K)^2 + \theta_6 (M + K)^2$

to M (N/M ranges from 1.67 to 3.43, averaging 2.31 with coefficient of variation 0.27), each of the formulas has, approximately, $(M + K)^2$ as a common factor. Thus comparative data for the three forms can be obtained as follows: for each problem, divide the total number of operations required to solve it by the number of iterations, and divide the result by $(M + K)^2$. The data of Table 8-2 were obtained in that way; for all forms, the ordinary simplex algorithm was used, and an S basis.

Table 8-2

OPERATIONS PER ITERATION/$(M + K)^2$

Problem	1D	2A	1E	1A	5A	1G	1F	2B	1B	avg.	c.v.
Standard form (run 12)	.88	3.00	2.11	.44	1.28	.79	.76	.59		1.23	.7
Explicit form (run 21)	.71	.95	.77	.49	.54	.31	.38	.29	.67	.57	.4
Product form (run 56)	.56	1.00	.54	.32	.45	.27	.25	.14	.26	.42	.4

The decrease of the ratios with size of problem is noteworthy; it is probably due to the decrease of the proportion of nonzero matrix entries. Table 8-3 makes a more direct comparison of these data, using the explicit form run as a base. Note that the relative efficiency of the product form tends to increase with the size of problem, owing, we think, to its greater ability to take advantage of the lower density of nonzeros.

Table 8-3

STANDARD AND PRODUCT COMPARED WITH EXPLICIT FORM

Problem	1D	2A	1E	1A	5A	1G	1F	2B	1B	avg.	c.v.
Standard form	1.28	4.67	3.03	.83	2.30	2.57	2.04	2.63		2.42	.4
Product form	.82	1.05	.74	.64	.79	.86	.67	.45	.43	.71	.3

9. ALGORITHMS COMPARED BY OPERATIONS

The algorithms of Section 6 may finally be compared in the total number of operations they require to solve a problem. In Table 9-1 they are all compared with the ordinary algorithm in explicit form (run 21). With the exception of that procedure, each algorithm given has been run in that form of the simplex method best suited to it; the ratio-pricing and the greatest-change (with F basis) procedures are omitted because they were not.

Table 9-1

VARIOUS ALGORITHMS COMPARED WITH ORDINARY, EXPLICIT

Problem	1D	2A	1E	1A	5A	1G	1F	2B	1B	avg.	c.v.
				Singleton basis							
PN1—standard; run 10	.75	2.14	2.42	.67	1.54	1.21	1.32	1.37		1.43	.4
PN2—standard; run 14	1.07	2.53	2.84	.53	1.79	1.52	1.18	1.82		1.66	.4
Greatest-change standard; run 15	1.15	3.66	3.72	.33	2.37		.99	1.66	2.36	2.03	.6
Ordinary-product run 56	.82	1.05	.74	.64	.79	.86	.67	.45	.43	.71	.3
				Full basis							
Symmetric standard; run 40	.57	4.80	6.04	.47	2.81	2.64	1.01	1.42		2.47	.8
Ordinary-Product run 55	.63	1.48	.81	.44	.89	.86	.25	.37	.38	.68	.5

We think that these figures constitute the best over-all assessment of these alternative algorithms from the point of view of calculation needed. The product form of the ordinary algorithm seems definitely superior, with use of a full basis probably being worthwhile for the larger problems.

We may try to predict the operation count for an unknown problem of given size. In Table 9-2, the counts of run 21 have been scaled in a manner intended to eliminate most of the influence of the size of the problem. Using the factor $(M + K)^2$ as in Table 8-2 to scale the count per iteration, and the factor M as in Table 6-3 to scale the number of iterations, we obtain the quotients of Table 9-2. The corresponding quotients for the other runs can be obtained by multiplying those of Table 9-1 by these numbers; the averages and coefficients of variation for those ratios are given in Table 9-3.

Table 9-2

OPERATIONS/$M(M + K)^2$ FOR ORDINARY EXPLICIT

Problem	1D	2A	1E	1A	5A	1G	1F	2B	1B	avg.	c.v.
	1.42	1.58	1.32	.62	.59	.40	.70	.34	2.22	1.02	.6

Table 9-3

OPERATIONS/$M(M + K)^2$ FOR OTHER RUNS

Algorithm	Form	Basis	Run	Average	C.V.
PN1	standard	S	10	1.36	.8
PN2	standard	S	14	1.59	.9
greatest-change	standard	S	15	2.04	1.0
ordinary	product	S	56	.73	.6
symmetric	standard	F	40	2.57	1.2
ordinary	product	F	55	.73	.9

Since in practice K is usually 1, we can say that around M^3 operations are required to solve a linear programming problem. A rough minimum for problems of no more than some 100 constraints is $0.3M^3$, and $2M^3$ is a rough maximum for smaller problems. A count of more than $3M^3$ indicates an uncommonly hard problem or a rather poor algorithm.

10. CONCLUSION

Three kinds of data have been used above: iterations, operations, and passes. We have come to the view that iterations alone is the least informative: on the one hand, the operation count measures the total work of a routine, and on the other passes measure the amount of data handled. Of course, except for those of Section 7, suboptimization is not used in any of the routines studied, so that in general the number of passes is equal to the number of iterations, which is the number we usually cite.

The results of Section 4 show that use of a full basis will reduce the iterations taken in Phase One. (In Section 9, however, we found that it is of little value in reducing the operation count for the most efficient procedure.) It appears that there is no excuse for using an entirely artificial basis.

In Section 5 we failed to find any measure of infeasibility with which to conduct Phase One which works better than the ordinary measure—the sum of all the infeasibilities.

The results of Section 6 show the positive-normalized procedures best in terms of iteration count, and that the full basis is good for the over-all problem. The first conclusion is consistent with the interesting re-sults of Kuhn and Quandt [8], who have experimented with several pivot-column selection procedures on a large number of randomly generated linear programming problems of special type having up to 25 constraints. In the only place where their results can be matched with ours, we agree in ordering these procedures in increasing effectiveness in iteration count: ordinary, greatest-change, and positive-normalized. Our data suggest M and 3M as bounds for the number of iterations to solve a problem starting from a singleton basis.

The extent to which suboptimization will be of value in a routine depends considerably on how its data-handling is organized. Section 7 shows that it can be used with little harm and under some circumstances with benefit to the total computational labor.

The comparison of operations per iteration in Section 8 shows pretty definitely that the order of the three main forms of the simplex method in increasing efficiency is: standard, explicit, product. The fact that those algorithms which are better than the ordinary in iterations need data which are conveniently obtained only in the standard form makes them less at-tractive from the point of view of operation count; Section 9 shows that the ordinary algorithm in product form leads the rest. There are other con-siderations, however, for general uses of a linear programming routine, which are hard to evaluate properly but which argue for the standard form: in that form most of the data needed for the usual postoptimal analyses—reduced costs, etc.—are immediately available and need not be especially calculated.

An important fact about the product form, whose detailed study is beyond the scope of this report, is that the product-form inverse is extremely compact for problems of low density. This fact has considerable bearing on the choice of a routine for larger problems. SHARE problem 4A, having 245 constraints, can be solved with an all-in-core routine [1] for the IBM 7090, which has 32,768 words of core. A similar routine using the explicit form would require 75,000 words, and using the standard form, 118,000 words.

At this time we feel that a product-form routine employing the ordinary or the greatest-change algorithm with suboptimization, with option for using a full basis, will pull together the best features of the procedures we have studied so far.

It may seem disappointing that our results have not allowed a more decisive ordering of the proposals studied. In part, of course, this is due to our having selected the more promising possibilites from a larger number of candidates; but it may also be the case that, as linear pro-gramming is presently understood, it is not possible to do a great deal better than some of these procedures do. A linear programming method has two parts: find the optimal basis, and calculate the optimal solution. If the optimal basis were known, it would still in the general case require some $1/3\,M^3$ operations to solve the linear equations thus identified (although a product-form method would do much better for problems, like ours, having a low density of data). Since some of our procedures do the whole job in about M^3 operations, there does not seem to be an enormous amount of room for improvement.

APPENDIX

The SCEMP Runs and Data

Nature of Run

(Note: These abbreviations are used; for bases: None, Singleton, Full;
for forms of the simplex method: Standard, Explicit, Product.)

Run	Starting basis	Form	Algorithm	
5	N	P	Ordinary	
6	S	E	Ratio-pricing	
8	N	E	Ratio-pricing	
10	S	S	Positive-normalized 1	
12	S	S	Ordinary	
14	S	S	Positive-normalized 2	
15	S	S	Greatest change	
21	S	E	Ordinary	
22	S	S	Ordinary with suboptimization;	L = 2
27	S	S	Ordinary with suboptimization;	L = 3
28	S	S	Ordinary with suboptimization;	L = 5
29	S	S	Ordinary with suboptimization;	L = 8
23	S	S	Greatest-change with subopt.;	L = 2
24	S	S	Greatest-change with subopt.;	L = 3
25	S	S	Greatest-change with subopt.;	L = 5
26	S	S	Greatest-change with subopt.;	L = 8
31	S	E	Sequential Phase One	
32	F	E	Fudge Phase One	
33	S	E	Least-infeasibility Phase One	
36	F	E	Sequential Phase One	
37	F	E	Least-infeasibility Phase One	
38	F	E	Extended composite Phase One	
39	F	E	Ordinary	
40	F	S	Symmetric	
41	F	E	Greatest change	
42	S	S	PN1 with suboptimization;	L = 2
43	S	S	PN1 with suboptimization;	L = 3
55	F	P	Ordinary	
56	S	P	Ordinary	

(These abbreviations are used: p1, iterations in Phase One; p2, total iteration count to solve problem; pa, number of passes to solve problem; op, total operation count to solve problem, where "K" stands for "000".)

Problem		1A	1B	1D	1E	1F	1G	2A	2B	5A
Run	Data									
5	p2	70	443	61	66	184		114	221	
6	p1	33		32	75	66	37	1	125	0
	p2	34		32	75	66	51	81	152	35
8	p1	40	306	37	88	113	92	69	151	46
	p2	40	365	37	88	113	92	99	151	49
10	p1	25		24	27	42	17	1	62	0
	p2	42		41	51	102	41	40	93	27
	op	15956		22532	151K	272K	55378	104K	440K	37692
12	p2	39		56	59	124	62	74	143	36
	op	19750		38456	189K	421K	118K	227K	845K	56327
14	p2	39		45	52	80	45	41	102	28
	op	12623		32297	177K	243K	69764	123K	585K	43829
15	p1	24		27	43	50	18	1	97	0
	p2	32		38	65	88	40	55	137	32
	op	7717		34449	232K	342K	45491	178K	758K	58127
21	p1	25	253	25	34	55	21	0	77	0
	p2	42	390	54	53	121	62	50	113	37
	op	23682	3620K	30045	62374	206K	45908	48569	321K	24502
22	p2	39		63	56	126	63	81	119	48
	pa	24		35	36	79	40	48	73	34
23	p2	38		56	64	111	53	61	108	53
	pa	25		35	43	82	36	42	73	37
24	p2	36		52	63	125	61	56	103	58
	pa	18		28	40	69	36	33	58	26
25	p2	33		50	75	104	57	57	102	63
	pa	12		22	36	43	26	24	37	25
26	p2	31		56	82	127	54	57	105	64
	pa	10		20	33	43	19	21	30	22
27	p2	39		64	71	141	73	98	145	43
	pa	16		28	37	68	35	45	64	22
28	p2	39		69	70	123	79	79	140	52
	pa	15		23	25	39	27	30	44	21
29	p2	37		56	97	143	71	98	131	48
	pa	9		14	31	38	17	31	38	14

Problem	1A	1B	1D	1E	1F	1G	2A	2B	5A
Run Data									
31 p1	38	263	24	32	54	21		75	
32 p1	15	135	10	26	6	34		71	
33 p1	34	238	27	35	68	22		86	
36 p1	14	145	9	32	6	51		80	
37 p1	12	186	9	33	6	50		80	
38 p1	17	136	8	26	3	22		55	
39 p1	12	134	8	24	3	34	0	53	0
p2	22	296	34	49	54	75	62	86	37
op	12439	3245K	14015	79322	79285	113K	70660	239K	24502
40 p2	19		23	81	59	46	41	83	31
op	11193		17012	377K	208K	121K	233K	455K	68736
41 p1	7	80	11	18	5	22	0	88	0
p2	23	105	21	36	46	58	41	102	31
42 p2	42		58	68	146	66	67	108	48
pa	24		33	43	94	39	43	67	34
43 p2	39		62	76	141	70	77	123	49
pa	16		28	39	67	34	36	55	26
55 p2	21	285	38	35	54	59	66	86	38
op	10342	1387K	18913	50594	52300	39554	72038	119K	21883
56 p2	41	421	56	56	121	62	50	106	35
op	15050	1540K	24531	45923	137K	39511	51179	144K	19278

REFERENCES

1. Clasen, Richard J., RSMFOR Linear Programming Routine, SHARE Distribution Agency, 1962.
2. Dantzig, George B., "Maximization of a Linear Function of Variables Subject to Linear Inequalities," Activity Analysis of Production and Allocation, T. C. Koopmans, ed., Wiley, 1951; pp. 339-347.
3. Orchard-Hays, William, A Composite Simplex Algorithm—II; Notes on Linear Programming—Part XII, RM 1275, The RAND Corporation, May 1954.
4. Dickson, J. C. and F. P. Frederick, "A Decision Rule for Improved Efficiency in Solving Linear Programming Problems with the Simplex Algorithm," Comm. Assoc. Comp. Mach., Vol. 3, September 1960, pp. 509-512.
5. Gass, S. I., Linear Programming—Methods and Applications, McGraw-Hill, 1958.

6. Hadley, George, Linear Programming, Addison-Wesley, 1962.
7. Harvey, Roy, et al., SCM3 Linear Programming Routine, SHARE Distribution Agency, 1962.
8. Kuhn, H. W. and R. Quandt, "An Experimental Study of the Simplex Method," undated.
9. Orchard-Hays, W., and D. M. Smith, "Computational Efficiency in Product Form Linear Programming Codes." This volume.
10. Smith, D. M., "Results on SHARE Test Problems," undated.
11. Talacko, J. V., and R. T. Rockafellar, "A Compact Simplex Algorithm for General Linear Programs," August 1960.
12. Wolfe, Philip, "RSM1 Linear Programming Routine," SHARE Distribution Agency #863, March 1960.
13. Wolfe, P., "Status Report: The SCEMP Project," The RAND Corporation, March 1961.
14. Wolfe, P., "An Extended Composite Algorithm for Linear Programming," P-2373, The RAND Corporation, July 1961.
15. Wolfe, P., "A Technique for Resolving Degeneracy in Linear Programming," RM-2995-PR, The RAND Corporation, May 1962.

Parametric Linear Programming

Robert L. Graves

As it is ordinarily discussed, parametric linear programming is concerned with two problems. In both of them it is desired to find the solution to a linear programming problem as a function of a parameter which enters the problem linearly. These problems are discussed in Refs. 1 and 2. There are two natural extensions which are investigated in Refs. 3, 4, and 5. Carpentier and Saaty discuss the problem when the parameter enters in a nonlinear manner. Simons gives some characterization of the solution when the parameter is a vector. Here the former problem is discussed and an analysis is given for polynomial functions. Naturally in this particular situation a more complete characterization of the solution can be given than is possible for more general nonlinear functions. Neither Ref. 3 nor 4 exhibits a complete constructive solution.

THE RESULTS IN THE LINEAR CASES

The situation in the two problems which arise when the parameter enters linearly is summed up in two theorems. In the following A denotes an m by n matrix ($n \geq m$), c an n-vector, b an m-vector, x an n-vector, u an m-vector, and y a scalar.

Theorem 1: Consider the linear programming problem

$$f(y) = \max (c_0 + yc_1)x$$

$$Ax = b$$

$$x \geq 0$$

and its dual problem

$$f(y) = \min bu$$

$$uA - (c_0 + yc_1) = d_0 + yd_1 \geq 0$$

Then the solutions, x and u, and the value, f, can be characterized as follows:

    a. There exists a finite connected set (possibly empty) of closed intervals, $[y_0,y_1]$ (some of which may be points) on which the problem has a solution. The set of intervals may include $(-\infty,y_1]$ and $[y_0,\infty)$ as well. Outside the set of intervals, the problem has no solution.

b. On each interval the components of x are constants.
c. On each interval the components of u are linear functions of y.
d. On each interval f is a linear function of y.
e. The function f is convex.

Theorem 2: Consider the linear programming problem

$$f(y) = \max cx$$

$$Ax = b_0 + yb_1$$

$$x \geq 0$$

and its dual problem

$$f(y) = \min (b_0 + yb_1) u$$

$$uA - c = d \geq 0$$

Then the solutions, x and u, and the value, f, can be characterized as in Theorem 1 by exchanging x and u and replacing f by $-f$.

Of equal importance is the fact that constructive methods exist which allow numerical solutions to be exhibited explicitly. The method which accompanies Theorem 1 is a variant of the primal simplex method while that for Theorem 2 is conveniently stated as a variant of the dual simplex method.

THE POLYNOMIAL CASE

The problem considered here is

$$f(y) = \max (c_0 + yc_1 + \cdots + y^g c_g) x = \max c(y)x \tag{1}$$

$$Ax = b_0 + yb_1 + \cdots + y^h b_h = b(y) \tag{2}$$

$$x \geq 0 \tag{3}$$

and its dual

$$f(y) = \min (b_0 + yb_1 + \cdots + y^h b_h) u = \min b(y)u \tag{4}$$

$$uA \geq c_0 + yc_1 + \cdots + y^g c_g = c(y) \tag{5}$$

Relation 5 may be written

$$uA - c(y) = d(y) \geq 0$$

The facts about the solution are contained in Theorem 3.

Theorem 3: There are solutions, x and u, and a value, f, of the problem defined by (1)-(5) which can be characterized as follows:

a. There exists a finite (but not necessarily connected) set of intervals $[y_0, y_1]$ (some of which may be points) in which the problem has a solution. The set of intervals may include $(-\infty, y_1]$ and $[y_0, \infty)$ as well. Outside the set of intervals the problem has no solution.

b. On each interval the components of x are polynomials in y of degree at most h.

c. On each interval the components of u and d are polynomials in y of degree at most g.

d. On each interval f is a polynomial in y of degree at most gh.

Proof: Let B be an arbitrary $m \times m$ submatrix of A. Consider the equations

$$B\bar{x} = b(y)$$

$$uB = \bar{c}(y)$$

where $\bar{x}$ and $\bar{c}$ are m-vectors whose components are defined by extraction from the relation of B to A.

If B is non-singular, then the equations have a unique solution and clearly the components of $\bar{x}$ and u are polynomials in y of the desired degree. There is, at most, a finite number of half open infinite and closed finite intervals (which may be points) in which

$$uA \preceq c(y)$$

$$\bar{x} \geq 0$$

are also satisfied since the finite set of polynomials have only a finite number of roots. In these intervals, the dual theorem asserts that a solution to the linear programming problem exists and the value of f(y) is given by the common value of b(y)u and c(y)x. This is a polynomial of degree at most gh.

If B is of rank $r < m$, either the matrix $[B|b(y)]$ has rank r for every y or it has rank r for a discrete set of y or it has rank r for no value of y. In the last case, there is no solution, $\bar{x}$, associated with B. In the first case, there are solutions to $B\bar{x} = b(y)$ which are polynomials of degree h in y. In the second case there are solutions for a set of discrete values of y. If the same analysis is made for the matrix $[B^T|\bar{c}(y)]$, it follows that the pair of equations have solutions of the desired polynomial form for every y or they have solutions for a discrete set of values of y. In either case, the same conclusions which were demonstrated when B is non-singular are true.

If there is any solution to the linear programming problem for a given value of y, there is a basic solution. Each basic solution arises from some matrix B of the sort just described. There are finitely many such matrices; hence there is only a finite number of intervals and points for which different polynomial representations of the solution exist. This concludes the proof.

A constructive method is probably of greater interest than the proof given above. The facts which will be needed in the proof that the constructive method is finite are that the number of submatrices, B, is finite and that the polynomial components of $\bar{x}$, and $uA - c(y) = d(y)$ have only a finite number of zeros. Before the algorithm is given a small numerical example will be examined.

An Example

Consider the problem

$$f(y) = \max -4(y-4)(y-9)x_3$$

$$x_1 + x_3 = 7(y-5)(y-6)$$

$$x_2 + x_3 = -3(y-1)(y-10)$$

$$x_1, x_2, x_3 \geq 0$$

This problem can be solved by exhibiting all of the bases with their tableaus and finding, for each of them, the intervals in which the associated solution is optimal. These tableaus are

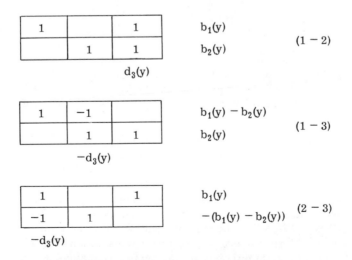

The formulas for the various polynomials are:

$$b_1(y) = \quad 7(y-5)(y-6)$$

$$b_2(y) = -3(y-1)(y-10)$$

$$b_1(y) - b_2(y) = \quad 10(y-3)(y-8)$$

$$d_3(y) = \quad 4(y-4)(y-9)$$

The intervals in which the various bases are optimal are easily obtained.

Basis	Intervals in which solution is optimal
$1 - 2$	$[1,4]$ and $[9,10]$
$1 - 3$	$[8,9]$
$2 - 3$	$[4,5]$ and $[6,8]$

In this example there are no isolated points which yield optimal solutions. Such examples are easy to construct. For let $d_3(y) = 1$, $b_2(y) = -(1-y)^2(3-y)^2$, and $b_1(y) = 1$. Then basis $(1 - 2)$ yields optimal solutions for $y = 1$ and 3 and the other bases yield no optimal solutions. These solutions are degenerate and suggest that special care must be taken to handle this particular kind of degeneracy in the constructive method now to be given.

The Algorithm

The algorithms associated with conventional parametric programming are variants of the simplex method and can be paraphrased as follows. Suppose that an optimal basic solution is available for $y = y_0$. Increase y to a value y_1 where y_1 has the property that the solution is not optimal when $y = y_1 + \epsilon$ for $\epsilon > 0$. If no such value y_1 exists, then the process terminates and the current solution is optimal for $y \geq y_0$. If y_1 can be found, then perform simplex iterations until a solution is found which is optimal at $y_1 + \epsilon$ for some (small) $\epsilon > 0$. The solution is optimal in $[y_0, y_1]$. Then replace y_0 by y_1 and repeat the process. If no such solution can be found for $y_1 + \epsilon$ then the process terminates and there is no optimal solution for $y > y_1$.

The path to be followed here is very much the same. The differences are that it is necessary to use both the primal and dual algorithms, it is necessary to "jump over" certain intervals, and the cases in which a basic solution is optimal in an interval must be distinguished from those in which a solution is optimal at an isolated point.

The algorithm finds (when possible) solutions which are "strongly optimal."

Definition: A function, p, is strongly nonnegative at a point, y_0, if it vanishes identically in some interval containing y_0 or if at y_0 its first nonvanishing derivative (including the zero[th] derivative) is positive. This is written $p(y_0) \,{}^+\!\!\geq 0$. The fact that $p(y_0) \,{}^+\!\!\geq 0$ but p does not vanish identically in any interval containing y_0 is denoted by $p(y_0) \,{}^+\!\!> 0$.

Definition: A solution to the linear programming problem given by

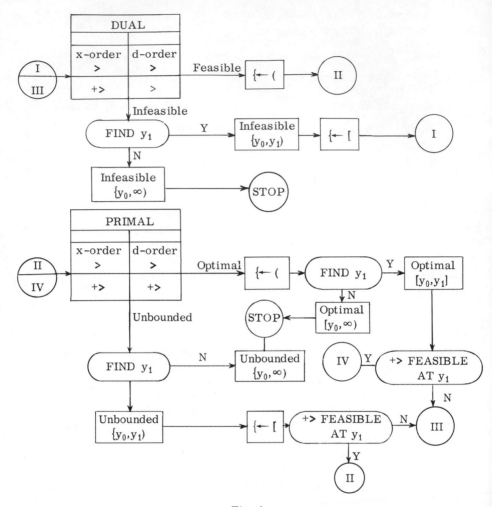

Fig. 1

(1)-(5) is strongly optimal at y_0 if the components of $x(y)$ and $d(y)$ are strongly nonnegative there.

It is clear that $p(y_0) +\geq 0$ implies that $p(y) \geq 0$ in some interval $[y_0,y_1]$. Further the relation $+\geq$ is an order relation which may be substituted for the usual one in the simplex algorithms. Actually both this relation and the conventional lexicographic ordering are used in certain of the simplex steps to follow.

The principal steps of the algorithm are exhibited in the flow chart shown in Fig. 1. The following paragraphs give a detailed commentary on the flow chart and a proof that the algorithm it embodies does yield a strongly optimal solution when one exists, an optimal solution when one

exists, and suitable signals when no optimal solution exists. It is also
shown that the entire process is finite.

At the heart of the method are the two versions of the dual simplex
method (I and III) and the two versions of the primal simplex method
(II and IV). When any of them is used, a basic solution is available and
the problem is modified as necessary to insure that only a finite number
of simplex steps is required. The differences between the methods arise
from the order relationship used. The descriptions are as follows:

I. The nonbasic components of d (i.e., the d_j associated with nonbasic variables) are set equal to one. This gives a basic solution
which is dual feasible. Then the standard dual simplex algorithm
is employed with lexicographic ordering in an attempt to find a
feasible solution to the given problem.

II. When this algorithm is used either a feasible or a strongly
feasible basic solution is available. The standard primal simplex
algorithm is used with lexicographic ordering in an attempt to find
an optimal solution to the given problem.

III. This algorithm is used when a basic feasible solution is available
which may be dual infeasible, dual feasible or strongly dual
feasible. In practice it would be desirable to distinguish these
cases. It is not logically necessary and, as in I, the nonbasic components of d are set equal to one to insure that the problem is
dual feasible. Then the dual simplex algorithm is used with the
usual lexicographic order relationship for the dual variables and
the strong lexicographic order relationship for the primal
variables in an attempt to find a strongly feasible solution to the
given problem.

IV. This algorithm is used when an optimal and strongly feasible
basic solution is available. The primal algorithm is used with
the strong lexicographic order relationship for both primal and
dual variables in an attempt to find a strongly optimal solution
to the given problem.

The over-all strategy is to have algorithms I and II determine the
isolated points at which optimal solutions exist while using III and IV
to find the solutions which are (strongly) optimal in nondegenerate
intervals. We now turn to the other parts of the flow chart whose purpose
is to determine the intervals. In the boxes in the chart which have the
label "Find y_1," one of the following tasks is to be performed. If the
current basis is optimal for the current value of y_0, then it is necessary
to find a value of $y_1 \geq y_0$ for which the basis is not strongly optimal. If,
at y_0, the current basis contains the information which shows that no
optimal (or strongly optimal) solution exists, then it is necessary to find
a value of $y_1 \geq y_0$ for which there may be an optimal solution.

In each of these cases it is necessary to find the smallest root of a set
of polynomials in some half interval. In conventional parametric programming one finds the smallest root of a set of linear functions in a
half interval.

We now follow the algorithm in detail. (The complete algorithm as given examines values of y greater than y_0. An obvious redefinition of strong ordering allows values of y less than y_0 to be treated.) To initiate the calculation, a value of y_0 and a basic solution are selected and algorithm I is executed.

If algorithm I terminates with a feasible solution to the given problem, then proceed to algorithm II. If it does not, then for some row, r, $b_r(y_0) < 0$ and all entries in the transformed row of A are nonnegative. Choose y_1 so that $y_1 > y_0$, $b_r(y_1) = 0$ and $b_r(y) < 0$ for $y_0 \leq y < y_1$. There is no feasible solution in the interval $\{y_0, y_1)$ and algorithm I must be used again with y_1 replacing y_0. If $b_r(y) < 0$ for $y > y_0$, then there is no feasible solution in $\{y_0, \infty)$.

The value of "$\{$" is either "$[$" or "$($". It is assigned one of these values at several points in the flow chart; initially it has the value "$[$" The intervals in which optimal solutions do not exist are open. However, one of these intervals may arise as the union of several subintervals. Evidently some of these subintervals must be closed on the left and the value of "$\{$" is chosen in such a manner that this assignment of open or closed on the left is accomplished.

Algorithm II terminates either with an optimal solution or with a signal that an unbounded solution exists. If an optimal solution is found then choose y_1 as the smallest value of $y \geq y_0$ for which either $b_i(y) <+ 0$ or $d_j(y) <+ 0$. If y_1 cannot be determined then the current solution is optimal in $[y_0, \infty)$. Otherwise, it is optimal in $[y_0, y_1]$ and if $y_0 < y_1$ it is strongly optimal in $[y_0, y_1)$. If $b_i(y_1) <+ 0$, then replace y_0 by y_1 and proceed to algorithm III; otherwise replace y_0 by y_1 and go to algorithm IV. If algorithm II does not produce an optimal solution, then for some column s, $d_s(y_0) < 0$, and all elements in the transformed column of A are nonpositive. Choose y_1 as the smallest value of $y \geq y_0$ so that either $d_s(y_1) = 0$ or $b_i(y_1) <+ 0$ for some i. There is no optimal solution in $\{y_0, y_1)$. If $b_i(y_1) <+ 0$, then replace y_0 by y_1 and then go to algorithm III. (Note that it is possible that $y_1 = y_0$). Otherwise replace y_0 by y_1 and return to algorithm II. (In this case it is necessary that $y_1 > y_0$.) If y_1 cannot be so chosen, then there is no optimal solution in $\{y_0, \infty)$.

The choices upon the termination of algorithm III are precisely the same as those in algorithm I. Similarly the choices upon the termination of algorithm IV are the same as those in algorithm II. The difference between II and IV is that when y_1 is chosen in IV, it is always true that $y_1 > y_0$. (It is quite easy to verify that $y_1 = y_0$ is impossible because all basic solutions which are considered are optimal and strongly feasible.)

To prove that the entire process is finite it is sufficient to show that as successive values of y_1 are determined, $y_1 = y_0$ cannot arise indefinitely, since it is known that each subalgorithm is finite and the possible values of y_1 are the zeroes of a finite set of polynomials. The cases where $y_1 = y_0$ is possible arise upon the completion of algorithm II when the path is directed to algorithm III or to algorithm IV. In the latter path we reach a point where $y_1 > y_0$. In the former path, we either reach such a point on the completion of algorithm III or we are directed back again to algorithm II. Upon emerging from algorithm II this time, we either go to algorithm IV or return to algorithm II still again via the path which ensures that $y_1 > y_0$.

Comments on the Computation

When the simplex algorithms III and IV are used it is necessary to have the derivatives of components of d and x evaluated at a point, y_0. If the derivatives (at y_0) associated with one basis are known then to calculate the derivatives (at y_0) associated with subsequent bases one simply uses the ordinary simplex transformations. The derivatives (at y_0) associated with a basis and a new value of y_0 are probably most easily calculated by multiplying the derivatives of the original quantities by the basis inverse.

To calculate the values of y_1 it is necessary to find the smallest root (in a half interval) of the components of d and x. To do this it is convenient to express the components as polynomials. This is probably most easily done by multiplying the original coefficients by the basis inverse. Thus we see that two forms are required for the different parts of the algorithm.

Extensions of the Method

Both theorem 3 and the algorithm can be extended to a wider class of functions. Functions which form a finite dimensional vector space and for which the range of the derivative operator is contained in the vector space are admissible. In order that the algorithm terminate in a finite number of steps, only intervals (on the parameter axis) in which the functions of the vector space have a finite number of roots can be considered. Thus finite Fourier series can be treated over finite intervals which is, of course, no restriction. In some situations it is desirable to consider costs or requirements which are rational functions in intervals in which no singularities occur. Here one may multiply the relevant set of coefficients by the least common multiple of their denominators and transform the problem into one in which the coefficients are polynomials. Then it is only necessary to divide by this factor to get the results as rational functions of the parameter.

Applications

One of the most fruitful areas for applications arises in those situations where the firm faces a market which is not perfectly elastic; that is, in cases where average price depends on the amounts sold or average cost depends on the amount purchased. In a linear programming model of a firm purchasing raw material in the amount Q, at a unit cost of C, it might be the case that $Q = C^{1.2}$. To convert the model to the proper form, it is necessary to replace Q in the requirements vector by y^6 and C in the cost vector by y^5.

This problem can be handled with the usual simplex method by examining a number of discrete cases, but the technique given here reveals precisely the nature of the solution. A very similar situation prevails in problems related to cash budgeting where the amounts of funds available as well as the cost coefficients depend on the interest rate. In the first example one might trace out the value of the functional and select the value of y (and hence of C) which optimizes. The second example merely permits a sophisticated sensitivity analysis.

It is possible to "block out" arbitrary open intervals on the parameter axis simply by adding an equation of the form $x_{n+1} = p(y)$ where p is a polynomial which is negative in the blocked out intervals and nonnegative elsewhere.

At the extreme, it is possible to block out everything but isolated points. Since the values of the costs and requirements at these points can be set arbitrarily by choosing the appropriate polynomials properly, a succession of problems with distinct costs and requirements may be solved. Needless to say, this approach to discrete programming is not practical but it does illustrate the generality of the method.

REFERENCES

1. Saaty, T. L., and S. I. Gass, "The Parametric Objective Function," Part I, Journal of the Operations Research Society of America, Vol. 2, 1954, pp. 316-19.
2. Gass, S. I., and T. L. Saaty, "The Computational Algorithm for the Parametric Objective Function," Naval Research Logistics Quarterly, Vol. 2, 1955, pp. 39-45.
3. Carpentier, J., "A Method for Solving Linear Programming Problems in Which the Cost Depends Non Linearly On a Parameter," Electricite De France, Direction Des Etudes et Recherches, May, 1959.
4. Saaty, T. L., "Coefficient Perturbation of a Constrained Extremum," Operations Research, Vol. 7, 1959, pp. 294-302.
5. Simons, E., "A Note on Parametric Linear Programming," Management Science, Vol. 8, 1962, pp. 355-358.

Computational Efficiency in Product Form LP Codes

David M. Smith
William Orchard-Hays

The superiority of carrying the inverse of the basis in product form for linear programming algorithms depends on: 1) having a sparse, packed, original matrix, 2) obtaining as small a number of nonzeros as possible when reinverting the basis, and 3) using an optimum reinversion frequency. These considerations are important because, when using the product form, recomputation of tableau entries as they are required is substituted for the storage and maintenance of a complete, current tableau. As demonstrated in the SCEMP tests of the SHARE Standard Test Problems [1] the product form (with optimal reinversion) required fewer operations than the standard form in all cases where the structural matrix was comprised of less than 50 per cent nonzero elements.

However, when the standard form is used, more data are available when the next vector to enter the basis is being chosen. If this information were profitably employed, it should be possible to reduce the total number of iterations and, consequently, the number of operations required to solve a problem. Better digital accuracy would also be maintained. In particular, it has long been suggested that the vector chosen to enter the basis should make the greatest possible change in the objective function, rather than only produce the greatest rate of change. In this volume, an algorithm [2] has been disclosed for obtaining this choice with little increase in the number of operations required in standard form calculations. On the other hand, choosing the vector of maximum change when using a product form code would require such an increase in operations as to be completely impractical.

Fortunately, a modest step in this direction is applicable to the product form; in fact, even at the same number of iterations it may reduce the operation count. A version of this technique has been coded, tested, and is incorporated in the current SHARE version of LP/90. In this code, the usual product form algorithm has been modified to select the two vectors producing the greatest rate of change in the objective (hence the name, "Double Pricing"), update both vectors, and compute in each case the extent of the change in objective. Then an iteration is performed with the better of the two. To date, the number of operations per iteration has been increased by about 25 percent; however, the vector that was not used is transformed by the last step as in the standard form. If its rate of change is still desirable, the second vector is also introduced into the basis making a "Double" iteration with almost no additional calculation. Since about 60 to 80 per cent of the second vectors were used in the SHARE problems, this resulted on the average in only $1.25/1.65 = .76$ times the usual number of operations per iteration.

Having two vectors expressed explicitly in terms of the current basis has an additional advantage in that it is less expensive to reject a vector from consideration on this iteration since its replacement may be on hand. The usual reason for rejecting a vector is that its pivot element is small enough that digital accuracy might be impaired by the indicated change of basis. Under these conditions it is better to select another vector, if possible, to enter the basis.

Another reason for vector rejection is to prevent nonmonotonic behavior of the sum of infeasibilities when using an inverse weighting function to drive out infeasibilities. The usual technique in approaching a feasible solution has been to select the vector to enter the basis having the greatest rate of change in the sum of infeasibility. Although this choice is guaranteed not to increase the total infeasibility, in many problems fewer iterations are required if the criterion for vector selection is the reduction in the number of infeasibilities rather than the amount. Such a choice function is obtained by weighting heavily the rows with the smallest infeasible value; that is, weighting the rows by the reciprocal of the value. Using this procedure, it is possible to select a vector which would increase the total amount of infeasibility. If it entered the basis without removing an infeasibility, cycling would be possible. Using the double pricing procedure, such vectors are cheaply rejected. The ratio test for the vector to leave the basis proposed by P. Wolfe [3] (which produces the greatest possible reduction in infeasibility) is modified to prevent the creation of a new infeasibility.

When the second vector is used, the reduced number of iterations expected as a result of the choice of the first vector is not always achieved. The comparison runs examined to date range from a 50 per cent reduction to a 90 per cent increase in the total number of iterations required. An increase of as much as 25 per cent in the number of iterations could be tolerated without increasing over-all solution time because of the computational efficiency of Double Pricing. The average effect in the SHARE test problems was a 10 per cent decrease in the number of iterations.

These efficiency improvements in the number of iterations and the percentage reduction in operations per iteration are independent of, and in addition to, control of the build up of nonzero elements in the product form of the inverse. The original work of H. Markowitz†[4] in this connection formed the basis of the two special techniques used in LP/90: an optimum reinversion policy, and special pivot choice to reduce the number of nonzeros generated. As to the first item, the reinversion point is com-

---

†The complete Markowitz pivot selection technique was implemented on the JOHNNIAC in 1955 by one of the authors, but it was so complicated that no further attempts have been made to code the complete selection procedure. The JOHNNIAC code was limited to 128 rows and the storage devices were particularly suitable; it was extremely efficient.

puted dynamically so as to maintain the average time per iteration (including the time for reinversion) at a minimum. This is accomplished by measuring the elapsed time since the start of the last reinversion on an on-line clock and computing the gross average time per iteration. If no control were exercised the average would first diminish, then reach a minimum, and finally start to increase. When an increase in average time greater than 1 per cent is detected, and the number of iterations between inversions is within ±25 per cent of the last number, reinversion is started. With this policy, the time spent in the inversion algorithm was about 15 per cent of the total computing time (including the time for reinversion).

The effect of speeding up the inversion algorithm is two-fold. First, the total time spent in the inversion algorithm will be reduced, but only by the square root of the speed ratio, since the more efficient algorithm will be used with greater frequency. Secondly, the time per iteration subsequently is also diminished in proportion to the reduction in average density of the product form. The very simple technique derived from the Markowitz method for inversion speed is to count the nonzeros in each row of the basis to be inverted, and to decrement the counts at each step so as to remain consistent with the counts of the as-yet-untransformed columns. The inversion agenda is then: take the next vector in original order (it is usually better to have the sparsest columns first), and choose as pivot that admissible row with least nonzero count.†

Records were kept in the SHARE problems of basic, structural nonzeros and product form nonzeros both before and after each inversion. They are summarized in Appendix II. The maximum number of nonzeros reached was four times the number in the original matrix. Reinversion reduced the entries in product form to between 0.5 and 1.7 times the nonzeros in the matrix. These densities correspond to 2-3 times that of the actual basis inverted. Substituting these values in the approximating formulas given in Appendix I for the number of operations gives a reasonably close check with the actual operation counts recorded in the SCEMP test runs.

The total running time for the 13 SHARE problems (starting from a feasible basis in IB and IVA) was about 35 minutes on the present distribution of LP/90 (Version 131) which incorporates all the features described in this paper. The time was divided as follows:

Iterations	25.0	minutes
Inversions	4.1	
Input & System	3.7	
Output	2.0	
	34.8	minutes

---

†This particular adaptation of the Markowitz technique was first published by Zoutendijk [5]. It was then coded for the IBM 7090 by Larsen of Esso Research and Engineering [6], based on a design of one of the authors. This code was released to C-E-I-R for inclusion in the SHARE version and after certain revisions is now incorporated in LP/90.

The compute time (iterations and inversions only) on these same problems with the first delivery of LP/90 (Version 99) was about 85 minutes† [7], but problem IVA was not completed. We estimate that 10 to 15 minutes more would have been required to reach a solution, so that the addition of these efficiency improvements has tripled the average speed of the code on these problems. In our other work, one problem has been found which ran 10 per cent longer; most problems run in slightly less than half the original time.

APPENDIX

I. Approximating Formulas for the average number of operations per iteration:

A. Product Form Single Pricing

Reverse transformations: $\dfrac{B}{2m} T$

Obtaining reduced costs: $\dfrac{B}{m} M$

Forward transformations: $\dfrac{B}{2m} T$

Total operations: $P = \dfrac{B}{m} (T + M)$

where m = number of rows
   B = number of non-slack vectors in basis
   T = number of nonzero transformation elements
   M = number of nonzero matrix elements
   P = number of operations

   In the SHARE problems total operations/iteration computed by the formula above ranged from 1.0 to 3.2 times M with the larger, sparser, problems having the higher values.

B. Standard Form (nonzero operations only)

Total operations: $E = \left[\dfrac{B}{m}\right]^2 mC$

where C = number of nonbasic columns.
    E = number of operations.

---

†All versions of LP/90 operate with double precision arithmetic. An intermediate code, Version 103, was distributed to SHARE in October 1961. This version incorporated all features of the present code except Double Pricing, but owing to clock failure we have no accurate times for its test runs. We estimate that it lies midway between Versions 99 and 131 in speed.

In the SHARE problems this formula gave values from 1.1 to 18.6 times M; again the larger problems had the larger values.

The spread of ratios of the formula values (Standard : Product) was from 1.2 to 3.8 except for the large, sparse 245 row matrix (Problem IV-A) whose ratio was 5.8. Except for problems III-A, III-B, and IV-A, the actual ratios of operation counts were computed from the SCEMP report; these values ranged from 1.05 to 2.9. The check between calculated and estimated ratios was considered sufficiently accurate considering the many variables not included. The trend, as expected, was toward larger ratios in sparse problems.

C. Product Form Double Pricing

Reverse transformations: $\dfrac{B}{2m} T$

Obtaining reduced costs: $\dfrac{B}{m} M$

Forward transformations: $\dfrac{B}{m} T$

Total operations: $D = \dfrac{B}{m} (3T/2 + M)$

The increase of $BT/2m$ for double over single pricing is estimated to require only about 25 per cent more operations for a double iteration than a single, since certain housekeeping and data transmission are not changed.

Thus, total operations per iteration = $1.25/1.65 = 0.76$ of the operations in single pricing if 65 per cent of the second vectors are used.

II. Summary of Test Run Results

Problem	IA	IB	IC	ID	IE
Description					
Rows	34	118	5	27	39
Columns (Structural)	64	225	9	20	100
Matrix Nonzeros (Structural)	245	1210	55	232	830
Average Values					
Nonunit Vectors in Basis	31	103	5	25	26
Nonbasic Columns	33	150	9	20	80
Basis Nonzeros	135	600	25	150	200
Eta Nonzeros before INVERT	200	3630	–	–	1215
Eta Nonzeros after INVERT	135	1700	–	–	415
$P = \dfrac{B}{m}(T/M + 1)$	1.4	2.8	–	1.5	1.3
$E = \dfrac{B^2}{m}(C/M)$	3.9	10.6	–	1.8	1.7
E/P Estimate	2.8	3.8	–	1.2	1.3
E/P from SCEMP	1.2	1.5	1.09	1.0	2.6
LP/90 Iteration to last Opt.					
Original Ver. 99	69	181*	8	56	163
SHARE Ver. 103 (Oct. 1961)	62	180*	8	28	168
Modified weighting and row choice.					
SHARE Ver. 131 (May 1962)	54	154*	10	53	169
Double Pricing					
Number of Doubles	18	52*	4	18	50
Compute time for Solution, minutes					
Original Ver. 99	.47	7.85	.14	.61	3.70
Double price Ver. 131	.24	4.30	.03	.37	2.36

*From supplied feasible starting basis. Numbers in parentheses for problem IV A were estimated by adding the number of iterations required in Ver. 131 (40) to go from the last profit value obtained in Ver. 99 to optimal on Ver. 103.

II. (Continued)

IF	IG	IIA	IIB	IIIA	IIIB	IVA	VA	TOTAL
67	49	32	99	79	18	245	34	846
72	62	78	79	87	25	352	44	1220
630	445	775	820	880	95	2125	355	8497
35	35	20	42	55	15	222	15	
100	65	84	120	110	12	200	63	
240	248	170	400	450	40	1250	100	
1900	900	1170	3300	2000	90	7000	826	
570	540	250	700	650	50	3400	140	
1.4	1.8	1.2	1.4	2.1	-	3.2	1.0	
3.0	3.6	1.4	2.6	6.4	-	18.6	.96	
2.1	2.0	1.2	1.9	3.0	-	5.8	1.1	
2.1	2.4	2.3	2.9	-	-	-	2.5	
102	86	167	118	183	22	(390)*	37	1586
116	82	172	115	166	22	(360)*	37	1516
62	74	156	126	135	25	309*	47	1374
20	24	45	47	41	6	79*	14	418
1.50	1.36	2.85	2.74	3.49	.11	(75.00)*	.26	100.0
.66	.74	2.08	1.50	1.35	.09	15.35	.26	29.0

*See footnote to first part of table.

REFERENCES

1. Cutler, Leola, and Philip Wolfe, "Experiments in Linear Programming," this volume.
2. Efroymson, M. A., "New Algorithms for Linear Programming," this volume.
3. Wolfe, Philip, "An Extended Composite Algorithm for Linear Programming," The RAND Corporation, P-2373, July 24, 1961.
4. Markowitz, H. M., "The Elimination Form of the Inverse and Its Application to Linear Programming," Management Science, Vol. 3, No. 3, April 1957, pp. 255-269.

5. Zoutendijik, G., <u>Methods of Feasible Directions</u>, Elsevier Publishing Company, June 1960, P. 43.
6. Larsen, L. J., "A Modified Inversion Procedure for Product Form of The Inverse-Linear Programming Codes," <u>Communications of ACM</u>, July 1962.
7. Larson, Robert H., "Final Report LP/90 Testing of SHARE Test Problems," Esso Research and Engineering, March 1, 1961.

SOME NEW ALGORITHMS FOR LINEAR PROGRAMMING

M. A. Efroymson

ABSTRACT

This paper presents two algorithms which improve the efficiency of the simplex method.

In addition to the conventional artificial vectors, a set of additional artificial vectors can be created which are linear combinations of the conventional artificial vectors and a selected group of real vectors. This set of variables has been named Implied Artificial Vectors since they can be generated at the time they are required and do not need to be included in the original matrix. Implied Artificial Vectors are used as an operational device which can markedly decrease the number of iterations required to obtain a first feasible solution. Implied Artificial Vectors are used until feasibility is obtained to maintain positive right-hand side elements for all restriction rows. Therefore, each iteration pivots on a row with a positive right-hand side and reduces the amount of infeasibility.

A vector selection based on maximum change in the objective function usually requires fewer iterations than a selection based on most negative d_j. However, the number of division operations per iteration is increased by the use of maximum change in objective function since a minimum ratio calculation is made on all vectors with negative d_j. When the right-hand elements are maintained at a zero or unit level these divisions operations can be replaced by a simple comparison operation. A matrix updating algorithm has been developed which maintains this condition of unity or zero levels on right-hand sides and requires the same number of multiplication and division operations as the original simplex updating algorithm.

A FORMULA FOR RANGING THE COST OF LIVING

S. N. Afriat

ABSTRACT

If a consumer's preference scale S is known, then any cost-of-living measurement has a point-determination. But such a scale S can only be known empirically to the extent that it is compatible with a scheme $\mathfrak{F}$ of expenditure data, necessarily finite, say in respect to some n commodities and some k occasions, giving the price and quantity consumed of each commodity on each occasion by k pairs of vectors (p_r, x_r) of order n. There will be an infinite class $S_{\mathfrak{F}}$ of such scales of the normal type compatible with $\mathfrak{F}$, in which case the data is consistent; otherwise $S_{\mathfrak{F}}$ is empty. For each $S \in S_{\mathfrak{F}}$ there is a determination $\rho_{rs}(S)$ for the ratio in which expenditure on occasion r must be changed to compensate, according to preferences in the scale S, for the price-changing from occasion s. With S ranging in $S_{\mathfrak{F}}$, $\rho_{rs}(S)$ describes a certain set $I_{rs}(\mathfrak{F})$. The problem of the cost of living index can be conceived of as the problem of evaluating the set $I_{rs}(\mathfrak{F})$ from the expenditure data $\mathfrak{F}$, assumed consistent. It turns out that this set is an interval, whose limits $\rho_{rs}^i(\mathfrak{F})$, $\rho_{rs}^0(\mathfrak{F})$ can be evaluated.

Let $u_r = p_r/e_r$, where $e_r = p_r'x_r$, and let $D_{rs} = u_r'x_s - 1$. Let (Λ, Φ), where $\Lambda = \{\lambda_r\}$, $\Phi = \{\varphi_r\}$, denote any solution of the system of inequalities

$$\lambda_r > 0, \quad \lambda_r D_{rs} > \varphi_s - \varphi_r \quad (r \neq s)$$

The consistency condition:

$$D_{rs} \leq 0, \quad D_{st} \leq 0, \quad \ldots, \quad D_{qr} \leq 0$$

impossible for all cycles of distinct elements r, s, t, ..., q from 1, ..., k, is necessary and sufficient for the existence of solutions.
Let

$$\alpha = \{\alpha_r\}$$

where

$$\alpha_r \geq 0, \quad \Sigma \alpha_r = 1$$

and let

$$x_\alpha = \Sigma x_r \alpha_r, \quad \varphi_\alpha = \Sigma \varphi_r \alpha_r.$$

Let

$$\rho_{rs}^i(\Lambda,\Phi) = \min_x \{u_r'x; \ (x - x_t)'u_t\lambda_t \geq \varphi_s - \varphi_t \ (t = 1, \ldots, k)\}$$

and

$$\rho_{rs}^0(\Lambda,\Phi) = \min_\alpha \{u_r'x_\alpha; \ \varphi_\alpha \geq \varphi_s\}$$

Then

$$\rho_{rs}^i(\mathcal{F}) = \min_{\Lambda,\Phi} \rho_{rs}^i(\Lambda,\Phi), \quad \rho_{rs}^0(\mathcal{F}) = \max_{\Lambda,\Phi} \rho_{rs}^0(\Lambda,\Phi)$$

It is noted that $\rho_{rs}^i(\Lambda,\Phi)$ is the minimum of a linear function subject to a system of linear inequalities in which the coefficients are themselves solutions of a further system of inequalities; and then $\rho_{rs}^i(\mathcal{F})$ is the minimum of this minimum for all such solutions.

A Stochastic Model for Programming the Supply of a Strategic Material

Herman Karreman

INTRODUCTION

Strategic materials are materials which a) are essential for the proper functioning of a country's economy, and b) rely at the same time heavily on importation for their acquisition. Iron and copper, for instance, are not strategic materials since the second part of the definition does not apply to them. But nickel is a strategic material and so is manganese, which is needed for the production of steel of good quality. As a matter of fact, much of what will be said in the following applies to this latter material.

Because of the reliance on imports, it will be clear that there is no automatic guarantee that these strategic materials will always be available at reasonable cost. This applies in particular to the case of "limited" war, which is understood to be a situation between "cold" war with no overt hostilities and "total" war. The Korean war, with hostilities confined to a local area and lasting for several years, is the type of "limited" war that is here envisaged. In such a situation, it will be difficult to obtain sufficient quantities of these strategic materials at reasonable cost by importation only. In fact, prices (including transportation costs and insurance premiums) paid in the last "limited" war period for these imported strategic materials were in many cases twice the normal ones.

To protect themselves against a repetition of this costly affair, countries have started to buy, in normal times, extra quantities of these foreign ores and to stockpile them. However, the amounts of money involved to provide adequate protection this way are enormous. Even the resources of the United States have been strained, despite its rich deposits of many essential materials (iron, copper, etc.) and the large amounts of money appropriated for the purchase of extra quantities of strategic materials from

†Second part of a study made on behalf of the Office of Defense Mobilization under Contract Nonr-1858(02) with the Office of Naval Research. Reproduction of this paper in whole or in part is permitted for any purpose of the United States government.

‡I am indebted to Harlan Mills for many helpful suggestions, in particular with respect to what is said at the end about the final state of the system, and to Stuart Dreyfus for drawing the flow-chart for the first computation.

foreign countries. The stockpiles of imported ores, built up in the past by the U. S. government, will in many cases provide industry with only a fraction of the extra quantities which it will need in a limited war period.

There are, of course, in some instances, deposits of these strategic materials in the country too. The quality of these domestic ores is on the average inferior to that of foreign ores, and they must first be upgraded to meet the standards set by industry. In normal times this makes them more costly than foreign ores (otherwise, they would have been used in the past). However, the technology of upgrading the ores of low quality is steadily improving and domestic ores might turn out to be profitable in a future period of limited war, when prices of imported minerals will again be high.

Assuming for a moment that we are on the eve of a limited war which will last for several years, the question then is: Given a small stock of ore at the beginning of the period, how much has to be imported and how much has to be produced domestically each year to meet the requirements of a certain strategic material in the following n years of limited war at minimum cost?

To answer this question, a model was constructed in which the various ways of meeting the requirements and the restrictions imposed on them were formulated. The objective function, being a cost function which had to be minimized, contained first order as well as many second order terms. This quadratic programming problem was solved twice, once by the simplex method, adapted to solve this sort of problem, and once by the gradient method.† The result obtained from that model showed that more than half of what was needed on top of the initial stockpile would have to come from domestic sources. Moreover, the solution appeared to be highly sensitive to a reduction in the costs of upgrading domestic ore on account of technological improvements.‡

So far, the underlying assumption was that of being on the eve of a limited war. This assumption was, of course, rather restrictive, since several other political situations are possible. To make the analysis more general, a stochastic model has been developed which takes the three possibilities of "no war," "cold war," and "limited war" into consideration. The probabilities of transition from one political situation into another have been assumed to be those found in the following matrix, P:

If situation in year n is that of	then probability of occurrence in year (n + 1) is assumed to be for:		
	no war	cold war	limited war
no war	.70	.20	.10
cold war	.05	.85	.10
limited war	.10	.40	.50

†The first method was developed by Philip Wolfe and the second by Ben Rosen.

‡A description of the model and the results obtained from it can be found in Ref. 1.

These transition probabilities reflect, of course, certain personal views of the political situation at the time they were decided upon. Still, they do not seem unreasonable and would perhaps even hold in the present situation.

It should be observed here that this matrix P of transition probabilities is not a doubly stochastic matrix, since the columns do not add up to 1 (the rows do). The characteristic values and corresponding characteristic vectors of P are:

$$\lambda_1 = 1 \qquad \lambda_2 = .65 \qquad \lambda_3 = .40$$

$$\xi_{1,1} = 1 \qquad \xi_{1,2} = 4 \qquad \xi_{1,3} = 1$$

$$\xi_{2,1} = 1 \qquad \xi_{2,2} = -1 \qquad \xi_{2,3} = 1$$

$$\xi_{3,1} = 1 \qquad \xi_{3,2} = 0 \qquad \xi_{3,3} = -5$$

These 3 characteristic vectors are independent so that the T-matrix formed by them has a nonzero determinant and an inverse

$$T = \begin{vmatrix} 1 & 4 & 1 \\ 1 & -1 & 1 \\ 1 & 0 & -5 \end{vmatrix}, \ \det T = 30, \ T^{-1} = \begin{vmatrix} \dfrac{5}{30} & \dfrac{20}{30} & \dfrac{5}{30} \\ \dfrac{6}{30} & -\dfrac{6}{30} & \dfrac{0}{30} \\ \dfrac{1}{30} & \dfrac{4}{30} & -\dfrac{5}{30} \end{vmatrix}$$

From this it follows that the matrix $T^{-1} P \, T$ will have the characteristic values as diagonal elements and that $\lim_{n \to \infty} P^n \neq 0$.

$$T^{-1}PT = \begin{vmatrix} 1 & 0 & 0 \\ 0 & .65 & 0 \\ 0 & 0 & .40 \end{vmatrix}, \ \lim_{n \to \infty} P^n = \begin{vmatrix} \dfrac{5}{30} & \dfrac{20}{30} & \dfrac{5}{30} \\ \dfrac{5}{30} & \dfrac{20}{30} & \dfrac{5}{30} \\ \dfrac{5}{30} & \dfrac{20}{30} & \dfrac{5}{30} \end{vmatrix}$$

The meaning of the latter is that if these probabilities were to remain the same for an indefinitely long period of time, then the probability of occurrence of these three political situations would be:

no war	$\dfrac{5}{30}$		1
cold war	$\dfrac{20}{30}$	or	4
limited war	$\dfrac{5}{30}$		1

These political situations influence the program in two distinct ways. First, the requirements will be different; a much larger quantity will be needed in a period of limited war than in one of no war, while the quantity needed in a cold war period will lie somewhere in between.

Secondly, the prices at which the imported ores can be obtained will be dependent on the political situation; prices will be high in a period of limited war and low in that of no war, with prices in a cold war period lying between these two extremes.

In addition, these import prices are found to depend on the quantities of foreign materials which will be purchased by the U.S. This merely reflects the important role the U.S. plays as buyer of these foreign ores. In other words, these import prices are a function of the quantities to be bought, which fact leads to quadratic terms in the objective function, as well as linear terms, of course.

The same holds for the costs of upgrading the domestic ores. They too are a function of the quantities which will be upgraded, due to economies of scale. However, there is this important distinction, that the quadratic terms in the objective function, resulting from the importation of foreign ores, have positive coefficients, while those associated with the upgrading of domestic ores have negative coefficients.

This is also true for the costs of processing the foreign and upgraded domestic ores into alloys; they too lead to quadratic terms with negative coefficients in the objective function in addition to linear terms. The same holds for the costs of constructing the plants designed to upgrade the domestic ores, combined or not with their processing into alloys.

The technological structure underlying the various activities is an essential element in the formulation of the problem. The relationships between the importation of foreign ores, the upgrading of domestic ores, the construction of upgrading plants, the storage of foreign and domestic ores, the processing of these ores into alloys, and the constraints imposed on each of them found their expression in a model, which will be described in more detail in the following section.

The problem has been solved by the technique of dynamic programming, which puts no limitations on the form of the objective function. On the other hand, this technique can handle discrete quantities only, so that much depends on the fineness of the grid. At the same time, the procedure is very time-consuming so that the available amount of computer time is crucial. In this particular case, a rather coarse grid was all that was feasible, given the limited resources.

The main result is, to a certain extent, a confirmation of the outcome of the nonstochastic model, namely that a much larger share of the requirements should be met by domestic production. Even in the case of a "no war" situation, the importance of developing domestic resources should not be entirely overlooked.

Another interesting feature brought out by the analysis is that the system has an interesting ergodic property, in the sense that it tends strongly to a particular final state, of which more will be said later.

THE MODEL

The technological structure underlying the model is pictured in the following diagram.

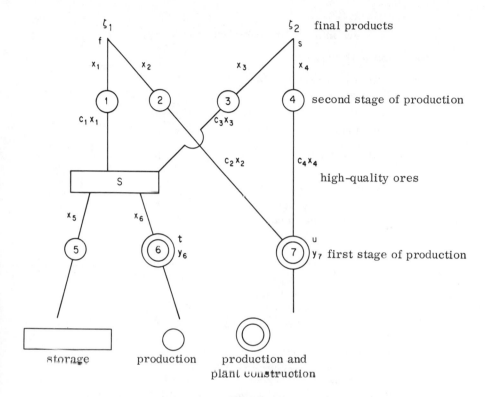

Fig. 1

Starting from the top, it can be seen that the final demand for manganese, the material for which this study was made, consists of two parts, one for ferro-manganese and one for silico-manganese. Each of these two types of alloys can be obtained from high-quality ores along conventional lines (processes 1 and 3) or from medium-quality ore by special treatment (processes 2 and 4). The high-quality ores, in turn, can be obtained by importation (process 5) or by upgrading domestic source-material (process 6). The quantities acquired this way are added to the stockpile, which, in turn, supplies part of the quantities needed in the production of alloys. Finally, there are two beneficiation plants in which the low-quality ores of domestic origin have to be upgraded before they can be further processed. The problem is to find that combination of stockpiling and construction of plants that will produce at minimum cost the quantities of alloys needed in the various possible sequences of political situations.

The formulation of this problem led to the model now to be described. The notation adopted for it is as much as possible in correspondence with that of a preceding article on the same subject, but it was necessary to deviate from that notation at certain points. The following symbols have been used for:

a) parameters in price and cost functions $\quad \alpha, \beta, \gamma, \delta$

b) quantities† required $\quad \zeta$

c) quantities† to be determined
      for each year $\quad$ x, y
      for a period of years $\quad$ s, t, u

d) technical coefficients $\quad$ c

e) transition probabilities $\quad$ p

f) indices
      individual years $\quad$ i
      summation of years $\quad$ j
      external states in particular
            no war $\quad$ I
            cold war $\quad$ II
            limited war $\quad$ III
      external states in general $\quad$ e, f, g
      internal states in general $\quad$ k, ℓ, m
      individual processes $\quad$ 1, 2, ..., 7
      summation of processes $\quad$ r

The quantities (x's) that have to be imported or produced domestically can be found in the diagram along the lines leading upwards from the circles that represent the corresponding activities. The increases in the plant capacities (y's) are located at the outer of two concentric circles.

Denoting the required quantities of ferro-manganese in year i by $\zeta_{1,i}$ and those of silico-manganese by $\zeta_{2,i}$, and looking at the diagram, the following two equalities become evident:

$$x_{1,i} + x_{2,i} = \zeta_{1,i} \qquad i = 1, 2, \ldots, n \tag{1}$$

$$x_{3,i} + x_{4,i} = \zeta_{2,i} \qquad i = 1, 2, \ldots, n \tag{2}$$

They simply state that what is required in a particular year also has to be produced in that year. In other words, there is no place in this model for a shortage of these alloys, since this would have disastrous consequences. On the other hand, there are also good reasons why no allowance for stockpiling alloys has been made either. It should, however, be noted that the requirements are now no longer supposed to be known beforehand,

---

† in net tons of pure manganese

as they were in the nonstochastic model, but depend on the sequence of political situations in the future.

The third equality merely states that what is added to the stockpile in a certain year plus what was there at the beginning of that year has to be equal to what is taken out of it in that year, plus what is left over at the end of that year, which equals the amount at the beginning of the next year.

$$s_i + x_{5,i} + x_{6,i} = c_1 x_{1,i} + c_3 x_{3,i} + s_{i+1} \qquad i = 1, 2, \ldots, n \qquad (3)$$

The letters c_1 and c_3 denote the quantities of manganese in the form of (high-quality) ores that are needed to produce 1 N.T. of manganese in the form of ferro- or silico-manganese. It has been assumed that these technical coefficients remain the same during the entire period that is covered by the program.

The fourth and fifth relationship assure that the quantity of ore that can be upgraded in any year cannot exceed the capacities of the upgrading plants at the beginning of that year. These capacities, in turn, are equal to the capacities at the beginning of the previous year, plus what has been added to them in that previous year:

$$x_{6,i} \leq t_{6,i} = t_{6,i-1} + y_{6,i-1} \qquad\qquad i = 1, 2, \ldots, n \qquad (4)$$

$$c_2 x_{2,i} + c_4 x_{4,i} \leq u_{7,i} = u_{7,i-1} + y_{7,i-1} \qquad i = 1, 2, \ldots, n \qquad (5)$$

$t_{6,i}$ and $u_{7,i}$ denote the capacities of the upgrading plants at the beginning of year i; $y_{6,i-1}$ and $y_{7,i-1}$ stand for increases in these capacities in the previous year.

As far as the alloy-producing plants are concerned, it can safely be assumed that their capacities will be large enough to process all the ore offered to them. Hence, there is no need for another set of constraints.

The same holds for the quantities of domestic ore to be extracted from the various deposits. Here, too, it can be assumed that these deposits contain sufficient quantities of ore to fill the needs for a good number of years.

Finally, there is the condition that all x and y variables are not allowed to assume negative values.

$$x_{r,i} \geq 0 \qquad r = 1, 2, \ldots, 6; \; i = 1, 2, \ldots, n \qquad (6)$$

$$y_{r,i} \geq 0 \qquad r = 6, 7; \; i = 1, 2, \ldots, n \qquad (7)$$

In summary, the model consists of 3 equalities and 2 inequalities (besides the 2 just mentioned) involving a total of 8 activities, of which 6 are related to the actual production of manganese and the other 2 to the construction and expansion of the upgrading plants.

The objective is to select that combination of the x's and y's, one combination for every year, that meets the requirements in all successive years at minimum-costs. These minimum-costs will depend on the situation at the beginning of the first year. Hence, there will be as many cost-minima as there are initial situations possible.

Each initial situation is characterized by an external and an internal state of the system. The external state is the political environment, being one of "no war," of "cold war," or of "limited war," the only three possibilities considered here. The internal state is determined by the capacity of each of the two upgrading plants and the quantity of ore in the stockpile at the beginning of the year.

The activities of a certain year not only have to meet the requirements of that year, but also transform the internal state of the system at the beginning of that year into a generally different one at the end of it. This latter state should then be the one that is most favorable from an economic point of view for meeting the requirements of future years in the light of what can be expected to happen politically.

Let $M_{e,k,j}$ denote the minimum-costs of a program covering j years, counting backwards in time, starting from the last year n, with the eth external and the kth internal state at the beginning of year j. Then $M_{e,k,j}$ can be defined as:

$$M_{e,k,j} = \min_{\ell} \left[C_{e,k,\ell,j} + \rho \sum_{f=I}^{III} p_{e,f} M_{f,\ell,j-1} \right] \tag{8}$$

Here $C_{e,k,\ell,j}$ stands for the cost of meeting the requirements of the jth year (being a function of the particular e^{th} external state) and transforming the kth internal state at the beginning of that year into the ℓth internal state at the end of it. Hence, $C_{e,k,\ell,j}$ is a function of the 8 activities that perform this dual function:

$$C_{e,k,\ell,j} = \sum_{r=1}^{6} x_{r,j} v_{r,j} + \sum_{r=6}^{7} y_{r,j} w_{r,j} \tag{9}$$

The $v_{r,j}$ variables in this expression stand for the prices of imported foreign ores, for the unit-cost of upgraded domestic ores, and for the unit-cost of alloys. The $w_{r,j}$ variables denote the cost of constructing or expanding the capacities of the plants by one unit per year.

The price to be paid for a unit of imported ore in any one year i, $v_{5,i}$, is first of all a function of $x_{5,i}$, the quantity of ore imported in that year:

$$v_{5,i} = \alpha_5 x_{5,i} + \beta_5 \qquad i = 1, 2, \ldots, n$$

It should be remarked at this point that the α-coefficient in this expression is positive. This is merely a reflection of the dominant position of the United States as a buyer of large quantities of ore in the foreign markets. Consequently, the resulting x_5 quadratic terms in the total cost expression of imported ores all have positive signs.

The price of imported ore is moreover dependent on the political situation. The reason is that the transportation costs and the insurance premiums, both of which are incorporated in the import prices, are greatly affected by the political situation. Hence there are actually 3 price functions for these imported ores, one for each political situation with its own β-coefficient:

no war $\qquad v_{5,i}^{I} = \alpha_5 x_{5,i} + \beta_5^{I}, \qquad i = 1, 2, \ldots, n$

cold war $\qquad v_{5,i}^{II} = \alpha_5 x_{5,i} + \beta_5^{II}, \qquad i = 1, 2, \ldots, n$

limited war $\quad v_{5,i}^{III} = \alpha_5 x_{5,i} + \beta_5^{III}, \qquad i = 1, 2, \ldots, n$

The unit-cost of the upgraded domestic ores as well as that of the alloys are also functions of their corresponding quantities:

$$v_{1,i} = \alpha_1 x_{1,i} + \beta_1, \qquad i = 1, 2, \ldots, n$$

$$v_{2,i} = \alpha_2 x_{2,i} + \beta_2, \qquad i = 1, 2, \ldots, n$$

$$v_{3,i} = \alpha_3 x_{3,i} + \beta_3, \qquad i = 1, 2, \ldots, n$$

$$v_{4,i} = \alpha_4 x_{4,i} + \beta_4, \qquad i = 1, 2, \ldots, n$$

$$v_{6,i} = \alpha_6 x_{6,i} + \beta_6, \qquad i = 1, 2, \ldots, n$$

Contrary to the α-coefficient in the price-function of imported ore, the α's in these last five expressions all have negative signs! In other words, the unit-costs will decrease with increases in the produced quantities, due to economies of scale. Consequently, the resulting quadratic terms in the corresponding x-variables of the total cost-functions all have negative signs.

Mention should also be made here of the fact that the expressions for $v_{2,i}$ and $v_{4,i}$ stand for the combined cost of upgrading domestic material and processing it into alloys. The α- and β-coefficients of these two expressions have been determined on the basis of the technical coefficients c_2 and c_4. They indicate how many units of manganese in the form of upgraded ore are needed to produce one unit of manganese in the form of alloys. As in the nonstochastic model, it has been assumed that these technical coefficients will remain the same during the period under consideration.

The unit-cost for constructing and expanding the upgrading plants in year i are:

$$w_{6,i} = \gamma_6 y_{6,i} + \delta_6, \qquad i = 1, 2, \ldots, n$$

$$w_{7,i} = \gamma_7 y_{7,i} + \delta_7, \qquad i = 1, 2, \ldots, n$$

As in the case of the unit-cost of the upgraded domestic ores and alloys, the γ-coefficients in these two expressions also have negative signs. Consequently, the resulting quadratic terms in the corresponding y-variables of the total cost-function have negative signs.

As for the write-off of these costs, the same depreciation rule has been adopted as in the nonstochastic model; the entire cost of construction or expansion is written off in 10 equal installments, starting with the year following that of construction or expansion. Hence, the total costs are also dependent on j, the number of years covered by the program, as long as $j \leq 10$.

Turning now to the second part of the right-hand side of equation (8), this can be written in a more explicit form:

$$\rho \sum_{f=I}^{III} p_{e,f} M_{f,\ell,j-1}$$

$$= \rho(p_{e,I} M_{I,\ell,j-1} + p_{e,II} M_{II,\ell,j-1} + p_{e,III} M_{III,\ell,j-1}) \tag{10}$$

The various costs of the program will occur in different years and will have to be put on a common basis, i.e., brought forward to the beginning of the first year; hence, the discounting factor ρ. The $p_{e,I}$, $p_{e,II}$, and $p_{e,III}$ are the probabilities of transition of the particular external state e (which is one of the three possible external states considered here) at the beginning of year j into the first, second, or third of these external states at the beginning of the next year, year $j-1$ (the years are being counted backwards in time).

$M_{I,\ell,j-1}$, $M_{II,\ell,j-1}$, and $M_{III,\ell,j-1}$ denote the minimum-cost of a $(j-1)$ years' program starting from the first (no war), second (cold war), or third (limited war) external state and the ℓth internal state, at the beginning of year $j-1$. It should here be observed that the ℓth internal state at the beginning of year $j-1$ is the same as that at the end of the preceding year j envisaged in expression (9) and implicitly in expression (8). Going back to the general expression for these minimum-costs, $M_{f,\ell,j-1}$, we can write for it:

$$M_{f,\ell,j-1} = \min_{m} \left[C_{f,\ell,m,j-2} + \rho \sum_{g=I}^{III} p_{f,g} M_{g,m,j-2} \right] \tag{11}$$

This formula is similar to (8) given for $M_{e,k,j}$ with the exception that the fth external and ℓ^{th} internal states at the end of year j = the beginning of year $j-1$ have been assumed to be replaced by the gth external and m^{th} internal states of the end of year $j-1$.

As for the internal states, they are in this model determined by a particular amount of manganese in the stockpile (s), a particular capacity of the first upgrading plant (t), and a particular capacity of the second upgrading plant (u). In other words, there are as many internal states as there are permissible levels of the stockpile times capacities of the first plant times capacities of the second plant.

From formula (8) it can be seen that a particular internal state has to be created at the end of year j which minimizes the cost of that year, plus the costs which can be expected to occur in the remaining years of the program on the basis of the probabilities of transition of external states. It should be kept in mind that this particular internal state ℓ at the end of year j depends on the internal state k at the beginning of that year, on the requirements of that year, given the political situation at the beginning of that year, and the quantities x and y which are ultimately the decisive elements of the program. The ideas in the last two sentences also apply to formula (11). How these quantities have been obtained will be discussed in the next section.

COMPUTATIONS AND RESULTS

The problem as it has been formulated belongs to the class of dynamic programming problems and has been solved by a recursive procedure based on the so-called "principle of optimality."[†] A peculiar feature of this procedure is that it starts with examining the last year of the program first, then the year before last, and so on, so that the first year of the program enters the computation last. The reason for this is that once the lowest-cost path has been found between the internal state at the beginning and that at the end of a period, it remains the lowest-cost path in all subsequent computations involving that particular initial internal state. This fact permits an enormous saving in the number of paths which have to be examined in the search for the least expensive one connecting the state of the system at the beginning of one year with that at the end of another year.[†]

Still, it is only possible to examine a rather limited number of states each year this way and the accuracy of the results depends to a great extent on the fineness of the grid. In this particular example, a mesh of 100,000 N.T. of manganese has been used which is rather coarse. It permits, however, a rather wide range for the quantity of manganese in the stockpile: from 0 to 2,000,000 N.T. In addition, three different capacities of each of the two upgrading plants have been taken into account. Consequently, there are $20 \times 3 \times 3 = 180$ different internal states for each of the three external states. Assuming for a moment that all paths connecting these internal states are feasible, 3×180^{10} paths would have to be examined for a program covering a 10-year period. However, by making use of the principle of optimality, this number is reduced to $3 \times 10 \times 180^2 = 972,000$. Of course, these are upper bounds, since the need of meeting the requirements eliminates a number of feasible internal states at the end of each year. Still, these figures give some idea of the amount of work that is saved by making use of this "principle of optimality."

Nevertheless, it will be clear that a high-speed electronic computer of the IBM-704 class is a prerequisite in performing the amount of work that remains to be done in applications of this kind. Besides computing the

---

[†]For a description of this principle, the reader is directed to Refs. 2 and 3.

[†]The interested reader will find a worked-out example in Ref. 5, pp. 18-33.

costs of each permissible path, the computer has been requested to print out for each internal state at the beginning of a year the cost of the least expensive path, the corresponding x and y values, and the resulting internal state at the end of that year. The latter provides first of all a check on the computations; in addition, it proves to be an important source of information, of which more will be said later.

From what has been said before, it will be clear that any n-year program will have as many minima as there are different states of the system at the beginning of that program. In this particular case, there are 3 different external states and 180 different internal states associated with each one of them. Accordingly, each n-year program has 540 minima and a selection of 540×n internal states, since the minimum-path corresponding to each one of these minima runs over n internal states in an n-year program.

The cost-minima of a 10-year manganese program prove to fluctuate between \$1.378 billion and \$1.986 billion, depending on the state of the system at the beginning of the program.† It is interesting to note that the differences between two neighboring minima in this table indicate how much extra has to be paid for or how much is saved by the difference in quantity between the two corresponding initial states. The nature of these differences is essentially the same as that of the shadowprices in the nonstochastic model.

The results of the nonstochastic model, designed for a 6-year period of limited war, have been compared with those of the stochastic model covering the same number of years. As one would expect, the costs of the nonstochastic model are higher than those of the stochastic model, since the latter also takes into account the possibilities of cold war and no war, while the former did not.

Also, it has been shown how two different sequences of external states would affect the minimum cost and the corresponding selection of internal states of a 4-year program. The same has been done for the first four years of a ten-year program, after which the two outcomes have been compared. These examples show how one can use the information contained in the tables of selected internal states to find the best course of action for every future sequence of external states. To put it differently, these tables of internal states of minimum-cost programs enable one to make full use of the information on the political situation as this becomes available in the course of time.

The tables of selected internal states are, moreover, interesting from another point of view. To demonstrate this, a 540 × 540 matrix Q will be used, in which each row and each column denotes one of the 540 possible states of the system. Figure 2 will make this clear.

This figure shows that, for instance, in the case of no war, an (1,1,19) internal state at the beginning of the first year will result in an (1,1,18) internal state at the end of that year. Furthermore, there is a 0.70 chance that there will still be a no-war situation at the end of the first year, a

---

†These cost-minima can be found in Table 5, pp. 35-36, and the corresponding selection of internal states in App. II, pp. 1-27 of Ref. 5.

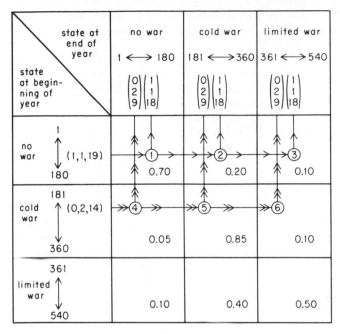

Fig. 2

0.20 chance that the no-war situation has changed into cold war, and a
0.10 chance into limited war, according to the earlier-described matrix P
of transition probabilities. Hence, a value of 0.70 will be assigned to the
element designated by ①, a value of 0.20 to element ②, and a value of
0.10 to element ③. It should here be observed that element ① takes the
same position in block I as element ② takes in block II and as element ③
takes in block III. To take another example, in the case of cold war, an
(0,2,14) internal state at the beginning of the first year will lead to an
(0,2,9) internal state at the end of that year. Hence, a value of 0.05 at ④,
of 0.85 at ⑤, and of 0.10 at ⑥. This process is continued until the
changes in all 540 initial states of the system have found their place in
the Q matrix, each nonzero element having an appropriate probability
value assigned to it. The final result will be a Q matrix with 3 × 540
= 1620 nonzero elements which can be partitioned in 3 identical strips of
540 rows and 180 columns. These nonzero elements indicate, then, how the
states of the system at the beginning of the first year of a ten-year program will be transformed into probable states of the system at the beginning of the second year. By probable states is here meant states with a
certain probability of realization assigned to them.

A particular initial state of the system will be represented in this con-
ception by a vector b of length 540 with all elements equal to zero except
one which will have the value of 1. If this vector b is now multiplied by
the matrix Q, then the resulting vector b' will indicate how that particular

initial state will have been transformed into various states at the beginning of the second year with a certain probability of appearance attached to each one of these states.

Now suppose that at the beginning of this second year the policy-maker again places himself at the start of a new ten-year program and asks himself how the situation in which he ended the first time will be further transformed. The answer to this question is given by another multiplication, this time of the vector b' times the same matrix Q as before.† The outcome of this second multiplication will be a vector b'' representing various states at the beginning of the second year of the new ten-year program, again with a certain probability of appearance attached to each one of these states.

If this process is repeated a number of times, an interesting property of the system comes to the fore: That is, the probability that one particular state of the system, namely the one with a (2,2,0) internal state, will appear becomes larger the more often this process is repeated and approaches the value of 1, while the probabilities of the other states gradually diminish and tend to 0. This means then that the repetition of a ten-year program year after year will ultimately lead to a (2,2,0) internal state of the system and will then remain in that state. This is what is meant by the technical phrase "convergence in policy space."

This property becomes even more interesting when other initial situations are considered as well. Then it turns out that whatever the initial situation is, i.e., wherever the value of 1 is located in the original vector b, the final state of the system will always be the one in which this particular internal state (2,2,0) has a high probability of appearance. This indicates that the system has an inherent ergodic property, which fact is of interest in itself.

At this point it should be observed that the same result would have been obtained if the matrix Q had first been multiplied by itself a number of times before the vector x matrix multiplication was done. Computing the powers of Q in ascending order will in the end result in a matrix $\lim_{n \to \infty} Q^n$ which will have only nonzero elements in the (2,2,0) columns and zero-elements everywhere else. The elements of the (n.w.; 2,2,0) column of this matrix will all have the value of 5/30, those of the (c.w.; 2,2,0) column will all have the value of 20/30, and those of the (l.w.; 2,2,0) column will all have the value of 5/30. This conjecture is based on the relationship between the matrices P and Q on the one hand, and that between $\lim_{n \to \infty} P^n$ and $\lim_{n \to \infty} Q^n$ on the other hand. It can then be said that a repetition of a

_____

†Because of the special feature of this problem, it was possible to perform this second computation on an IBM 650 equipped with index registers and able to perform floating-point arithmetic. By making extensive use of the table-look-up facility, it took this machine about three minutes to carry out one such multiplication.

10-year policy year after year will render the system, as it has been described here, into an absorbing Markov chain.†

At this point it should be remarked that the (2,2,0) internal state of the system is the one in which both plants have their largest admissible capacity and in which the stockpile does not contain any ore at all. This then stresses the importance of the domestic resources and the value that is to be attached to the development of the technology by which these low-quality domestic ores can be made suitable for the production of alloys. Of course, this conclusion is subject to the assumption that the price-cost relationships between imported and domestically produced ores will not materially change in favor of the foreign ores. Moreover, this result is subject to the assumption that the probabilities of transition of the three political situations will remain the same during the period under consideration.

---

†For a description of the properties of an absorbing Markov chain, the reader is directed to Ref. 4, in particular Chapter XV, Section 6, and Chapter XVI, Sections 1 and 4.

REFERENCES

1. Karreman, Herman F., "Programming the Supply of a Strategic Material, Part I: A Nonstochastic Model," Naval Research Logistics Quarterly, Vol. 7, No. 3, Sept. 1960.
2. Bellman, Richard, Dynamic Programming, Princeton University Press, 1957.
3. Bellman, Richard, and Stuart E. Dreyfus, Applied Dynamic Programming Princeton University Press, June 1962.
4. Feller, William, An Introduction to Probability Theory and its Applications, Vol. I, John Wiley and Sons, 1957.
5. Karreman, Herman F., "Econometric Analysis of the United States Manganese Problem, Part II," Research Memorandum No. 14, Econometric Research Program, Princeton University, March 1960.

MATHEMATICAL PROGRAMMING APPLIED TO SHORT TERM SCHEDULING OF INTERCONNECTED HYDRO-THERMAL ELECTRIC POWER SYSTEMS

B. Bernholtz

ABSTRACT

In addition to its practical importance, the problem of utilizing stored water so as to minimize the cost of supplying electric energy has been historically important in the development of recursive techniques for solving multi-stage decision problems. Pierre Massé, formerly of the Électricité de France, was among the originators of these methods. He dealt with a single reservoir only, and was concerned with operation over long periods of time. The complexity of this decision problem is due to its stochastic nature. Subsequent mathematical interest has centered essentially on the same model.

This paper deals with the equally important but mathematically neglected problem of economic operation of an electric power system over short periods of time, say 24 hours. To date this problem has been left largely in the hands of those who actually operate power systems. A brief perusal of the pertinent engineering literature will show that they have not always treated it with proper mathematical respect.

Daily operation may be considered as a deterministic process. Those elements, such as future load demands and river flows, which are stochastic when viewed in the long term can be assumed to be known 24 hours in advance. The complexity of this scheduling problem is due to the number of variables and the variety of constraints to which they are subject. The method of solution must be able to produce schedules fast enough so that they may be used on a daily basis.

An iterative procedure for determining economic daily schedules is presented, in which successive system schedules are determined each yielding a greater profit than the preceding. The method takes transmission losses into account and satisfies all applicable constraints. This work was done while the author was with the Hydro-Electric Power Commission of Ontario and has been published elsewhere [1, 2, 3, 4, 5].

A realistic model of part of the system operated by the Commission contains 16 sources of generation. These include thermal-electric stations, "fixed head" hydro-electric stations, a variable head hydro-electric station (actually a pumped-storage reservoir and pumping-generating station operated in conjunction with a major hydro-electric station), "contract" sources and simple and multiple interconnections with neighboring power systems. A daily schedule consists of average hourly outputs for each source in the model. Because of the constraints on water usage, each hour's operation cannot be considered separately so that the problem involves 16 × 24 = 384 variables.

REFERENCES

1. Bernholtz, B., and L. J. Graham, "Hydro-Thermal Economic Scheduling, Part I, Solution by Incremental Dynamic Programming," AIEE Transactions, Vol. 79, Pt. III, 1960.
2. Bernholtz, B., and L. J. Graham, "Hydro-Thermal Economic Scheduling, Part II, Extension of the Basic Theory," AIEE Transactions, Vol. 80, Pt. III, 1961.
3. Bernholtz, B., and L. J. Graham, "Hydro-Thermal Economic Scheduling, Part III, Scheduling the Thermal Sub-System Using Constrained Steepest Descent," AIEE Transactions, Vol. 80, Pt. III, 1961.
4. Bernholtz, B., and L. J. Graham, "Hydro-Thermal Economic Scheduling, Part IV, A Continuous Procedure for Maximizing the Weighted Output of a Hydro-Electric Generating Station," AIEE Transactions, Vol. 80, Pt. III, 1961.
5. Bernholtz, B., and L. J. Graham, "Hydro-Thermal Economic Scheduling, Part V, Scheduling a Hydro-Thermal System with Interconnections," submitted to the AIEE Transactions for publication.

An Application of Linear Programming to the Fairing of Ships' Lines

S. A. Berger
W. C. Webster

1. INTRODUCTION

When a shipyard contracts to build a ship it is given a small drawing, called the "lines plan," which describes the geometrical shape of the ship's hull. This drawing consists of three interrelated curves. One set of these curves represents the intersection of the hull and a series of horizontal planes parallel to the keel. These cuts are called "waterlines." A vertical set perpendicular to the centerplane is called "stations"; and another set parallel to the centerplane is called "buttocks." Fig. 1 is the lines plan of a typical ship.

A naval architect has drawn these curves using a spline--a thin, pliable beam held in place with weights. He insures that these curves are "fair" or smooth and pleasing to the eye, because he desires the ship's surface to have this property also. It has been felt that ships so designed will not suffer from the loss of performance sometimes associated with bumps or unfairness of the ship's hull.

As it stands, this drawing (Fig. 1), about one-fiftieth or one-hundredth the size of the full ship, is far too inaccurate for direct use in building a ship. The full-scale tolerance of about $\frac{1}{8}$-inch cannot be perceived on such a small drawing. It then becomes the task of the shipyard to expand the scale of this plan. Since these curves have no mathematical definition, such scaling up is not at all a trivial matter.

The traditional method of attack for this problem is to measure from the lines plan a sufficient number of points to describe the curves. These points are laid down, full scale, on a mold loft floor. The loftsman then reconstructs the lines plan by drawing fair curves through or as close as possible to these scaled points. During this process any reading errors or inaccuracies caused by scaling are detected visually and corrected.

The problem we have undertaken is to perform the same task mathematically. In itself, this mathematical lofting would not offer any particular

†The application of linear programming to curve fitting, as presented here, is the result of work performed by Todd Shipyards Corporation, Research and Development Group, in partial fulfillment of the U.S. Navy Department's Bureau of Ships Contract NObs-4427, administered by Code 770, with the joint sponsorship of the U.S. Maritime Administration.

241

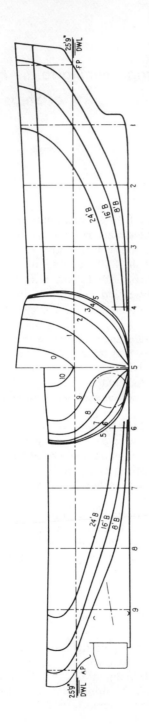

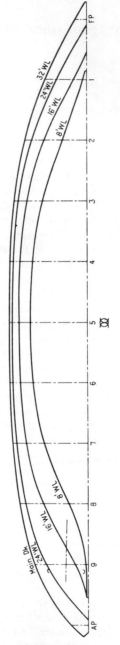

Fig. 1. Lines of USS Glacier

advantages over the previous manual approach. However, with the advent of automation, it is imperative that such a mathematical definition exist in order to use computer-controlled fabricating machines.

2. FAIRNESS CRITERIA

In order to be able to produce a curve which is fair, it is first necessary to isolate the properties determining fairness. With current practice as our guide, we find that fair curves must at least:

2-a. Be class C^2 functions. The naval architect insures that the curves are smooth by using a spline to draw them. Thin beam theory predicts that these curves will be functions whose second derivative is continuous everywhere.

2-b. Have no extraneous inflection points. When a naval architect draws the lines plan he arranges the spline and its constraining weights so that the curve it assumes is free from bumps. This process is again repeated in the mold loft. For a curve given by 2-a above, a bump is the occurrence of two closely spaced inflection points. Since the curves of the lines plan are drawn by the naval architect and are fair, we must be sure that the curves which result from the fitting process have only those inflection points indicated on this drawing.

These two criteria are not sufficient, since it is possible to construct curves which do satisfy them and which are not pleasing to the eye. However, experience has indicated that the curve which satisfies 2-a and 2-b, and which is the best fit to a set of points scaled from a fair curve, is satisfactory. Here we define "best fit" as the curve whose maximum deviation from the given points is a minimum.

3. PRELIMINARY SMOOTHING

The data one obtains from the lines plan usually consists of offsets, that is, the scaled distances of the waterlines and stations from the centerplane. These data are prone to certain difficulties. First, the accuracy of the data is limited by the measuring method. The offsets are read from a drawing with lines of finite width by a scale of finite precision. Second, since there are usually at least two hundred points given to describe a ship, it is not at all unreasonable to assume that some of them might embody large errors due to reading errors, transcribing errors, etc. Thus these data need not be exact. There may be a few points that are totally in error and do not bear any information. Superimposed on all the rest of the points are small, random errors due to the mensuration. It is crucial that these bad points be rejected if the naval architect's intentions are to be preserved in the curve fitting process.

Such errors are now detected in the mold loft when the loftsman notices that it is impossible to pass a spline through a set of points without producing a bump. A similar procedure can be performed numerically.

We shall assume that:

3-a. The offsets to be examined are, for the most part, reasonable points and the bad points are not closely spaced.

3-b. The set of points sufficiently describe a ship which was intended to be fair. Presumably, the points form a matrix of waterlines and stations faired by the navàl architect. Thus it is reasonable to expect to be able to pass fair curves through, or at least very near, the good points representing the individual waterlines and stations.

The strategy for detecting bad points involves determining if these points which were scaled from, and which represent, a fair curve are compatible with the fairness criteria. Any incompatibility will be interpreted as the existence of a bad point. Since continuity of any order cannot be a property of discrete points the question of compatibility becomes: From the myriad of class C^2 functions which pass through these points, is it possible for one of them to be free of bumps?

Consider the three points shown in Fig. 2. By the mean value theorem there must be some region in the interval from points 1 to 3 in which the second derivative of any class C^2 function has the same sign as the second difference computed at point 2. For the points shown the second difference is negative and there must be at least a region in this interval with negative second derivative.

If there is a fourth point adjoined to these three such that the second difference computed at 3 is positive then there must be some region, near 3 in the interval 2 to 4 which has a positive second derivative. Thus, in the interval 1 to 4 the second derivative must change in sign and there must be an inflection point. Two consecutive sign changes at three neighboring points indicates two inflection points. Since this would be the shortest interval in which one could predict the existence of two inflection points, i.e.,

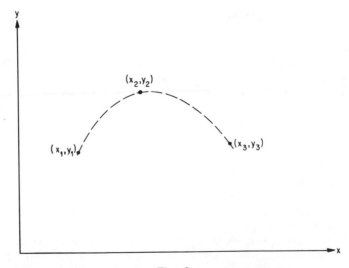

Fig. 2

a bump, we must conclude that they contradict our assumptions. It seems unreasonable to assume that a naval architect would have intended such a set of points since, if he had desired the curvature to change so often he would have given more information to describe the shape of the curve in this region.

Once an inconsistancy is discovered it is an easy matter to locate the bad point from the pattern of second differences in the neighborhood of this difficulty. We have written a program which goes through this process of detecting and locating the bad points. This program adjusts the bad points so that they become compatible with the other points.

4. CURVE FORMS

There are two possible general approaches to the problem of mathematically fairing a ship's hull. The first method, the analogue of current manual lofting practice, is to fair all of the waterlines and stations individually, and since, in general, the set of waterlines will not be compatible with the set of stations, to repeat the process in an iterative fashion until convergence criteria are met. The second method is to treat the problem directly as a surface fairing problem in three dimensions. The advantage of the first method as compared to the second is that it reduces the complex problem of fairing a three-dimensional surface to the conceptually simpler one of fairing a number of closed curves in a plane. However, this advantage could be partly or completely offset by such difficulties as convergence of the iteration and lack of fairness of intermediate waterlines and stations. Putting aside such considerations for a while, let us first consider the problem of fairing individual waterlines and stations as two-dimensional fairing problems. The difficulties indicated above, as well as the direct problem of fairing in three dimensions will be considered in later sections of the paper. The problem of interpolating between these faired waterlines and stations (a difficulty which does not exist in fitting a surface) can be solved by a method given recently by Birkhoff and Garabedian [1].

The first decision one must make in fairing a set of points in a plane involves the selection of the equation to be employed.

In attempting to fit a waterline or station with one analytic expression certain difficulties arise; these may be traced to the fact that current lofting practice (using splines) makes these contours into segmented analytic curves, and hence not representable by one analytic function [2]. As indicated earlier, the current practice is to fair waterlines and stations using a spline. Under small deflections splines assume the shape of a segmented polynomial of third degree. That is, this curve is a set of cubic equations joined in such a way that the resulting curve is of class C^2. The non-analyticity of this curve allows greater freedom in obtaining acceptable ship forms. In particular, straight portions being special cubic curves are easily included in such a curve, and in addition, and most significantly, one can readily control inflection points on this type curve. Here, the second derivative varies linearly in the regions between—and is continuous at—the joins. An inflection point occurs in the interval between two adjacent joins if and only if the second derivative at one join is opposite in sign to the second derivative at the other. If the joins of the spline curve are taken at the points where the original data are given and if one constrains the spline curve to have second derivatives of sign matching the second differences at these points, then this curve will not have any extraneous inflection points. Here pre-smoothing prevents any undesired behavior of the second derivatives in the neighborhood of these points and the properties of the spline curve prevent any difficulties from arising between these points.

For these reasons it was apparent that the spline curve is eminently well suited for the fitting of fair curves on a ship.

5. LINEAR PROGRAMMING FORMULATION

The formulation of fitting a fair curve to these points is now quite obviously a linear programming problem. Suppose we are given n points through which we would like to pass a fair curve. The resulting linear program is given by:

$$-\lambda + Y(x_i) \leq y_i \tag{1}$$

$$-\lambda - Y(x_i) \leq -y_i \qquad i = 1, \ldots, n \tag{2}$$

$$-r_i \cdot Y''(x_i) \leq 0 \tag{3}$$

The Eqs. (1) and (2) constrain the spline curve $Y(x)$ to be within λ of the given data. The Eq. (3) constrains the second derivative at the ordinates of the given data to have the same sign as the second difference r_i. Minimizing λ produces the best fit according to our definition.

Notice that Eq. (3) is location independent. That is, a curve so fitted is still fair even if one translates the curve up or down by any amount. This property allows us to draw the very important conclusion that it is impossible for the process of iterating waterlines and stations to diverge. At worst the solution can oscillate. However, our experience has shown that indeed the iteration converges and does so quite rapidly.

In order to solve this linear program one has to represent $Y(x)$ as a linear function of positive parameters. We have used the representation for the spline curve suggested by Theilheimer [3] which is:

$$y = a_0 + a_1 x + a_2 x^2 + \sum_{j=1}^{n-1} A_j (x - x_j)_+^3 \tag{4}$$

where:

$$(x - x_j)_+^3 = (x - x_j)^3 \qquad \text{if } x \geq x_j$$
$$(x - x_j)_+^3 = 0 \qquad \text{if } x < x_j$$

The "plus" notation in the summation permits one to represent this non-analytic curve with one equation and a minimum of parameters. In order to make Y(x) a function of positive parameters (to satisfy the requirements of a linear program), no generality is lost if one lets:

$$a = (a' - a''), \qquad a', a'' \geq 0$$

In these terms, the linear program becomes

$$-\lambda + (a_0' - a_0'') + (a_1' - a_1'')x_i + (a_2' - a_2'')x_i^2 + \sum_{j=1}^{i-1} (A_j' - A_j'')(x_i - x_j)^3 \leq y_i \qquad (5)$$

$$-\lambda - (a_0' - a_0'') - (a_1' - a_1'')x_i - (a_2' - a_2'')x_i^2 - \sum_{j=1}^{i-1} (A_j' - A_j'')(x_i - x_j)^3 \leq -y_i \qquad (6)$$

$$-2r_i(a_2' - a_2'') - 6r_i \sum_{j=1}^{i-1} (A_j' - A_j'')(x_i - x_j) \leq 0 \qquad (7)$$

$$i = 1, \ldots, n$$

Equations (5) $\rightarrow$ (7) represent a tableau of

3n equations,   2n + 5 variables

We have done a great amount of work with this formulation and have found the results very satisfactory. However there are some undesirable features. First, the tableau is very dense. That is, more than one half of the possible elements are nonzero. This leads to storage problems with certain codes. Second, there is no immediate feasible solution. This is not terribly important but it does first require some time to find a feasible solution.

These two problems can be helped somewhat if one adds inequalities (5) to (6). This eliminates about half of the nonzero elements but requires the addition of one slack per point to maintain the sense of the inequalities. This slightly revised formulation increases the linear program tableau to (3n + 5) variables.

It is quite clear that even small curve fitting problems become large linear programs. As a result, several steps were taken to improve efficiency.

6. IMPROVEMENTS

Duality

As originally noted by Kelly [4], curve fitting tableaus, and this one is no exception, tend to have more constraints than variables. Thus it is advantageous to use the dual formulation. This is of particular interest since it is obvious that the corresponding dual problem has an immediate feasible solution due to the simple cost vector in the primal problem. For our problems duality thus offers significant advantages.

Representation

Notice that Theilheimer's notation is by no means unique. A spline curve fitted to n points, of the type previously assumed, has n + 2 degrees of freedom. In principle one could choose any (n + 2) independent properties of the curve and these will determine the curve.

Offset Representation

One set of parameters that appears obvious to consider is the final ordinates after the fairing is complete. Suppose that the curve $Y(x)$ which is fitted to the points (x_i, y_i) passes through the points $(x_i, \bar{y}_i)$. We can choose these $\bar{y}_i$ as (n) of the (n + 2) parameters. Obviously they are independent. The additional two necessary parameters chosen were a_1, slope at the initial point x_1, and a_2, the second derivative at x_1.

As before we must assure that all the parameters are positive if a linear programming formulation is to be used. Since we are dealing with curves which represent a real ship's lines, it is unreasonable to allow any of the offsets to be negative. (Because ships are symmetric about the center-plane we need fair only the positive half of the hull.) The requirement $\bar{y}_i \geq 0$ is not only compatible with linear programming requirements but also with natural requirements.

In terms of equations (1) $\rightarrow$ (3), we have:

$$-\lambda + \bar{y}_i \leq y_i \tag{8}$$

$$-\lambda - \bar{y}_i \leq -y_i \tag{9}$$

$$-r_i \cdot Y''(x_i) \leq 0 \tag{10}$$

In this representation, one notices that Eqs. (8) and (9) are considerably simpler than Theilheimer's representation, Eqs. (5) and (6). However, with Theilheimer's notation it was possible to write out the counterpart to Eq. (10), Eq. (7), explicitly. In the above notation this is not as simple to do. However one can derive a set of recurrence relations which permit the construction of $Y''(x_i)$.

Equations (8) $\rightarrow$ (10) represent a linear program of (using duality):

n + 5 equations,   3n variables

This is a considerable decrease in the size of tableau required. It is worth noting that besides being smaller, the tableau formed by (8) $\rightarrow$ (10) is less dense than (5) $\rightarrow$ (7). The conclusion is then that the offset notation greatly decreases the tableau size and even more greatly decreases the nonzero entries required for a problem.

Deviation Representation

Let us consider the case when (n) of the independent variables are the deviations, δ_i, from the given ordinates, y_i. Thus:

$$\bar{y}_i = y_i + \delta_i \tag{11}$$

The reasons for going to such a notation are not at all obvious. If one tries to use these δ_i as a basis for a linear program, of the type previously formulated, it is immediately clear that two variables δ_i' and δ_i'' are needed at each point in order that the deviation be unrestricted in sign. This would, to be sure, undermine the effort to simplify the solution. Instead let us consider a slightly different problem. Let us take the δ_i as legitimate linear programming variables, where the δ_i are required to be equal to or greater than zero. Let us suppose that we subject the spline curve to the following constraints:

$$-\lambda + \delta_i \leq 0 \tag{12}$$

$$-r_i \cdot Y''(x_i) \leq 0 \tag{13}$$

Equation (13) is the same as Eq. (3). Equation (12) insures that λ is equal to or greater than any deviation, δ_i, since all of the δ_i are constrained to be positive. When one minimizes λ subject to (12) and (13) one determines the spline curve which:

(a) has the minimum, maximum deviation from the given points,
(b) lies wholly above the given points. That is, $\bar{y}_i \geq y_i$.

Clearly this is not the same solution obtained from equations (1) → (3). This solution is denoted by $\bar{Y}(x)$ and the corresponding values of λ and δ_i as $\bar{\lambda}$ and $\bar{\delta}_i$.

Consider the curve given by translating $\bar{Y}(x)$ down by $\bar{\lambda}/2$. That is:

$$\bar{\bar{Y}}(x) = \bar{Y}(x) - \bar{\lambda}/2$$

Several things can be proved about the curve $\bar{\bar{Y}}(x)$. First, the maximum deviation of $\bar{\bar{Y}}(x)$ from the original points is $(\bar{\lambda}/2)$. This follows immediately from the fact that the curve, $\bar{Y}(x)$, is wholly above the points but is still within $\bar{\lambda}$ of them. Second, $\bar{\bar{Y}}(x)$ is exactly the curve one would obtain if one had used Eq. (1) → (3). Obviously this curve satisfies Eq. (3). If there were another curve with a smaller deviation, $\hat{\lambda}$, from the points then this curve, this new curve, translated up by $\hat{\lambda}$, would contradict (a) and (b) above. This not very obvious result means that if we use the deviations from the given points as (n) of the independent variables, a linear program can be set up that requires only two constraints per point. One subtracts one half of the calculated maximum deviation from this curve to get the desired curve.

This process requires (using duality):

n + 5 equations,   2n variables

The value of $Y''(x_i)$ for this case can, of course, be calculated by the same recurrence relations as used in the offset notation.

Second Derivative Representation

There is another representation which can match the gains achieved by the deviation representation and may have some ultimate advantages. This time let us take C_i, the second derivatives at the points x_i, as (n) of the (n + 2) required variables. For the other two variables let us choose $\bar{y}_1$ the faired abscissa at x_1 and $(a_1' - a_1'')$ the slope at x_1.

Again we are faced with the problem of the nonnegative requirement. However, notice that the sole purpose of (3) is to impose a certain sign, that of r_i, on $Y''(x_i)$.

Consider a new set of independent variables $\bar{C}_i$, given by

$$\bar{C}_i = r_i C_i \equiv r_i Y''(x_i) \tag{14}$$

Whenever C_i satisfies Eq. (3), $\bar{C}_i$ is positive. Thus if $\bar{C}_i$ are chosen as independent variables, they can be taken as linear programming variables and as such obviate the necessity of using Eq. (3) for each point.

It is not necessary to let $\bar{y}_1$ take on negative values for the reasons discussed in the development of the offset notation. In this case Eqs. (1) and (2) become:

$$-\lambda + Y(x_i) \leq y_i \tag{15}$$

$$-\lambda - Y(x_i) \leq -y_i \tag{16}$$

Here again it is difficult to express $Y(x_i)$ in explicit form. However, as before, recurrence relations can be found from which it is easy to construct $Y(x_i)$.

This formulation yields a linear program of (again using duality):

n + 4 equations,   2n variables

This is then equivalent to the reduction afforded by the deviation approach.

7. SURFACE

As indicated earlier one could treat the problem of mathematically fairing a ship hull directly as a surface fairing problem in three dimensions. Such an approach leads to a much more complex mathematical formulation;

it does, however, completely eliminate the need to apply an iterative scheme and the consequent problem of convergence is thereby avoided.

Since, according to current practice, individual waterlines and stations are segmented spline curves, the most natural approach in attempting a surface fit would be to use the direct analogue of such curves in three dimensions, that is, choose a surface equation with the property that the curves of intersection of the surface with two families of mutually perpendicular planes results in waterlines and stations which are segmented spline curves. Such a surface would be analytic in the domain bounded by two successive waterlines and stations; at the boundaries the second derivative normal to the boundaries must be continuous, along the boundaries of each small surface element all the derivatives in the direction of the boundaries are continuous.

The equation having the properties indicated above can be written

$$y(x,z) = \sum_{i,j=0}^{2} a_{ij}x^i z^j + \sum_{i=1}^{n-1} A_i(x - x_i)_+^3 + \sum_{j=1}^{m-1} B_j(z - z_j)_+^3$$

$$+ \sum_{\substack{i=1 \\ j=1}}^{\substack{i=n-1 \\ j=m-1}} C_{ij}(x - x_i)_+^3(z - z_j)_+^3 \qquad (17)$$

where the symbol $(\ )_+$ is as defined earlier. This equation represents a segmented cubic surface over the domain

$$x_1 \leq x \leq x_n$$
$$z_1 \leq z \leq z_m$$

The continuity requirements are automatically satisfied by Eq. (17). The linear programming formulation of this problem then involves requiring that the deviation at each point of the x-z grid of given points be bounded by λ and that the sign of the curvature in the waterline and station planes agree with the sign of the corresponding second difference. Apart from the fact that y is now also a function of z the only substantial difference between fairing in two or three dimensions using linear programming lies in there being two curvature constraints in the latter case and only one in the former. If r_{ij} and s_{ij} denote the second differences in the x and z directions respectively evaluated at the point (x_i, z_j) then the linear programming formulation of the problem is as follows:

Minimize λ subject to the conditions

$$\left.\begin{array}{l} |y(x_i,z_j) - y_{ij}| \leq \lambda \\[2mm] -r_{ij}\dfrac{\partial^2 y}{\partial x^2}(x_i,z_j) \leq 0 \\[3mm] -s_{ij}\dfrac{\partial^2 y}{\partial z^2}(x_i,z_j) \leq 0 \end{array}\right] \quad \begin{array}{l} i = 1, 2, \ldots, n \\[2mm] j = 1, 2, \ldots, m \end{array}$$

$$(18)$$

where $y(x_i, z_j)$ represents equation (17) evaluated at the point (x_i, z_j), while y_{ij} is the given value of y at this point.

The other representations of splines previously presented can be easily extended to give a surface representation. However, these representations, although they offer a savings over the Theilheimer-type surface as they do with the Theilheimer curve, require a much more complicated procedure to develop the matrix given by Eq. (18).

8. CONCLUSIONS

Each of the methods presented above has been successfully used in fairing ships' lines. In general, it is found that the surface representation requires about two orders of magnitude more time before reaching a solution than does the iteration procedure. The surface method, however, results in a solution with a smaller maximum deviation than one obtained by iterating. Although we can not prove convergence, no difficulty has thus far arisen in any of our runs using this latter scheme.

Throughout the discussion in this paper we have neglected mention of certain areas of the ship's hull which do not conform to the general statements made about ships' lines. In particular, there are places where the second derivative is not continuous. Also, nothing has been said about the ends of curves, where one cannot calculate second differences to be used in the linear programming formulation. These difficult areas do require special attention, but can be effectively included in an over-all linear programming ship fairing program.

There is one additional feature of linear programming which enhances its suitability for this problem. This is concerned with the ability to add additional constraints to the program without changing the basic formulation. This feature could be particularly useful in introducing such constraints as fixed cargo capacity, given beam, etc. That is, it would be possible for the ship user or naval architect to designate certain parameters which he wished held fixed in the fairing process; the only limitation, of course, would be that these constraints be linear.

In conclusion, we feel that linear programming finds an ideal application in the fairing of ships' lines.

Acknowledgements

We would like to thank Donald Atkins and Richard Tapia of Todd Shipyards, San Pedro, for having done much of the programming required in the present study. We would also like to thank Dr. M. Juncosa of the RAND Corporation for originally suggesting the use of linear programming in the ship fairing problem.

REFERENCES

1. Birkhoff, G., and H. L. Garabedian, "Smooth Surface Interpolation," J. Math. and Phys., Vol. 39, No. 4, Dec., 1960, pp. 256-268.

2. Kerwin, J. E., "Polynomial Surface Representation of Arbitrary Ship Forms," J. Ship Res., Vol. 4, No. 1, June 1960, pp. 12-21.

3. Theilheimer, F., and W. Starkweather, "The Fairing of Ship Lines on a High-Speed Computer," David Taylor Model Basin, Appl. Math. Lab., Report 1474, January 1961.

4. Kelley, J. E., Jr., "An Application of Linear Programming to Curve Fitting," Univac Application Res. Center, Tech. Rept., No. 5, March 31, 1957.

The Simulation of Multi-component Distillation †

E. C. De Land
M. B. Wolf

A new method is proposed for the simulation of multicomponent petroleum distillation columns. This method takes advantage of the power of mathematical programming techniques for computing the equilibrium states of physiochemical processes. The formal procedure was proposed and developed for other chemical systems, but it is perfectly general, being able to incorporate changes of phase, external sources or sinks of mass or energy, and differential equations which describe system dynamics if they are relatively slow with respect to the chemical dynamics.

Using a theorem of the mathematician Gibbs, a chemical equilibrium may be defined in terms of the thermodynamic free-energy of each of the components. At equilibrium, the sum of the free energies will be minimized. In the present paper a free energy (nonlinear) function is defined and then minimized under the natural physical (linear) restraints of the system. On the analog computer—chosen because of the ease of representing the system dynamics, (nonlinear) heat and mass balance equations—the solution method is by steepest descent. A digital solution has also been devised, but not yet implemented because the digital program will be much more comprehensive than the basic idea which is presented here.

1. INTRODUCTION

Several procedures have been devised for the simulation of particular subsystems in a refinery operation, and in particular, since the advent of computer technology, practical methods have been developed for modeling multistage, multicomponent distillation on the computer. Amundsen [2], Lyster [3], Greenstadt [4], and others have described successful programs on the digital machine; Marr [5], Worley [6], Rijnsdorp and Maarleveld [7], Computer Systems, Inc. [8], and others discuss simulations on the analog. Usually these methods are based upon the equations and techniques devel-

---

†This paper is an abridgment of research sponsored by the United States Air Force under Project RAND and initially reported in RM-3258-PR. Views or conclusions presented in this paper should not, however, be interpreted as representing the official opinion or policy of the sponsoring agency.

oped formerly for hand calculation. Maar [5] is an exception in that he proposes a set of partial differential equations for the temperature and composition profiles of the column as a whole.

We propose, here, to apply a basic notion of thermodynamic equilibrium, the Gibb's free-energy function, to provide a model for simulation. This will require that we take full advantage of the high speed, capacity, and flexibility of the modern computer. There are several advantages, which we will discuss, to be gained from this method, but principally they arise from the fact that the method is perfectly general. It is a natural format for representing the subsidiary chemical reactions and states of a complex system and for representing classical equilibrium, but also it can be used to model irreversible thermodynamic processes (deGroot [16], and others) such as elution, ion exchange, and forcing functions (potentials) of various kinds. Thus, the method may be used to simulate other elements of the refinery. Here, we illustrate an application to multicomponent distillation.

The procedure originates in a paper by White, et al. [9], and has been applied in biological systems [10], combustion, planet atmospheric studies, and others. The present application was suggested in an earlier paper [11]. The analog computer results were obtained from research for a master's thesis by one of the authors [12]. Details of the analog techniques are contained in Reference 13.

2. A FRACTIONAL DISTILLATION COLUMN

It will not be necessary, here, to describe the fractional distillation column in great detail (see Reference 1). The basic idea is that a homogeneous input mixture of n components (the Feed) is to be separated into two principal fractions, a condensed vapor phase (the Distillate) and a liquid remainder (the Bottoms), with reasonable efficiency and control by means of a series of m staged distillations. Fig. 1 illustrates a typical distillation (a Plate) with communication to the plate above and the plate below. The scalar L_k represents the rate of flow of liquid from the kth plate with mole fraction composition vector $X_k = (x_{k1}, x_{k2}, \ldots, x_{kn})$ and V_k, the flow of vapor from the kth plate of composition $Y_k = (y_{k1}, y_{k2}, \ldots, y_{kn})$. Feed, at rate F and composition X_f, is entered at plate f and we assume either that the feed has the same temperature, pressure, and composition as X_f or that it has the same temperature and pressure but a composition which would produce X_f and Y_f at equilibrium.

We assume total condensation of the top plate vapor, having composition Y_m, at rate V_m, some of which, the reflux ratio $R = L_D/L_D + D$, is returned to the top plate. Heat at rate Q is entered at plate 1, where also a Bottoms product $L_1 = B$ of composition $X_1 = (x_{11}, x_{12}, \ldots, x_{ln})$ is withdrawn.

Heat and mass conservation equations may be written over the column as a whole or over any idealized internal section, e.g., a single plate. These equations plus the vapor-liquid equilibrium equations completely specify the operation of an idealized column when the boundary conditions and physical specifications of the tower are given. The composition of the

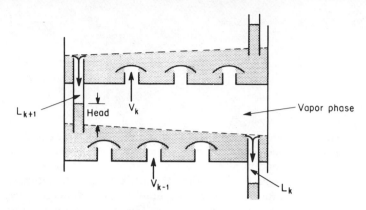

Fig. 1. A Bubble-cap Plate

product B or D will essentially be a function of Q, m, F, X_f, and R, but actually many parameters affect the product. In addition, important sources of error are heat losses, pressure losses due to viscous flow, undesirable chemical reactions, and the possibility that equilibrium is not attained on each plate.

A sufficient set of equations for an idealized tower may easily be written. For example, an analysis may begin by considering the conservation of mass on the bottom plate. For the bottom plate, from Fig. 1, we have $k = 1$, $V_{k-1} = 0$, $L_k = B$, and Q, not shown, is added. Therefore

$$L_2 = V_1 + B \tag{1}$$

or, for each component j,

$$L_2 x_{2j} = V_1 y_{1j} + B x_{1j} \tag{2}$$

Using H_k and h_k for the enthalpies of the vapor and liquid on plate k, we have

$$V_1 H_1 + B h_1 = L_2 h_2 + Q \tag{3}$$

For the vapor-liquid equilibrium equation we may write

$$y_{1j} = K_j(T, P) x_{1j} \tag{4}$$

where T and P are the temperature and pressure of plate 1 and K_j is the partial-pressure equilibrium constant, a tabulated function. With B, X_1, and Q given there are six unknowns so that two additional equations are required. Two equations which prove to be convenient for machine computation are derived from the fact that the sum of the mole fractions in a given phase is 1:

$$\sum_j x_{2j}(T_2) = 1 \tag{5}$$

and

$$\sum_j y_{1j}(T_1) = 1 \tag{6}$$

Therefore, since x_{2j} and y_{1j} are functions of plate temperature, for known volume and pressure the temperatures, required for the computation of H, h and K, may be obtained implicitly.

This sample set of equations is appropriately modified for other plates of the tower and, in practice, will be supplemented with subsidiary equations (relating to heat losses, etc.) as required but which we do not need for the present purpose. For the present, from equations 1-6, it is plausible that, given B, X_1, and Q, one may compute the initial conditions for plate 2. Computing in this manner, matching boundary conditions between each plate, D and Y_m are eventually determined. Then if Y_m does not equal the desired composition X_D, either (a) an iterative procedure is instituted to correct Y_m by varying Q, m, F, X_f, or R or (b) the loop is automatically closed, i.e., an error term may be fed back and used to correct the given input parameters until the system considered as a whole is in steady state and gives the desired output.

3. PREDICTION OF CHEMICAL EQUILIBRIUM

Computer methods, devised for the description of complex chemical equilibrium, are in terms of the reaction rate equations or the equilibrium constant algebraic equations or finally in terms of the thermodynamic free energy of the equilibrium condition which may be obtained by mathematical programming. At equilibrium, of course, all methods give essentially the same information, but in addition the last method has a standard format which is more flexible, yields additional data on the enthalpy of each species, and can incorporate the so-called irreversible, time-invariant processes.

For mixtures of a single phase equilibrium, conditions may be predicted, as described in previous papers [11, 14], by minimizing the (nonlinear) Gibb's free-energy function

$$F(Y) = RT \sum_j \bar{n} y_j [c_j + \ln y_j] \tag{7}$$

where

$Y = (y_1, y_2, \ldots, y_n)$ the set of mole fraction numbers,
$c_j = (F_j^0/RT) + \ln P$, standard free energy per mole of the jth species,

$\bar{n} = \Sigma_j n_j$, total number of moles of all species,
y_j = mole fractions of jth species,

under the (linear) conditions of conservation of mass and that $y_j > 0$ for each j. The right side of Eq. (7) is simply the sum of the Gibb's free energy of each species. For mixtures of two phases, one phase may be regarded as the "standard state" and the other phase may be computed with respect to this state. Thus, if $F_j^0/RT = 0$ in vapor phase, and using z for either x or y,

$$F(Z) = RT\bar{n}_1 \sum_j y_j[0 + \ln P + \ln y_j] + RT\bar{n}_2 \sum_j x_j[\bar{C}_j + \ln x_j] \qquad (8)$$

where

$\bar{C}_j \quad = (\Delta F_j^0/RT) + \ln P = \Delta F_j^0/RT$, liquid phase,
$\Delta F_j^0 \quad$ = change in standard free energy per mole for the jth species,
$\bar{n}_1, \bar{n}_2$ = total moles in liquid and vapor phase.

For vapor-liquid equilibria, ln P = total pressure in atmospheres for the vapor phase, = 0 for the liquid phase. Alternately, Eq. (8) may be regarded as the statement of a chemical reaction in either phase, in which case $\bar{C}_j$ becomes the free energy of formation of the product species. For the present distillation:

$$\bar{C}_j = \ln \frac{y_j}{x_j} = \ln \frac{P_j}{P \text{ Total}} = \ln K_j(T, P) \qquad (9)$$

Thus, for the distillation column, we replace equation (4) by equation (8) and minimize (8) under the restrictions or conditions

$$x_j \geq 0, \quad y_j \geq 0, \quad \text{the output species are not negative} \qquad (10)$$

and conservation of mass

$$N_i = n_{1i} + n_{2i} = \text{total moles of } i^{th} \text{ input species}$$
$$\text{in both phases on a plate} \qquad (11)$$

However, since the equilibrium concentrations are independent of the amount of the total mixture, we may either assume the total moles in either phase equals a constant, or, from Pv = $\bar{n}$RT and the dimensions of the tower, compute the actual N_i. Assuming $\bar{n}_1 = 1$ and $\bar{n}_2 = 1$, we may replace equation (11) with

$$\phi_i \equiv N_i - x_i - y_i = 0, \quad \text{for each i} \qquad (12)$$

Chemical reactions may be incorporated and the resulting stoichio-

metric restrictions [including Eq. (12)] may be organized into a matrix
format by writing, instead of (12)

$$\phi_i = N_i - \sum_j a_{ij} z_j = 0 \tag{13}$$

where the a_{ij} are formula numbers indicating the atoms of species i in
product j. For ideal vapor-liquid equilibrium, all $a_{ij} = 1$ and the matrix is
diagonal for each phase (z represents either x or y).

For computational purposes we incorporate the restrictions (12) or (13)
into (8) using Lagrange multipliers and find the min-max of

$$G(Z, \pi) = F(Z) - \sum_{i=1}^{n} \pi_i \phi_i \tag{14}$$

under (10), which clearly has the same minimum with respect to z as the
original problem. At equilibrium the vectors Z and π satisfy (14) and give
respectively the moles (or mole fraction) of each species and the free
energy contribution of each species present. To see this latter definition
of the components of the vector π, we may consider the first partial derivatives of G, which arise for purposes of computation by the method of
steepest descent.

To compute, either on the analog or the digital computer, we may write

$$\frac{\partial G}{\partial z_j} = \overline{C}_j + \ln z_j - \Sigma a_{ij} \pi_i = 0, \quad \text{for each } j$$

$$\frac{\partial G}{\partial \pi_i} = \phi_i(z) = 0, \quad \text{for each } i \tag{15}$$

and $z_j > 0,$ all j

and require that these partials be satisfied for all i and j. The first equation of (15) clearly defines the π_i as in the above paragraph, the second
is the conservation of mass. Detailed procedures for computing a chemical
equilibrium on the digital machine are given in Ref. [9], an example in Ref.
[10]. The analog procedure is given in Refs. [11], [12], and [13]. But, generally speaking, we can satisfy zero sum equations as in (15) by implicit
computation. In the first two equations of (15) we begin by defining the unknowns π and Z arbitrarily and arrange matters so that if they are in
error, a negative feedback signal forces the system to correct their values.
A certain amount of analysis is required for convergence and stability, but
the idea is not new. Kose [15], in 1956, demonstrated the conditions for
convergence.

4. DISCUSSION, AN APPLICATION, AND CONCLUSIONS

Reduced to its essential content the suggestion of this paper is to re-place the computation represented by Eq. (4), Sec. 2 by the procedure of Sec. 3. But in practice, the remaining equations of Sec. 2 will be altered and the amount of computation reduced. However, in a feasibility study, Eq. (4) was replaced by Eqs. (15) and a problem in the stabilization of natural gasoline was simulated on an analog computer [13]. The feed con-tained six components and under the conditions of the experiment, the desired separation was attained with six plates.

Computationally some of the detailed changes involved are:

(a) The $\bar{C}_j = \ln K_j$ are no longer functions of two variables since the ambient pressure is introduced as an additive term in Eqs. (8) and (14)

(b) Although this is an advantage only on the analog computer, the vari-able multiplications of Eq. (4) have been replaced by log function genera-tion.

(c) On the analog, more amplifiers were required than we presume to be the case for Eq. (4).

(d) The computation time for a new equilibrium is usually very short, a few milliseconds, hence the computed equilibrium is responsive to a con-tinuously changing parameter, and would continuously follow.

(e) In the usual procedure, Eq. (6) implicitly determines the vapor temperature along with Eq. (4) from the fact that the total pressure is equal to the sum of the partial pressures.

$$P = \sum_j P_j = \sum_j K_j x_j P \qquad\qquad (16)$$

The temperature is changed until Eq. (16) is satisfied. This procedure is still possible and was used in the example problem; however it may be more convenient to have n and T fixed and determine P as in (12). The T may be computed from the enthalpy and mass flow rate.

(f) Chemical reactions may be incorporated with no changes in format; the matrix of coefficients, a_{ij}, becomes nondiagonal.

(g) Following classical procedures, unequal chemical potentials across phase boundaries or membranes may be simulated by incrementing $(\Delta F^0/RT)$ for the affected species. The $(\Delta F_j^0/RT)$ may thus depend upon variables other than temperature and pressure, for example, flow rate, concentration (activity), or electrochemical potential across phase bounda-ries or membranes. Each of these phenomena have been simulated for time-invariant, steady-state systems where the activities or potential are assumed to be parameters.

(h) For these cases, either the analog or digital solution methods have been found to give stable solutions with good precision.

More generally, this procedure separates the equilibrium computation from the mass flow. With respect to the temperature and pressure profiles

of a tower, one could regard the tower as a sequence of equilibria completely determined at each plate with the over-all heat and mass flow boundary conditions, B, R, F, X_f, and Q, as forcing functions. That is, even
though, for a fixed distillate composition, these functions form a dependent
set; they do determine the pressure and temperature profiles as monotone
"step-like" functions. As such, the column may be regarded as a thermo-
dynamically bounded system open to the environment, the interior determined by the boundary conditions. Then the usual procedures of partial
differential equations, e.g., relaxation, may be indicated, where the nodes
are determined by equilibrium computation. Practically, this simulation
will be much enhanced if the pressure profile can be assumed. It is still a
conjecture that there will be a unique solution if both the pressure and temperature profiles must be computed, although the conjecture is reasonably
founded on the simpler case of constant pressure.

Finally, the natural extension of the steady-state computation procedure
of Sec. 3 is being considered. This procedure will include all m plates of
the tower in a single conceptual format of restriction equations applying to
a single Gibb's free-energy function for the entire tower. The alternative
was to have a free-energy function and restriction for each plate, the
plates being linked together either by iteration from plate to plate or by a
method from partial difference equations as above. This conceptual format
has not been implemented on the digital computer, but would be constructed
by formal compartmentalization of the matrix a_{ij} in a manner similar to
Ref. [10], a compartment for each plate. The difficult analytic problems
are to show that this nonlinear mathematical programming problem is sufficiently determined and that it will converge.

Although a distillation column may ideally be time-invariant, actually it
probably is not. Oscillatory states and transients—as well as nonideal
plate conditions—are considered more likely. It would be curious to use
this approach to analyze the system as a whole for its intrinsic natural
frequencies and transient response as in Ref. [17]. Also, it would be interesting to know whether the present procedure involving a minimization
could be incorporated into the linear programming routine for product distribution throughout the refinery.

REFERENCES

1. Robinson, C., E. R. Gilliland, Elements of Fractional Distillation,
        Revised and rewritten by E. R. Gilliland, 4th ed. McGraw-Hill,
        New York, 1949.
2. Admunsen, N. R., A. S. Pontinen, "Multicomponent Distillation Calcu-
        lations on a Large Digital Computer," Industrial and Engineering
        Chemistry, Vol. 50, May, 1958, pp. 730-736.
3. Lyster, W. N., S. L. Sullivan, Jr., et al, "Figure Distillation This New
        Way," Petroleum Refiner, Vol. 39, August, 1960, pp. 121-126.
4. Greenstadt, J., Y. Bard, B. Morse, "Multicomponent Distillation Cal-

culation on the IBM 704," Industrial and Engineering Chemistry, Vol. 50, November, 1958, pp. 1644-1647.

5. Marr, G. R., Jr., "Distillation Column Dynamics: A Suggested Mathematical Model," a publication of Electronics Associates, Inc., Princeton Computation Center, Princeton, New Jersey, May 1962.

6. Worley, C. W., "The Application of Analog Computers to Steady State Multicomponent Distillation Calculations," a publication of Electronics Associates, Inc., Princeton Computation Center, Princeton, New Jersey, 1961.

7. Rijnsdorp, J. E., A. Maarleveld, "Use of Electrical Analogues in the Study of the Dynamic Behavior and Control of Distillation Columns," Proceedings of the Joint Symposium on Instrumentation and Computation, London, 1959.

8. Computer Systems, Inc., "Multi-component Distillation," Technical Data Sheet 80-105-001.

9. White, W. B., S. M. Johnson, G. B. Dantzig, "Chemical Equilibrium in Complex Mixtures," Journal of Chemical Physics, Vol. 28, No. 5, pp. 751-755, May, 1958.

10. Dantzig, G. B., J. C. DeHaven, et al, "A Mathematical Model of the Human External Respiratory System," The RAND Corporation, Research Memorandum RM-2519, September 28, 1959.

11. DeLand, E. C., "Continuous Programming Methods on an Analog Computer," The RAND Corporation, P-1815, September 29, 1959.

12. Wolf, M. B., "The Simulation of Fractional Distillation by Mathematical Programming," a thesis, University of California, Los Angeles, May 1962.

13. DeLand, E. C., M. B. Wolf, "The Simulation of Multicomponent Distillation," The RAND Corporation, to be published.

14. DeLand, E. C., "Simulation of a Biological System on an Analog Computer," The RAND Corporation, P-2307, May 23, 1961.

15. Kose, T., "Solutions of Saddle Value Problems by Differential Equations," Econometrica, Vol. 24, January 1956, pp. 59-70.

16. deGroot, S. R., "Thermodynamics of Irreversible Processes," (North-Holland Publishing Company, Amsterdam) Interscience Publishers, Inc., New York, 1952.

17. Williams, T. J., C. L. Johnson, and A. Rose, "Transients and Equilibration Time in Continuous Distillation," Industrial and Engineering Chemistry, Vol. 48, July 1956, p. 1172.

18. Nelson, W. L., Petroleum Engineering, 3rd Ed., McGraw-Hill, New York, 1949.

19. Rossini, F. D., K. S. Pitzer, et al., Selected Values of Properties of Hydrocarbons, (Circular of the National Bureau of Standards-461). Prepared as part of the work of the American Petroleum Institute Research Project 44, U. S. Govt. Printing Office, Washington 25, D.C., November 1947.

OPTIMAL CAPACITY SCHEDULING

Arthur P. Veinott, Jr. and *Harvey M. Wagner*

ABSTRACT

The purpose of this paper is twofold: (1) to exhibit simple and efficient algorithms for solving a particular class of optimization problems, and (2) to demonstrate the wide applicability of this class, which includes, as significant models, capacity scheduling, equipment replacement and overhaul, labor force planning, and multi-commodity warehouse decisions. Of some importance is the fact that not only do our algorithms assist in solving generalized versions of these models, but in many cases, such as equipment replacement, they actually improve on computational schemes heretofore proposed for simplified versions. We have tried to avoid confusion that would be engendered by simultaneously referring to several of the models, by keeping our exposition in terms of one particular problem, capacity scheduling; we do, however, turn attention to the other interpretations of the model. The specific capacity scheduling problem is described as follows: a decision maker must contract for warehousing capacity over n time periods, the minimal capacity requirement for each period being deterministically specified. His economic problem arises because savings may possibly accrue by his undertaking long-term leasing or contracting at favorable periods of time, even though such commitments may necessitate leaving some of the capacity idle during several periods. Clearly this programming model might also apply to other types of capacity, such as transport facilities, insurance protection, and leased telephone lines.

REFERENCES

1. Veinott, A. F., Jr., and H. M. Wagner, "Optimal Capacity Scheduling," RM-3021-PR, Santa Monica: The RAND Corporation, February 1962.
2. Veinott, A. F., Jr., and H. M. Wagner, "Optimal Capacity Scheduling— I, II," Operations Research 10, 518-546 (1962).

THE PERSONNEL ASSIGNMENT PROBLEM

David J. Fitch

ABSTRACT

The personnel assignment problem was formulated and in a sense solved by Brogden in his 1946 Psychometrik paper. He stated the problem as one of devising a procedure "for maximizing efficiency of selection and assignment when each individual may be eligible for several assignments." This means assigning men in such a way as to both maximize the sum of the expected contributions and to meet the required quotas.

The paper (1) points out the fact that the Army has a large problem in assigning men and has substantial information which could help in making assignment decisions, and that the absence of a computerized model which can handle the rather complex situation means that decisions made are poorer than are necessary, (2) traces the history of the problem, (3) compares the Brogden approach where each iteration is optimal and convergence is toward a feasible solution with the simplex procedure where each iteration yields a feasible solution and convergence is toward one which is optimal, (4) outlines Dwyer's contribution for solving for the job constants needed in the Brogden solution, and (5) describes a program we have written and which is running on the IBM 1401 for assigning up to 10,000 men with as many as 100 jobs and which is able to solve this size problem in a very reasonable length of time.

An Algorithm for Integer Solutions to Linear Programs[†]

Ralph E. Gomory

INTRODUCTION

This report describes a method—based on G. B. Dantzig's simplex
algorithm—for solving linear programming problems in integers. This
method has been outlined before in [3] and [3a] and is closely related to
previous work by Dantzig, Fulkerson, and Johnson [1] and Markowitz and
Manne [2].

A general description of the method is given in Section 1. In Section 2
the main class of inequalities used in the method is derived and shown to
form a group. Section 3 gives a geometrical interpretation of the inequalities. In Section 4 some properties of the inequality group are derived. Section 5 discusses briefly ways of choosing particularly effective
inequalities. In Section 6 a variant of the basic inequalities is discussed.
Section 7 contains a description of the lexicographical dual simplex method
used in the finiteness proofs. Section 8 gives two versions of the method
and shows that they obtain the integer answer in a finite number of steps.
Section 9 contains miscellaneous comments including remarks on possible
extensions, programming experience, etc. Section 10 contains a summary
of the procedure and small worked out problems illustrating some of the
results of the preceding sections. The later sections depend only on
Sections 1 and 2, with an occasional reference to the beginning of 4.

The idea of adding inequalities to a linear programming problem to
progress toward an integer solution has already been used in [1] and [2].
Here we show how to add such inequalities automatically, and prove that
by use of a certain class of inequalities the integer solution is actually
attained.

The notation and general approach to the simplex method used
throughout is that of A. W. Tucker. Both A. W. Tucker and E. M. L.
Beale have contributed many valuable suggestions.

1. GENERAL DESCRIPTION

The integer programming problem is the problem of finding nonnegative integers x_j maximizing

†This work appeared originally as Princeton-IBM Mathematics Research
Project Technical Report Number 1, November 17, 1958.

$$z = a_{0,0} + \sum_{j=1}^{j=n} a_{0,j} (-x_j)$$

subject to the conditions

$$\sum_{j=1}^{j=n} a_{i,j} x_j \leq a_{i,0} \qquad i = 1, \ldots, m$$

The inequalities above can be replaced by equations involving additional nonnegative "slack" variables $\bar{x}_i$, and, for purposes of exposition, the whole problem will be enlarged by the addition of a series of trivial relations $x_j = -1(-x_j)$ (unit rows). This way <u>all</u> the variables involved are expressed in terms of the independent (or nonbasic) variables appearing on the right in the enlarged set

$$z = a_{0,0} + \sum_{j=1}^{j=n} a_{0,j} (-x_j)$$

$$\bar{x}_i = a_{i,0} + \sum_{j=1}^{j=n} a_{i,j} (-x_j) \qquad i = 1, \ldots, m$$

$$x_s = \sum_{j=1}^{j=n} -\delta_{s,j} (-x_j) \qquad s = 1, \ldots, n \tag{1-1}$$

Here the $\delta_{s,j} (\delta_{s,j} = 1$ if $s = j$, $\delta_{s,j} = 0$ otherwise) indicate the unit rows.

Whenever it is convenient to have a complete set of unit rows, i.e., a set with a -1 in every column including the zero-column, we can also adjoin the trivial equation $-1 = -1(1)$.

Rewriting (1-1) in matrix form gives

$$X = A^0 T^0 \tag{1-2}$$

with X the $m + n + 1$ vector with z as first component representing <u>all</u> the variables, T^0 the $n + 1$ vector with 1 as first component and other components $-t_j$ representing the variables on the right in Eq. (1-1), and A^0 the matrix of <u>all</u> constants appearing on the right in (1-1).

To solve the ordinary linear programming problem one applies George Dantzig's simple algorithm (or the dual algorithm) to Eq. (1-2) and by a series of pivot steps (which are equivalent to choosing different sets of nonbasic variables) produces a series of new equations

$$X = A^k T^k$$

in which T^k represents the variables that are nonbasic after the kth pivot step, and the A^k are transformed into their successors by right multiplication by non-singular matrices. (The dual simplex method in this form is described in more detail in Section 7.)

The solution to the ordinary linear programming problem is obtained when an A^k is obtained with the special properties

$$a_{0,j} \geq 0 \qquad j = 1, \ldots, n$$

$$a_{i,0} \geq 0 \qquad i = 1, \ldots, n + m \tag{1-3}$$

the solution then being $X = \alpha_0$ with α_0 the first column or column of constants in A^k.

We can now outline an algorithm for obtaining the solution to the integer programming problem.

The initial matrix A^0 (we will assume here that it is a matrix of integers) is transformed by the simplex method into the form (1-3). If the solution X is not in integers a new equation or equations (each representing a new inequality and its slack variable) is added to the set A^k. It will be shown that this inequality is satisfied by any nonnegative integer solution to (1-2), so that its addition does not eliminate any nonnegative integer solution to the original problem. Each additional equation introduces a single negative element into the zero column so the enlarged matrix is not in the form (1-3). The (dual) simplex method is then applied to the new matrix to bring it back to the desired form. If the new solution is still non-integer the process is repeated. During this process a new row can be dropped as soon as its slack variable becomes strictly positive. It is shown that in a finite number of steps a final matrix $A^{k'}$ is obtained with the following properties

(i) it is of the form (1-3),
(ii) all entries are integers,
(III) it contains n or less additional rows, all unit rows.

If we disregard the trivial equations represented by the additional unit rows we have the equations represented by the first $n + m + 1$ rows

$$X = \overline{A} \, T$$

where T, the vector of the current nonbasic variables, can include some of the new slack variables, and X (since the extra rows have been dropped) is simply the vector of original variables. Just as in the standard simplex method, a solution is now obtained by setting all variables in T equal to zero. Because $\overline{A}$ is an integer matrix and in form (1-3) the solution so obtained is integer, nonnegative, and maximizes z. Thus it is the solution to the integer programming problem.

We will also show that $\overline{A}$ is a unimodular transform of A^0 and that if the (readily available) inverse of this transformation is applied to the extra rows of the final matrix, the resulting rows represent the set of additional inequalities expressed as all-integer inequalities (or equations) in the original variables.

2. THE BASIC INEQUALITIES

We will now proceed to show that each matrix A^k has implicit in it a class of additional inequalities satisfied by any nonnegative integer solution to the problem.

In terms of X and T^k the equations of A^k are

$$X = A^k \, T^k \tag{2-1}$$

However, any nonnegative integer solution X', also satisfies the relation

$$X' \equiv 0 \qquad (\text{modulo } 1) \tag{2-2}$$

where we say that two numbers are equivalent ($\equiv$) modulo 1 if they differ by an integer.

From (2-1) and (2-2) we have for T', which consists of the nonbasic variables from the integer solution X',

$$0 \equiv A^k \, T' \qquad (\text{modulo } 1). \tag{2-3}$$

This gives a set of equations which T' must satisfy if it is to produce an integer X'; however, these are not the only equations that must be satisfied by T'. Any integer multiple of an equation of (2-3) produces another equation satisfied by T', and so does any sum of the equations of (2-3). If we regard any equation as being given by its row vector, we find a whole class of equations satisfied by T'. This class is the module M generated by the rows of A^k over the integers.

From some of these equations (rows) we will deduce new inequalities. Suppose that an equation of M

$$0 \equiv a_0 + \sum_{j=1}^{j=n} a_j \, (-t_j') \tag{2-4}$$

has the property that $a_j \geq 0$ for all $j \geq 1$. Then from this equation an inequality can be deduced.

Rewriting (2-4) we have

$$a_0 \equiv \sum_{j=1}^{j=n} a_j \, t_j'$$

Now the right hand side of this equation is nonnegative since everything appearing there is nonnegative. It is also equivalent to the left hand side which can be represented as the sum of an integer n_0 and a nonnegative fractional part f_0. Since the right side is nonnegative and differs from the left by an integer, it must be either f_0, $1 + f_0$, $2 + f_0$, etc. Consequently

$$f_0 \leq \sum_{j=1}^{j=n} a_j\, t_j'$$
(2-5)

This inequality can be expressed in the form of an equation by introducing the slack s

$$s = -f_0 - \sum_{j=1}^{j=n} a_j\, (-t_j')$$
(2-6)

which is the difference of the two sides of (2-5). The inequality is then expressed by the requirement that s be nonnegative. Since s is the difference of two equivalent numbers [the two sides of (2-5)] s is also an integer.

Equation (2-6) then is a new equation in nonnegative integers which must be satisfied by the T' of any integer solution and represents a new inequality. If $f_0 \neq 0$, i.e., a_0 is not an integer, the T^k of the present trial solution, $t_j = 0$, $1 \leq j \leq n$, does not satisfy the new inequality, for these t_j values, substituted in (2-6), give s a negative value $-f_0$. Equation (2-6) then represents a new equation which could be added to the equations of A^k. Since s is required to be a nonnegative integer, the new problem is still a problem in nonnegative integers.

Since there are many (in fact a countable infinity) of equations in M satisfying the condition $a_j \geq 0$, $1 \leq j \leq n$, a whole family of new inequalities could be deduced by this reasoning and applied. However we will be able to do something better. We will replace this large family by a smaller (finite) family F of inequalities. The inequalities of F will be generated from A^k in a very simple way, and every inequality of the larger family will be implied by some inequality of F.

To do this we consider the effect of decreasing by integer amounts the a_j, $j \geq 1$, that appear in (2-4). First of all, changing the a_j by integer amounts does produce equations satisfied by T' since this change can be accomplished simply by adding or subtracting the appropriate unit rows of A^k. (This change is also justifiable directly. Since the t_j' are integers, this change changes the right hand side only by an integer.) Secondly, any decrease in the a_j which leaves them still nonnegative results in a new inequality. This inequality is just like (2-5) only it involves the new smaller coefficients. It is easily seen that this new inequality is stronger and in fact implies (2-5). Any T' satisfying the new inequality automatically satisfies (2-5).

The strongest possible inequality obtainable from (2-4) by this process of coefficient reduction is

$$f_0 \leq \sum_{j=1}^{j=n} f_j\, t_j$$
(2-7)

where the f_j are the fractional parts of the a_j, each a_j being represented as an integer plus some nonnegative fractional part $f_j < 1$. We will call an inequality like (2-7), in which the coefficients cannot be reduced any more, a reduced inequality.

As before we can represent this inequality by an equation

$$s = -f_0 - \sum_{j=1}^{j=n} f_j \, (-t_j) \qquad (2\text{-}8)$$

and we will let the row vector of fractional parts

$$(f_0, \, f_1, \, f_2, \, \ldots, \, f_n)$$

stand for either (2-7) or for the equation form of the inequality.

This leads us to consider the mapping J which sends <u>any</u> row vector of M into the row vector of its fractional parts.

<u>We assert that this sends an equation satisfied by T' into an inequality satisfied by T'.</u>

To see this take <u>any</u> equation of M

$$0 \equiv a_0 + \sum_{j=1}^{j=n} a_j \, (-t_j)$$

and, if there are negative elements among the a_j, $j \ge 1$, make them nonnegative by changing the element by some integer amount. This process results in a new equation with nonnegative coefficients but with the same fractional parts. The new equation is of course still satisfied by T'. From this new equation with all nonnegative coefficients, the inequality involving the fractional parts can be derived just as above. Thus the inequality represented by the row of fractional parts is a legitimate one satisfied by T'.

Furthermore the mapping J sends an equation like (2-4), which does have nonnegative a_j into the inequality of (2-7), rather than the inequality (2-5) which is deduced directly from (2-4). Consequently we need only consider the inequalities which are represented by the fractional row vectors. Any other inequality, such as (2-5) is already implied by its reduced inequality which is its image under the mapping J.

Suppose that under J two rows R_1 and R_2 go into two rows of fractions F_1 and F_2. Then J $(R_1 + R_2)$ is easily seen to be the row vector

$$F = (f_0, \, f_1, \, \ldots, \, f_n)$$

where the components of F are obtained by adding the components of F_1 and F_2 <u>modulo 1</u>, i.e., adding them and dropping the integer parts. The same observation applies to J (nR_1) where n is some integer. The result of the mapping is the vector of fractional parts obtained by taking J (R_1), multiplying by n and reducing modulo 1.

Because of this we are able to describe the class of reduced inequalities in a very simple way. Since all the elements of M are integer combinations of the rows of A^k, all the reduced inequalities are integer combinations of the images of rows of A^k. <u>Hence all reduced inequalities are integer combinations of the fractional part rows of A^k,</u> addition and multiplication being interpreted modulo 1.

Under these rules of combination the fractional rows representing the reduced inequalities form a finite† additive group F, some of whose properties will be discussed in Section 4. The main result that will be produced is that under many circumstances F is <u>actually cyclic</u>, all the inequalities being produced as multiples modulo 1 of a single fractional row.

Also because of their origin all these inequalities have the following property: if either they, or their slack equations, are expressed in terms of the original nonbasic variables, they become all integer inequalities (or equations). Thus the original problem as expressed in terms of its original variables is being enlarged by adding more <u>all integer</u> inequalities.

(In actual machine programming so far we have produced the additional inequality by simply choosing a row of A^k with non-integer constant term and writing the new equation

$$s = -f_0 - \sum_{j=1}^{j=n} f_j \, (-t_j)$$

by simply taking the fractional parts of that row. If you are doing things in this simple way it helps noticeably to take the row with the largest fractional f_0.)

3. A GEOMETRICAL INTERPRETATION

The inequalities such as (2-5) can be given a simple geometrical interpretation. To see this most easily let us suppose that the linear programming problem was given originally in terms of integer inequalities in which we now designate the variables by Y.

$$AY \leq B$$

We will consider the convex body C that these inequalities cut out in the space of the variables Y. Confining ourselves to this space makes geometrical interpretation easier. If we assume that no s-variables have yet been added, the other variables in any solution X are simply the slacks added in converting the inequalities above into equations. Clearly each of these slacks is an integer combination of the y_j.

We are now ready to consider the origin of an inequality like (2-5). Equation (2-4) was obtained as an integer combination of the equations represented by the rows of A^k. If X is any solution, (integer or not), each

---

†F will be finite whenever the matrix A^0 is in integers or has entries which can be written as integers over some greatest common divisor. See Section 4.

right hand side of the equations (the rows of A^k) equals some variable x_i. Consequently the right hand side of (2-4) satisfies

$$a_0 + \sum_{j=1}^{j=n} a_j (-t_j) = \sum_i n_i x_i$$

where $\sum_i n_i x_i$ is some linear <u>integer</u> combination of variables x_i. Since each slack among the x_i is an integer combination of the variables y_j, we actually have by substitution

$$a_0 + \sum_{j=1}^{j=n} a_j (-t_j) = \sum_{j=1}^{j=n} n_j' y_j \tag{3-1}$$

So the right hand side of (2-5) represents a linear integer form L in the original variables Y.

The trial solution to (2-1) $t_j^k = 0$ gives a certain X and hence a Y. The Y, as is well known, is a vertex P of C.

If in Y space we consider the hyperplane $L = a_0$, (3-1) shows that the hyperplane passes through P (see Fig. 1).

If the a_j of (3-1) are all nonnegative, L takes on its maximum value at this vertex. Hence it is drawn externally tangent in Fig. 1.

If a_0 is non-integer, and hence a sum $n_0 + f_0$, $f_0 > 0$, we can push the $L = a_0$ line (hyperplane) into C as far as the line $L = n_0$ without cutting off any lattice points. (These all-integer coordinate points are dots in Fig. 1). This is because if there were a lattice point between $L = a_0$ and $L = n_0$, it would, since L is an integer form, give an integer value to L. But L has no integer value between a_0 and n_0. Thus L can safely be pushed in and $L \le n_0$ gives a new inequality. (Unless L has a common factor in its co-efficients it is actually pushed until it strikes some lattice point some-where.)

With regard to s-variables it is necessary only to note that from their construction, they are an integer combination of the variables x_i already present when they were constructed. Hence they too are integer combinations of the original Y_j, and the geometrical interpretation goes through unchanged.

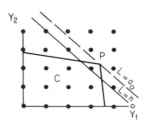

Fig.1

4. THE GROUP OF INEQUALITIES

We already know that the inequalities we need be concerned with are those formed by integer combinations of the fractional parts of the rows of A^k. The main part of this section is devoted to showing that under many circumstances the whole group F of inequalities can be obtained as multiples modulo 1 of a single row vector.

We will also show that F always contains D or less elements when D is a number defined below.[†]

All these conclusions depend on a theorem of A. W. Tucker [6] which we restate here in the (weaker)form most suitable for our immediate purposes. Let A^0 be an $m' \times n'$ matrix, $m' \geq n'$. Let P^{-1} be the inverse of an $n' \times n'$ matrix P consisting of any n' rows of A^0. Let A^k be given by

$$A^k = A^0 P^{-1}$$

Then the theorem asserts that each subdeterminant of A^k is obtained by multiplying an appropriate subdeterminant of A by $\pm |P^{-1}|$, where $|P^{-1}|$ indicates the determinant of P^{-1}.

We outline the proof of this theorem. Let β be any square submatrix of A^k. By interchanging rows and adding the appropriate unit rows from among the complete set of unit rows in A^k, β can be enlarged to a square $n' \times n'$ submatrix, β', with β a block on the main diagonal of β'. Since β' consists of n' rows of A^k it is the transform by P^{-1} of the square submatrix $M(\beta')$ consisting of the corresponding rows of A^0. Thus we have $\beta' = P^{-1} M(\beta')$ and taking determinants $|\beta'| = |P^{-1}| |M|$. But β' consists only of diagonal 1's and the block β, so $\pm |\beta| = |P^{-1}| |M|$ as desired.

The P^{-1} which transforms our original A^0 into A^k in the simplex method is the inverse of an $n + 1$ rowed matrix P consisting of rows taken from A^0, so the theorem applies in the case in which we are interested. Of course our P^{-1} is simply the product of the matrices P_i representing the individual pivot operations[‡] and each of these P_i has determinant $1/p_i$ where p_i is the pivot element. Consequently, as is well known, $|P^{-1}| = 1/p_1 p_2 \cdots p_k$. Clearly $p_1 p_2 p_3 \cdots p_k = |P|$ and since P is made up from the integer matrix A^0, $|P|$ is an integer D.

Similarly <u>any</u> subdeterminant of A^0 is an integer. Consequently Tucker's theorem, applied here, states that any subdeterminant of A^k is of the form m/D, where m is some integer (the value of a subdeterminant of A^0), and D is the (integer) product of all preceding pivots.

We will need this property not for A^k itself but rather for the matrix $F(A^k)$ whose rows are the fractional parts of the corresponding rows of A^k. However it is not hard to show that this property does carry over from A^k to $F(A^k)$.

[†]Actually it contains exactly D elements (see concluding paragraphs, this section).

[‡]This matrix is shown in Section 7.

To see this we can split A^k into the sum of two matrices U and F'. The rows of F' are all the unit rows of A^k and the fractional parts of the other rows. The U consists of zeros in the rows corresponding to unit rows of A^k and contains the integer parts of the other rows. Then

$$F' = A^k - U = A^0 \ P^{-1} - U = (A^0 - UP) \ P^{-1} = \overline{A} P^{-1}$$

$\overline{A}$ is an integer matrix since UP is, and $\overline{A}$ still contains all the rows of P unchanged; the addition of UP to A only adds zeros to these rows. Consequently P^{-1} is still the inverse of the $(n + 1) \times (n + 1)$ matrix P made up now from rows of $\overline{A}$, and the conditions for Tucker's theorem are still satisfied. So by the same reasoning as before we have all sub-determinants of F' are of the form m/D and finally, since the sub-determinants of $F(A^k)$ are included among those of F', we have the same result for the subdeterminants of $F(A^k)$.

Our problem is to find out something about the row vectors generated by integer combinations of the rows of $F(A^k)$ (components being combined modulo 1). We can now recast this problem into a familiar form. Since the elements of $F(A^k)$ (1×1 subdeterminants) are of the form m/D, multiplication by D produces a matrix $\overline{F}$ of integers. (These integers, of course, are simply the numerators that appear if all the fractions in A^k are written in the form m/D.) The subdeterminant property of $F(A^k)$ translates readily into the following property of $\overline{F}$. Every $r \times r$ subde-terminant of $\overline{F}$ is divisible by D^{r-1}.

Combining rows of $F(A^k)$ modulo 1 is clearly equivalent to combining rows of $\overline{F}$ modulo D, and our problem is to find in the group G whose elements are all possible vectors with entries from the additive group of integers modulo D, the subgroup F generated by the rows of $\overline{F}$. In order to apply the standard elementary divisor theorem we will change viewpoint slightly and regard G as a module over the integers with the basic elements

$$e_0 = (\overline{1}, \overline{0}, \ldots, \overline{0})$$
$$e_1 = (\overline{0}, \overline{1}, \ldots, \overline{0})$$

etc., with 1 the unit of the integers modulo D. Then a row $(m_0, m_1, \ldots, m_n)$ of integers represents the element

$$m_0 \ e_0 + m_1 \ e_1 + \cdots + m_n \ e_n$$

Now to find the submodule F generated by the rows of $\overline{F}$ we apply the elementary divisor theorem (van der Waerden [7]), and find that by choosing new bases in the module G and submodule F we obtain a new matrix of the form

$$\begin{pmatrix} \varepsilon_0 & & & & \\ & \varepsilon_1 & & & \\ & & \varepsilon_2 & & \\ & & & \cdot & \\ & & & & \cdot \end{pmatrix}$$

whose rows generate the submodule. As is well known, ε_i divides ε_{i+1} and ε_0 is the greatest common divisor of all the elements of $\overline{F}$. More generally $\prod\limits_{i=0}^{i=r} \varepsilon_i$ is the g.c.d. of the $(r+1) \times (r+1)$ subdeterminants of $\overline{F}$. Hence $\prod\limits_{i=0}^{i=r} \varepsilon_i$ is divisible by D^r.

Now let us consider a special case. Let us suppose that ε_0, the g.c.d. of all the elements of $\overline{F}$, is a number relatively prime to D. (Unless the numbers in the original problem had common factors or were arranged with a good deal of symmetry it seems reasonable to suppose that this g.c.d. actually will be 1 a good part of the time, so this special case is expected to be prevalent, and in fact it has been prevalent in the examples done so far.) Then, since D divides $\varepsilon_0 \varepsilon_1$ it must divide ε_1 and hence all succeeding ε_i. Since D annihilates every member of G (i.e., $Dg = 0$ for all $g \in G$) the rows containing ε_i, $i > 0$ all represent the zero element of G and consequently the module F is cyclic and is generated by the single element g represented in the new basis by $(\varepsilon_0, 0, 0, \ldots, 0)$.

Of course it is also generated by any multiple ng where n is relatively prime to D. This result can be restated to refer directly to F regarded as the group whose elements are rows of fractions of the form m/D. Here we can say that if an element of F cannot be rewritten as a row of fractions over some new common denominator smaller than D, then the multiples of this row (modulo 1) already generate all F.

This property shows up in the example at the end of this paper.

By using the fact that $\prod\limits_{i=0}^{i=r} \varepsilon_i$ is divisible by D^r we can obtain a more general statement about the rank of F.

Let p be any prime, let $\alpha_i(p)$ be the power to which the prime divides ε_i, let $\overline{\alpha}(p)$ be the power to which it divides D. Then since ε_i divides ε_{i+1}

$$\alpha_i(p) \leq \alpha_{i+1}(p)$$

and the condition which expresses divisibility by D^r is

$$\alpha_0(p) + \sum_{i=1}^{i=r} \alpha_i(p) \geq r\,\overline{\alpha}(p) \tag{4-1}$$

If R(p) is the largest i for which

$$\alpha_i(p) < \alpha(p)$$

we have the inequality on the rank R of F,

$$R \leq 1 + \max_{p \, \varepsilon \, D} R(p) \tag{4-2}$$

where $p \, \varepsilon \, D$ means that only primes dividing D are considered. Clearly once the index i exceeds $\max\limits_{p \, \varepsilon \, D} R(p)$, every prime in D appears in ε_i to as high a power as it does in D. Hence these ε_i represent the zero element, and hence (4-2).

Also if $\alpha_0(p) \geq \overline{\alpha}(p)$, then $R(p) = 0$, so we need consider only primes for which $\alpha_0(p) < \overline{\alpha}(p)$.

We next get an estimate for $R(p)$ in terms of $\alpha_0(p)$. From (4-1) and the definition of $R(p)$, we have for any $p \, \varepsilon \, D$

$$R(p) \, \overline{\alpha}(p) \leq \alpha_0(p) + \sum_{i=1}^{i=R(p)} \alpha_i(p) \leq \alpha_0(p) + R(p)[\overline{\alpha}(p) - 1] \tag{4-3}$$

Comparing the extreme right and left sides gives

$$R(p) \leq \alpha_0(p) \tag{4-4}$$

so

$$R \leq 1 + \max_{\begin{cases} p \, \varepsilon \, D \\ \alpha_0(p) < \overline{\alpha}(p) \end{cases}} \alpha_0(p) \tag{4-5}$$

Or in words, if p_i divides ε_0 to a lower power than it divides D, then the rank of the submodule is equal or less than one plus the largest of these powers.

In particular if D has no repeated primes in its factorization the rank of the submodule is again 1.

In all the cases where F is cyclic, it clearly has D elements or less. We will next show that this property of having D or less elements holds whether F is cyclic or not.

The elementary divisor theorem has been used to exhibit F as the direct sum of cyclic subgroups. If we give each subgroup the index of the corresponding ε_i, it is obvious that each is annihilated by multiplication by $D/(\varepsilon_i, D)$ where (a, b) is used to indicate the greatest common divisor of a and b. Consequently each subgroup contains at most $D/(\varepsilon_i, D)$ elements and the total number of elements then is at most

$$\prod_{i=0}^{i=r} D/(\varepsilon_i, D)$$

In this product we need consider only the ε_i up to the first one that is divisible by D (call it ε_r), since the ratios are only 1's from that point on.

Using the notation of the preceding theorem and the division property of D we have, for any prime p in D

$$R(p)\,\bar{\alpha}(p) \le \sum_{i=0}^{i=R(p)} \alpha_i(p)$$

In this range of i the $\alpha_i(p)$ are individually less than $\bar{\alpha}(p)$, while for $i > R(p)$ we have [by the definition of R(p)] $\alpha_i \ge \bar{\alpha}$. Hence

$$\sum_{i=0}^{i=r} \min\,(\alpha_i(p),\,\bar{\alpha}(p)) \ge R(p)\,\bar{\alpha}(p) + (r - R(p))\,\bar{\alpha}(p) = r\,\bar{\alpha}(p) \qquad (4\text{-}6)$$

But the sum on the left is exactly the power to which p appears in $\prod_{i=0}^{i=r} (\varepsilon_i,\,D)$. Eq. (4-6), repeated for each prime, then assets that D^r divides $\prod_{i=0}^{i=r} (\varepsilon_i,\,D)$. Consequently the order of the group F is equal or less than

$$\prod_{i=0}^{i=r} \frac{D}{(\varepsilon_i,\,D)} = \frac{D^{r+1}}{\prod_{i=0}^{i=r} (\varepsilon_i,\,D)} = \frac{D^{r+1}}{m\,D^r} = \frac{D}{m}$$

and hence is D or less.

If, as we have assumed throughout, the original problem contains a set of unit rows (i.e., it is given as an inequality problem, rather than one involving equations), this result can be improved to show that the order of F equals D. A derivation of this is sketched here. The transformation P^{-1} sets up an isomorphism between the module $M(A^0)$ generated by the rows of A^0 over the integers and the module generated by the rows of A^k. The mapping J of Section 2 then gives a homomorphism of this last module with the group F of inequalities, and hence a homomorphism of $M(A^0)$ and F. Taking into account the nature of the mapping J it follows that the elements going into zero in this correspondence are those generated by the rows of A^0 that go into unit rows in A^k. Designating the matrix of these rows by P, we have F is isomorphic to the factor module $M(A^0)/M(P)$. Since A^0 contains a complete set of unit rows, $M(A^0)$ is simply all the integer n + 1 vectors. The elementary divisor theorem can now be applied to show that the number of elements in the factor module, and hence in F, is $|P| = D$. It is assumed here that A^0 also has been enlarged whenever a new row is added to its transform A^k. Although this isomorphism still holds when there is no set of units in the original problem, and D is taken to be the product of pivots, the inequality given above is all that is obtained.

5. CHOOSING INEQUALITIES

When choosing among desired inequalities certainly the goal is to choose an inequality in which the ratios f_0/f_i are as large as possible. Geometrically this is choosing the new inequality whose equality plane intercepts the t_i axes as far as possible from the origin. Since in one inequality some of these ratios may be large and some small, there is no clear-cut comparison among inequalities except in the case where all ratios from one inequality are greater than all ratios from another. However there are many criteria which seem sensible that can be used.

First is the one that has been used in actual programming so far. Choose the largest f_0 in the matrix and use this row. The basis of this choice is largely an argument from ignorance. If you don't want to bother to look at the various f_i in the rows or generate new fractional rows by addition or multiplication, you don't know anything about them. Consequently you try to get favorable f_0/f_i ratios simply by choosing a large f_0.

This criterion is certainly subject to improvement in many ways, involving different amounts of work.

This seems to be the crudest possible criterion; at the opposite extreme one can generate a whole series of much better criteria by using the Euclidean Algorithm. The Euclidean Algorithm explicitly computes the representation of the greatest common divisor of two integers a and b as an integer combination of a and b,

$$(a, b) = ma + nb$$

and of course the g.c.d. is the smallest positive number that can be represented in this way.

The Euclidean Algorithm is especially useful when you want to predict the effect of multiplying a given row (inequality) by an integer. Suppose it is decided to multiply in such a way that f_0 is transformed into a new constant term f_0' which is as large as possible, but still less than 1. If $f_0 = h/D$ find the representation of (h, D)

$$(h, D) = mD + nh$$

Multiplication by n will then produce $f_0' = (h, D)/D$, which is the smallest possible nonzero f_0', and, as is easily seen, multiplication by $(D - n)$ will produce $1 - (h, D)/D$ which is the largest possible f_0'. If the group F is cyclic, and the initial row is one of the generators, you will have found in this way the reduced inequality with largest possible constant term.

This constant reference to a large constant term should not be taken too seriously. It may well be more important to have a row with small average f_i.

Another approach would be to ask for the inequality with deepest possible intercept with, for example, the t_i axis. This is obtained by computing

(h_i, D), where $f_i = h_i/D$. Clearly $f_i \times (D/(h_i, D)) \equiv 0$ modulo 1, so if
$f_0 \times (D/(h_i, D)) \not\equiv 0$, the deepest possible intercept is obtained by multiplying
by $D/(h_i, D)$. If $f_0 \times (D/(h_i, D)) \equiv 0$, then it is not hard to prove that the
deepest intercept is obtained by multiplying through by n_i where n_i is
given by

$$(h_i, D) = m_i D + n_i h_i$$

This produces the multiple with the smallest nonzero f_i'.

The row obtained in this way gives the deepest intercept of all possible
multiples of the original row. Again if the original row was one of the
generators of the group and the group is cyclic, the deepest possible intercept by a reduced inequality has been obtained.

It would be reasonable to choose as t_i the variable whose column is
(lexicographically) least negative. This is equivalent to choosing to make
the deepest possible intercept in the axis along which the objective
function decreases most <u>slowly</u>.

Still another approach would be to throw on several or even many new
inequalities and let the simplex method itself do the choosing by its
choice of pivots. In the course of making all the elements in the zero
column nonnegative, pivots will occur in some but not usually all new
rows. Rows in which pivots occur represent inequalities that are used,
while the rows whose constant term goes positive without a pivot in that
row, represent inequalities that have been satisfied as a result of satisfying other ones. These rows can be dropped as soon as this occurs.

Although the very crudest sort of criteria have been very successful so
far, it may well be that a criterion of the Euclidean Algorithm type used to
get deep cuts in particular directions will be needed in problems in
which D, and hence the number of reduced inequalities, becomes very
large.

6. SOME ADDITIONAL INEQUALITIES

The reasoning that produced the inequality (2-5) can be summarized
this way. The right hand side is known to be nonnegative, the left hand
side is written as $n_0 + f_0$. Since the two differ by an integer, the right
hand side is either f_0, or $1 + f_0$, etc., and hence is $\geq f_0$. Now if (i) $f_0 = 0$,
(ii) all the a_j are strictly > 0, and (iii) the current X is not an integer
solution, a stronger inequality can be deduced. Since $f_0 = 0$ is assumed,
the inequality would only say

$$0 \leq \sum_{j=1}^{j=n} a_j t_j'$$

Since all the a_j are strictly positive, the equality can be obtained only when
all the t_j' are zero. However by assumption (iii) the current X, which is
given by these values of t_j', is not an integer solution, therefore the

equality does not hold for the T' of any <u>integer</u> solution and we must
actually have

$$1 \leq \sum_{j=1}^{j=n} a_j t_j'$$ (6-1)

This inequality can then be improved by reducing the a_j as in Section 2.
However those a_j that are integers cannot be reduced to 0, as in Section 2,
because of the requirement that the coefficients be strictly positive; consequently they are reduced to 1.

This reduction can be carried out systematically as before; the only
differences from the procedure of Section 2 are in dealing with equations
in which the a_0 term is an integer. The final inequalities obtained are
simply these: all members of F having $f_0 \neq 0$ are obtained just as before,
each member of F having $f_0 = 0$ is replaced by a new vector having a 1
written wherever a 0 appeared in the original F element. These represent the new inequalities, and they are easily obtained from F.

It is important to remember that these inequalities can be used only
when the current solution is non-integer. They cannot be used, for example, to convert from a noninteger to an integer matrix after an integer
solution (0 column) is obtained. They also do not have the properties
required in either of the two convergence proofs.

It is interesting that by this method we obtain from the zero element of
F the row vector

$$(1, 1, \ldots, 1)$$

which arises when all the zeros are replaced by ones as prescribed above.
This particular inequality is the one obtained by Dantzig [4] in a very
simple and direct way at a time when only the inequalities described in
Section 2 of this paper were known.

7. LEXICOGRAPHICAL DUAL SIMPLEX METHOD

George Dantzig's simplex method is the fundamental algorithm on which
this integer algorithm is based. Since the simplex method exists in many
forms and many notations, the particular variant used in these proofs
needs to be described.

In order to facilitate proofs, a lexicographical† version of the simplex
method is used. This ensures that even in cases of degeneracy the simplex
method still goes through.

In order to facilitate adjoining or dropping equations as required in this

---

†See Dantzig, Orden, Wolfe [5].

algorithm, the dual simplex method (applied to the primal problem) will be used.†

Let us assume then that the original inequalities of a linear programming problem have been turned into equations as in Eq. (1-1) and that the unit rows have also been added as in (1-1). We then have an array in which all the variables are expressed in terms of some of them, specifically in terms of the initial collection of nonbasic variables.

Thus the linear programming problem is to maximize

$$z = a_{0,0} + \sum_{j=1}^{j=n} a_{0,j} \, (-t_j^0)$$

subject to

$$x_1 = a_{1,0} + \sum_{j=1}^{j=n} a_{1,j} \, (-t_j^0)$$
$$\vdots$$
$$x_{m+n} = a_{m+n,0} + \sum_{j=1}^{j=n} a_{m+n,j} \, (-t_j^0) \tag{7-1}$$

and the condition that all variables be nonnegative. It is to the above array which includes the unit rows that we will apply the lexicographical dual simplex method. We will refer to all coefficients on the right in Eq. (7-1) as the $a_{i,j}$.

The fundamental operation used is pivoting or Gaussian elimination on rows. Here this means that an element a_{i_0,j_0} is designated as pivot element. Then the i_0^{th} equation is used to express $t_{j_0}^0$ in terms of x_{i_0} and the t_j^0, $j \neq j_0$. This expression is then substituted for $t_{j_0}^0$ wherever $t_{j_0}^0$ appears on the right hand side of the Eqs. (7-1). The result is to make x_{i_0} nonbasic in place of $t_{j_0}^0$ while $t_{j_0}^0$ becomes a basic variable. The effect on the matrix A^0, whose elements are the $a_{i,j}$ is simply this: the j_0 column α_{j_0} is replaced by $(-1/a_{i_0,j_0}) \, \alpha_{j_0}$ then the appropriate multiples, $a_{i_0,j}$, of this new column are added to the other columns so that in the resulting matrix A^1 the $a_{i_0,j}^1$ elements are zero except for a_{i_0,j_0}^1 which is -1. In other words A^1, the matrix whose coefficients express all the variables x_i in terms of the new nonbasic set t_j^1, is simply

---

†It is also possible to dualize the problem and use the primal method on the dual problem. This has the advantage that new variables (columns) rather than new equations (rows) are added during the computation, and this is easier in the usual simplex machine codes. See Markowitz and Manne [2].

$$A^0 \; P^{-1}$$

where the $(n + 1) \times (n + 1)$ matrix P^{-1}

$$
\begin{pmatrix}
1 & & & & & & \\
& 1 & & & & & \\
-\dfrac{a_{i_0,0}}{a_{i_0,j_0}} & & 1 & -1/a_{i_0,j_0} & -\dfrac{a_{i_0,j}}{a_{i_0,j_0}} & -\dfrac{a_{i_0,n}}{a_{i_0,j_0}} & \\
& & & & 1 & & \\
& & & & & 1 & \\
& & & & & & 1
\end{pmatrix}
\qquad (7\text{-}2)
$$

is the negative of the inverse of the $(n + 1) \times (n + 1)$ matrix consisting of the i_0 row of A^0 and all the unit rows except the one involving $t^0_{j_0}$.

The dual simplex method consists of a succession of such pivot steps, resulting in a sequence of matrices A^k. With each A^k is associated a "trial solution" obtained by setting the current nonbasic variables t^k_j equal to zero, and then choosing the current basic variables, the x^k_i to satisfy the equations, i.e.,

$$x^k_i = a^k_{i,0}$$

The matrix and trial solution are usually said to be "dual feasible" if the $a_{0,j}$, $j \neq 0$ are all nonnegative. They are feasible (or primal feasible) if all the $a_{i,0}$, $i \neq 0$ are nonnegative. If A^k is both primal and dual feasible, the associated trial solution is the solution to the linear programming problem, since the primal feasible property makes the x_i values nonnegative and, since

$$z = a_{0,0} + \sum_{j=1}^{j=n} a_{0,j} \, (-t^k_j)$$

with all $a_{0,j}$ nonnegative, $z = a_{0,0}$ is the largest possible value of z.

We will depart from this nomenclature in one way due to the fact that a lexicographical method is being used. We will say that a column vector β is (lexicographically) positive ($\beta > 0$) if the first nonzero entry of β, counting from the top down, is positive. Negative is defined similarly. A column vector β is greater than another column vector β' if $\beta - \beta' > 0$.

Using positive and negative for columns in this sense we will say that a matrix is dual feasible if all columns α_j, $j \neq 0$, are positive. This notion coincides with the meaning of dual feasible given above except when some of the elements of the top row are zero.

We will assume throughout that our starting matrices A^0 are such that they can be led into dual feasible form by a succession of pivot steps. (This is always the case if, for example, the convex body cut out by the original inequalities is bounded.) It is also worth noting that, since the transforming matrices P^{-1} are nonsingular and A^0, because of the unit rows, is of maximal rank, no all zero columns can appear in any A^k.

Once a dual feasible form is achieved, the dual simplex method proceeds to obtain the solution in the following way: choose some row i_0 ($i_0 \neq 0$) with $a_{i_0,0}$ negative. Then consider the columns α_j for which $(1/a_{i_0,j}) \alpha_j$ is negative, and select from these that column which is the least negative. Then pivot on a_{i_0,j_0}. It is easily verified that this pivot step results in a new matrix A' in which the columns are still positive and since

$$-(a_{i_0,0} /a_{i_0,j_0}) \, \alpha_{j_0}$$

(a negative vector) has been added to α_0, it follows that $\alpha_0' < \alpha_0$.

A succession of such steps results in a succession of strictly decreasing α_0^k. There can only be a finite number of these since there are only a finite number of possible sets of nonbasic variables, and any choice uniquely determines an α_0^k. Consequently the process must stop. This can happen either if there are no negative elements in the current α_0^k, or if there is a negative $a_{i_0,0}^k$ but no negative columns $(1/a_{i_0,j}) \alpha_j^k$. In the first case the solution has been obtained, in the second it is easily seen that the negative value $a_{i_0,0}^k$ is the largest value that the variable x_{i_0} can attain, and consequently no solution in nonnegative numbers exists.

8. FINITENESS PROOFS

In these proofs we will use the lexicographical dual simplex method described in Section 7. It is not implied that this simplex method need be used in practice or that it is necessary to the proof. It is simply that its use in the proof has reduced the original rather long and tedious proofs to relatively simple ones.

Let us assume then that we have obtained a (lexicographically) dual feasible solution, and that in all succeeding pivot steps we choose pivot elements in accordance with the lexicographical dual simplex method. After each pivot then we obtain a new "trial solution" α_0^{k+1} which is strictly lexicographically smaller than its predecessor α_0^k.

We will also assume that some <u>lower</u> bound is known for the value of z. That is we assume it is known that if an integer solution exists, it gives a z-value $\geq$ some known (possibly large negative) M. This is always the case if we are dealing with a bounded convex body.

First Method of Proof

Let us assume that we adopt the following procedure. Proceed with the simplex method until an optimal solution is obtained; if this solution $\alpha_0^k = (a_{0,0}^k, a_{1,0}^k, \ldots, a_{m+n,0}^k)$ is not in integers, let $a_{i_0,0}^k$ be the first noninteger component. Then introduce the new equation

$$s = -f^k_{i_0,0} - \sum_{j=1}^{j=n} f^k_{i_0,j} \, (-t^k_j)$$

and adjoin it to the bottom of the existing set. (We know from Section 2 that any nonnegative integer solution of the original set of equations satisfies the new set and gives the new variable s a nonnegative integer value.)

We now apply the dual simplex method to obtain a new feasible maximum, for the $-f^k_{i_0,0}$ term has introduced a negative element into the zero column. This new application of the simplex method either gives a new optimal solution or indicates that no feasible solution exists. In this second case we know that no solution to the original problem exists in integers. In the first case if the new maximum is still noninteger, we repeat the process. If remaximization is always possible we will show that an integer solution is attained in a finite number of repetitions.

Let us suppose the contrary. Then the process would produce an infinite sequence of trial solutions

$$\alpha^k_0 > \alpha^{k+1}_0 > \alpha^{k+2}_0 > \cdots$$

We will consider only the first $m + n + 1$ components of these trial solutions. Since the trial solutions are monotone decreasing; the successive first components $a^k_{0,0}$ are also monotone decreasing, since we assume that z has a lower bound M, so do the $a^k_{0,0}$ or else clearly no integer solution exists. Let $n_{0,0}$ be the largest integer such that $n_{0,0} \le a^k_{0,0}$ for all k. We will first show that $a^k_{0,0} = n_{0,0}$ for all $k \ge$ some k_0.

From the definition of $n_{0,0}$ it follows that after a certain point the $a^k_{0,0}$ can all be written as $n_{0,0} + f^k_{0,0}$ with $f^k_{0,0} < 1$. A finite number of pivot steps after this point is reached, a new maximum must be obtained. If k' is the index at this point and $f^{k'}_{0,0}$ is not zero, our procedure will select the fractional parts of the 0-row to form the new equation

$$s = -f^{k'}_{0,0} - \sum_{j=1}^{j=n} f^{k'}_{0,j} \, (-t_j)$$

The dual simplex method next selects a pivot element from this new row. If the j_0 column is selected, the new value of z after the pivot is

$$a^{k'+1}_{0,0} = a^{k'}_{0,0} - \frac{a^{k'}_{0,j_0} f^{k'}_{0,0}}{f^{k'}_{0,j_0}}$$

Since all the $a^{k'}_{0,j}$ are nonnegative at an optimum point we have

$$a^{k'}_{0,j_0} \ge f^{k'}_{0,j_0}$$

and hence

$$a_{0,0}^{k'+1} \leq a_{0,0}^{k'} - f_{0,0}^{k'} = n_{0,0}$$

so for k equal or greater than $k' + 1$, $a_{0,0}^{k} = n_{0,0}$.

Since the first component is now fixed at $n_{0,0}$, the second components of the trial solutions are now monotone decreasing and bounded from below by zero for $k > k' + 1$. (If the component fell below zero, reoptimization would then fail to be possible.)

We can now repeat word for word the argument given above for the first component by simply changing the first subscript from 0 to 1. This shows that the second component attains and remains at some integer value. The only point that requires any explanation is the reason why $a_{1,j_0}^{k''}$ should be nonnegative. $a_{1,j_0}^{k''}$ is nonnegative because the first entry in the j_0 column is 0, and, since the column itself is (lexicographically) positive, the second element, which is $a_{1,j_0}^{k''}$, could not be negative. The top element is 0, because otherwise the pivot step would actually strictly decrease $a_{0,0}^{k''}$ below its already attained minimum value $n_{0,0}$.

Just as above then we can conclude that the second component attains some integer value and then remains at it. This argument is then repeated for all the original $m + n + 1$ variables. This gives the integer solution.

What has been shown of course is that an integer 0-column α_0^k is eventually attained. To obtain an all-integer matrix you simply continue. Take any row of the matrix that still contains fractions, and use the fractional parts as a new relation as before. Of course now the f_0 term will be zero. Consequently the next pivot step will leave all the values in the zero column unchanged and we are still at the same optimum point and in optimal form. If fractions still remain anywhere, the process is repeated. Since the D number which forms the denominator of all the fractions (as discussed in Section 4) is the product of all pivots, and these pivot elements are now all proper fractions, $|D|$ constantly decreases. Since $|D|$ is an integer and $\neq 0$, either $|D|$ becomes 1, or else the process stops because the matrix has no fractions in it. Actually these two cases coincide; if the matrix is all integer, $|D|$ is necessarily 1. To see this remember that the transforming matrix P^{-1} has determinant $1/D$. The inverse of this transformation (i.e., P) sends $n + 1$ rows of A^k into the unit rows of A^0. Hence P is the (negative) inverse of of a square submatrix of A^k. If A^k is all integer, this implies that the determinant of P is $1/D_2$ where D_2, the determinant of the square matrix in question, is an integer. Since the determinant of P also equals D, it follows that $D = D_2 = \pm 1$. Hence the final matrix is related to the initial one by a <u>unimodular</u> transformation.

The procedure given above can be greatly modified without changing the proof. For example it is not necessary to choose the new equation at each optimum point by the rule given above. If this rule of choice is applied every tenth time or every hundredth time the proof still goes through and you are free to add any new relation or relations whatsoever at all the other optimum points. Another way to relax the choice restriction is to use, instead of the fractional parts of the i_0 row, any multiple m of the row of fractional parts that has the property $mf_{i_0,0} < 1$. This new relation provides a stronger inequality and is easily seen to have the same effect on the next trial solution as does the inequality used in the proof.

This proof, as well as the next one, goes through unchanged if the row representing a new variable (s variable) is dropped as soon as the s variable involved becomes positive, or more exactly, as soon as the s variable leaves the nonbasic set and becomes basic. Dropping such a row does not affect the lexicographical positiveness of any column as this is determined by the topmost element, and a column with nothing but zeros above the s-row cannot occur (see Section 7).

Since there can be at most n nonbasic s variables, the number of additional rows need never exceed n + 1.

Dropping the extra inequality is allowable, of course, as only the original inequalities need be satisfied to give a solution.

Second Method of Proof

This proof will show the finiteness of a different sort of process, one in which there is no distinct repetition of optimization, new relation, re-optimization, etc., but rather a process in which (at least up to a certain point) the adding of new equations and pivot steps of the dual simplex method can be interspersed at random.

If it is assumed that the first step is to obtain a dual feasible matrix, the remaining choices to be made in carrying out the algorithm can be summarized in this way.

If the matrix is both nonoptimal and contains fractions, one can either make a step of the dual simplex method, or first choose and add some reduced inequality, and then make a pivot in the row of the new inequality. If the matrix is in integers but not optimal, one must make some step of the dual simplex method. If the matrix is optimal but not all in integers, one must choose some new reduced inequality, add it, and pivot on its row. If the matrix is in integers and optimal, the problem ends and no further steps are made.

The sequence of choices results in a sequence of trial solutions. In order to have an infinite sequence of trial solutions α_0^k, let us assume that after an integer optimal matrix is achieved, the corresponding trial solution is simply repeated in the sequence from that point on.

In the following, D^k indicates the value of D after the kth pivot.

We can now assert that <u>if an integer solution exists, any way of making the above choices which ensures that $\lim_{k \to \infty} \inf |D^k| < \infty$ will actually attain the solution (in fact an integer optimal matrix) in a finite number of steps</u>.

An example of such a procedure would be to make all the choices quite freely until $|D^k|$ rises above some predetermined value N_0 (if it ever does). With $|D| \neq 1$ the matrix can not be all integer (this is easy to prove) so it is possible to add a new relation. Add any new relation and pivot on its row thus producing a new D^{k+1} with $|D^{k+1}| = f|D^k|$ with f the pivot element (of course $|f| < 1$). If D^{k+1} is still greater than N_0 repeat the process. Eventually the D value will decrease below N_0 and then choices can be made quite freely again. Clearly this process provides a $\liminf_{k \to \infty} |D^k| \leq N_0 < \infty$.

To proceed with the proof, let us suppose that we have a procedure which guarantees a sequence of matrices with $\liminf_{k \to \infty} |D^k| < \alpha$. Since the D^k are integers, there is a value M which is attained by D^k for an infinity of values of k. If we denote these k by k_i, then we have a decreasing subsequence of trial solutions

$$\alpha_0^{k_1} \geq \alpha_0^{k_2} \cdots$$

and all entries in these vectors are of the form m/M with m integer. Since we assume the existence of an integer solution, the first components are bounded from below, decrease, and hence have a limit point. Since they are all rational numbers with denominator M, they can have a limit point only if they reach some final value and then repeat it. Consequently the first component attains and remains at some fixed value for k_i greater than some fixed k_0. The second component must be monotone decreasing from this point on. It is ≥ 0 since a negative value would imply that the problem now has no feasible solutions (further dual simplex steps can only make it more negative), which would in turn imply that the original problem has no integer solution, contrary to assumption. Consequently the second component has a limit value which it too attains. This argument is repeated for all components, so finally the $\alpha_0^{k_i}$ reach some final vector α which is then repeated. The only step of the algorithm which does not cause a strict decrease in the α_0^k is the addition of a reduced inequality with $f_0 = 0$ followed by a pivot on this row. A finite sequence of these steps will produce an integer matrix. Since there is no further decrease in α at any later step, this must be an integer optimal matrix. This ends the proof.

Unlike the first proof this one assumes that an integer solution exists and shows that the process finds that solution in a finite number of steps. The first proof either found a solution or else showed that none existed. If the second procedure is applied just as described to a problem not having an integer solution, this fact is not guaranteed to become apparent in any obvious way. This situation can be remedied if the procedure adopted provides for some periodic reoptimization (obtaining a primal feasible solution). Then at any point the impossibility of reoptimization indicates nonexistence of a solution.

A particularly intriguing procedure of this type was suggested by E. M. L. Beale and stimulated the search for the above finiteness proof. In this procedure N_0 is taken to be 1; thus the matrix is constantly being returned to all integer form.

9. MISCELLANEOUS COMMENTS

Computational Experience

This is largely limited to small problems. Many small problems, similar to those in Section 10, have been done by hand with very encouraging results. The method was programmed on an E101 computer and the results, again on small problems, were also encouraging. During a stay at RAND a FORTRAN I program [8] was written for the RAND 704. Since only single precision arithmetic was available in FORTRAN I, the method was programmed exactly, numerators and the denominator (D) being stored separately. (This happens to be very easy to do in these integer problems, and is shown in one example in Section 10.) This numerical approach avoids dealing with round-off error. However it has the drawback that the program fails if some of the numbers involved get too large and overflow. Eight problems were run with the following results:

E	5	5	7	7	12	12	15	15
P	6	4	6	9	8	1	34	20

Here E is the number of inequalities in the original linear programming problem, and P is the number of pivots required <u>after</u> reaching the original noninteger maximum by the simplex method. The number of variables involved in the inequalities was approximately the same as the number of inequalities in each case. Of course the number of variables was later approximately doubled when the inequalities were turned into equations by the addition of slack variables.

This experimental program involved the crudest possible criterion (the max $f_{i,0}$ criterion) and added inequalities one at a time. Only small D numbers (in the hundreds at most) were encountered in these eight problems. One other fifteen inequality problem failed when the run ended in an overflow.

Some Direct Extensions

Extension of the method to the case where there are equations in the original problem in place of inequalities is straightforward. So is the extension to the case where some of the variables are unrestricted in sign. Also the inequalities of Section 2 are still valid if the starting matrix is not a matrix of integers, as no use was made of this face in Section 2. The main point of having all integer inequalities was to assure that the slack variables are integers. If this is assumed separately, or if the problem is an equation problem with no slacks, the integer matrix is not needed.

An example of a problem in which some of the variables are unrestricted in sign is the problem of finding the greatest common divisor of 2 (or more) integers a_i. Of course the g.c.d. is the smallest nonzero integer that can be expressed as an integer combination of the numbers involved. Hence it is the solution to the problem.

$$\text{minimize } z = a_1 x_1 + \cdots + a_n x_n \text{ subject to } z \geq 1$$

The x_i are integers and the only variable restricted in sign is the slack introduced by the inequality. If the method of this report is applied here it solves the problem by doing the Euclidean Algorithm. There are various forms of the Euclidean Algorithm and they correspond to the various ways the method can be applied when unrestricted variables are present.

An example of a problem involving only unrestricted variables is the problem of solving a set of linear diophantine equations, i.e., of obtaining all integer solutions to a set of linear equations with no maximum problem and no restriction in sign on the variables involved. The method of this report also solves this problem in a very simple and rapid way.

It is interesting that in this last application the method is still successful (for purely algebraic reasons) even though there are no sign restricted variables present, and hence an interpretation in terms of additional inequalities, or cutting off parts of a convex body, is completely inapplicable.

In a different direction is the question of solving not one integer programming problem, but a family of such problems. Here we can make use of the fact that the final matrix is a unimodular transform of the original one, for if an integer change is made in the right hand sides of the original inequality, the result on the final matrix is also an integer change. If the right hand sides are decreased by an integer step, the various extra inequalities deduced during the computation are still valid; thus the s variables are still required to be nonnegative. The effect of such a decrease on the final matrix is merely to add certain of the columns to the zero column. If the elements of the zero column remain nonnegative, the solution to the new problem has been obtained. If some go negative, some additional steps are required. This is entirely analogous to the usual notion of parametric programming.

The Mixed Problem

This is the problem in which some, but not all, of the variables involved are required to be integers. This is not a direct extension. However extensions to this case have been made, first by Beale [9] and later, more directly, by Gomory [10]. Both methods are almost completely computationally untested.

Finiteness Proofs

Although much work remains to be done on the material in all sections of this report, the situation seems especially unsatisfactory in Section 8. The finiteness proofs given there allow a good deal of choice, especially if the choices of inequality that they dictate are made only occasionally.

However there is no proof that if the choices described in Section 5 are made <u>all</u> the time, the integer answer will be obtained; yet these choices seem to be the desirable ones from the point of view of making rapid progress and have been used on the machine programs. Actually in all problems done so far, <u>any</u> method involving the reduced inequalities has worked. It would be desirable to know whether or not this is true in general.

Applications

Examples of combinatorial problems reducible to integer programming problems were given by Dantzig [11]. In another direction the fact that nonconvex problems are reducible to (usually mixed) integer programming problems has been known at RAND for some time. A device involving a nonconvex objective function was given by Markowitz and Manne [2], and the subject is first treated systematically by Dantzig [12] in a paper containing many interesting applications.

Round-off Error

Most of the method does not appear to pose problems of round-off error very different from those encountered in the usual simplex method. It seems that the round-off problems arising in those features that <u>are</u> different from the simplex method can be overcome.

10. EXAMPLES

In these examples we will not require a lexicographical simplex method. We will follow A. W. Tucker in using a "condensed" form and so will not include unit rows (see the examples).

The simplex rule for choice of pivot element in both primal and dual methods can be summarized as follows: if the problem is primal [dual] feasible, i.e., $a_{i,0} \geq 0$, $i \geq 1$ [$a_{0,j} \geq 0, j \geq 1$], choose a column j_0 [a row i_0] with first element a_{0,j_0} [$a_{i_0,0}$] negative. From among the positive [negative] elements in this column [row] select the one for which the ratio $a_{i,0}/a_{i,j_0}$ [$a_{0,j}/a_{i_0,j}$] attains its least absolute value. This is the pivot element element a_{i_0}, j_0.

The effect of pivoting on pivot element a_{i_0,j_0} can be summarized as follows: a new array is obtained in which the variables at the end of the i_0 row and top of the j_0 column have been exchanged, and in which the new coefficients $a'_{i,j}$ are given by

$$a'_{i,j} = a_{i,j} - a_{i_0,j}\, a_{i,j_0}/a_{i_0,j_0} \qquad i \neq i_0,\ j \neq j_0$$

$$a'_{i_0,j} = a_{i_0,j}/a_{i_0,j_0} \qquad j \neq j_0$$

$$a'_{i,j_0} = -a_{i,j_0}/a_{i,j_0} \qquad i \neq i_0$$

$$a'_{i_0,j_0} = 1/a_{i_0,j_0}$$

When by a succession of pivots an array is obtained which is both primal and dual feasible (and hence optimal), a new equation (or equations) representing a new inequality is added. This equation is simply

$$s = -f_0 - \sum_{j=1}^{j=n} f_j (-t_j)$$

where the f_j are the fractional parts from some row and the t_j are the current nonbasic variables, or are the fractional parts obtained by combining (modulo 1) several of the fractional part rows, or multiplying a row by an integer. For rules of choice see Section 5. Here by fractional part f of an element a, we mean the number obtained if an element a is written as n + f with n an integer and $0 \le f < 1$.

After such an equation is added, the array is not primal feasible, so further steps of the simplex method (usually the dual method) are made until the array is again optimal. This process is then repeated until an integer answer (integer column of constants) or an all integer matrix (whichever is desired) is obtained.

S variables can be dropped whenever they emerge from the nonbasic set, and of course many variations on the above procedure are possible.

In order to have a fixed procedure for these examples, inequalities will be added one at a time and the fractional parts of some chosen row in the matrix will be used directly. The row will be chosen as follows: select the column with the smallest entry in the top row (min $a_{0,j}$, $j \ge 1$). Then select the row having the smallest fractional part in that column. (An all integer row is not considered.) This choice of row is an attempt to get a deep "cut" in the direction of least rapid decrease of z. The row used is marked by an arrow in each case.

The pivot element is marked by an asterisk.

The entire inequality group will be listed for some arrays.

Example 1.

Maximize $z = 4x_1 + 5x_2 + x_3$

Subject to: $3x_1 + 2x_2 \qquad \le 10$

$\qquad\qquad x_1 + 4x_2 \qquad \le 11$

$\qquad\qquad 3x_1 + 3x_2 + x_3 \le 13$

Introduce slack variables $\bar{x}_1, \bar{x}_2, \bar{x}_3$

Starting array, primal feasible.

		1	$-x_1$	$-x_2$	$-x_3$
	z =	0	−4	−5	−1
	$\bar{x}_1$ =	10	3	2	0
|D| = 1	$\bar{x}_2$ =	11	1	4*	0
	$\bar{x}_3$ =	13	3	3	1

	1	$-x_1$	$-\bar{x}_2$	$-x_3$
z =	$13\frac{3}{4}$	$-2\frac{3}{4}$	$1\frac{1}{4}$	-1
$\bar{x}_1 =$	$4\frac{2}{4}$	$2\frac{2}{4}*$	$-\frac{2}{4}$	0
$x_2 =$	$2\frac{3}{4}$	$\frac{1}{4}$	$\frac{1}{4}$	0
$\bar{x}_3 =$	$4\frac{3}{4}$	$2\frac{1}{4}$	$-\frac{3}{4}$	1

$|D| = 4 \times 1 = 4$

	1	$-\bar{x}_1$	$-\bar{x}_2$	$-x_3$
z =	$18\frac{7}{10}$	$1\frac{1}{10}$	$\frac{7}{10}$	-1
$x_1 =$	$1\frac{8}{10}$	$\frac{4}{10}$	$-\frac{2}{10}$	0
$x_2 =$	$2\frac{3}{10}$	$-\frac{1}{10}$	$\frac{3}{10}$	0
$\bar{x}_3 =$	$\frac{7}{10}$	$-\frac{9}{10}$	$-\frac{3}{10}$	$1*$

$|D| = 4 \times 2\frac{2}{4} = 10$

$|D| = 10$. Optimal

Solution:

$$z = 19\frac{4}{10}, \quad x_1 = 1\frac{8}{10}$$

$$x_2 = 2\frac{3}{10}, \quad x_3 = \frac{7}{10}$$

Inequality Group F:

1/10 (3, 9, 3, 0) (8, 4, 8, 0)
$x_2 \equiv$ (6, 8, 6, 0) (1, 3, 1, 0)
$x_3 \equiv$ (9, 7, 9, 0) (4, 2, 4, 0)
$\vdots$ (2, 6, 2, 0) (7, 1, 7, 0)
$\vdots$ (5, 5, 5, 0) (0, 0, 0, 0)

	1	$-\bar{x}_1$	$-\bar{x}_2$	$-\bar{x}_3$
z =	$19\frac{4}{10}$	$\frac{2}{10}$	$\frac{4}{10}$	1
$x_1 =$	$1\frac{8}{10}$	$\frac{4}{10}$	$-\frac{2}{10}$	0
$x_2 =$	$2\frac{3}{10}$	$-\frac{1}{10}$	$\frac{3}{10}$	0
$x_3 =$	$\frac{7}{10}$	$-\frac{9}{10}$	$-\frac{3}{10}$	1
$s_1 =$	$-\frac{7}{10}$	$-\frac{1}{10}$	$-\frac{7}{10}*$	0

In the original coordinates the inequality $s_1 \geq 0$ becomes the new integer inequality:

$$-\frac{7}{10} + \frac{1}{10}(10 - 3x_1 - 2x_2) + \frac{7}{10}(11 - x_1 - 4x_2) \geq 0$$

or

$$x_1 + 3x_2 \leq 8$$

$|D| = 7$. Optimal $\longrightarrow$

Integer solution is:

$z = 19$ $x_1 = 2$

$x_2 = 2$ $x_3 = 1$

$F: \dfrac{1}{7}$ (0, 1, 4, 0) (0, 5, 6, 0)
  (0, 2, 1, 0) (0, 6, 3, 0)
  (0, 3, 5, 0) (0, 0, 0, 0)
  (0, 4, 2, 0)

	1	$-\bar{x}_1$	$-s_1$	$-\bar{x}_3$
$z =$	19	$\dfrac{1}{7}$	$\dfrac{4}{7}$	1
$x_1 =$	2	$\dfrac{3}{7}$	$-\dfrac{2}{7}$	0
$x_2 =$	2	$-\dfrac{1}{7}$	$\dfrac{3}{7}$	0
$x_3 =$	1	$-\dfrac{6}{7}$	$-\dfrac{3}{7}$	1
$\bar{x}_2 =$	1	$\dfrac{1}{7}$	$-1\dfrac{3}{7}$	0
$s_2 =$	0	$-\dfrac{1}{7}^*$	$-\dfrac{4}{7}$	0

$|D| = 1$. Integer matrix

	1	$-s_2$	$-s_1$	$-\bar{x}_3$
$z =$	19	1	0	1
$x_1 =$	2	3	-2	0
$x_2 =$	2	-1	1	0
$x_3 =$	1	-6	3	1
$\bar{x}_2 =$	1	1	-2	0
$\bar{x}_1 =$	0	-7	4	0

Example 2.

Maximize $z = 3x_1 - x_2$

Subject to: $3x_1 - 2x_2 \leq 3$

$-5x_1 - 4x_2 \leq -10$

$2x_1 + x_2 \leq 5$

$|D| = 1$

	1	$-x_1$	$-x_2$
$z =$	0	-3	1
$\bar{x}_1 =$	3	3^*	-2
$\bar{x}_2 =$	-10	-5	-4
$\bar{x}_3 =$	5	2	1

	1	$-\bar{x}_1$	$-x_2$
z =	3	1	-1
$x_1 =$	1	$\frac{1}{3}$	$-\frac{2}{3}$
$\bar{x}_2 =$	-5	$\frac{5}{3}$	$-7\frac{1}{3}$
$\bar{x}_3 =$	3	$-\frac{2}{3}$	$2\frac{1}{3}{}^{*}$

$|D| = 3$

F: $\frac{1}{3}$ (0, 1, 1)
       (0, 2, 2)
       (0, 0, 0)

	1	$-\bar{x}_1$	$-\bar{x}_3$
z =	$4\frac{2}{7}$	$\frac{5}{7}$	$\frac{3}{7}$
$x_1 =$	$1\frac{6}{7}$	$\frac{1}{7}$	$\frac{2}{7}$
$\bar{x}_2 =$	$4\frac{3}{7}$	$-\frac{3}{7}$	$3\frac{1}{7}$
$x_2 =$	$1\frac{2}{7}$	$-\frac{2}{7}$	$\frac{3}{7}$
$s_1 =$	$-\frac{6}{7}$	$-\frac{1}{7}$	$-\frac{2}{7}{}^{*}$

$|D| = 7.$ Optimal

Solution:

$z = 4\frac{2}{7}$ $x_1 = 1\frac{6}{7}$ $x_2 = 1\frac{2}{7}$

F: $\frac{1}{7}$ (6, 1, 2) (2, 5, 3)
       (5, 2, 4) (1, 6, 5)
       (4, 3, 6) (0, 0, 0)
       (3, 4, 1)

$\longrightarrow$

	1	$-\bar{x}_1$	$-s_1$
z =	3	$\frac{1}{2}$	$\frac{3}{2}$
$x_1 =$	1	0	1
$\bar{x}_2 =$	-5	-2^{*}	11
$x_2 =$	0	$-\frac{1}{2}$	$\frac{3}{2}$
$\bar{x}_3 =$	3	$\frac{1}{2}$	$-\frac{7}{2}$

$|D| = 2.$ Dual feasible

F: $\frac{1}{2}$ (0, 1, 1)
       (0, 0, 0)

	1	$-\bar{x}_2$	$-s_1$
$z =$	$\frac{7}{4}$	$\frac{1}{4}$	$4\frac{1}{4}$
$x_1 =$	1	0	1
$\bar{x}_1 =$	$2\frac{2}{4}$	$-\frac{2}{4}$	$-5\frac{2}{4}$
$x_2 =$	$1\frac{1}{4}$	$-\frac{1}{4}$	$-\frac{5}{4}$
$\bar{x}_3 =$	$1\frac{3}{4}$	$\frac{1}{4}$	$-\frac{3}{4}$
$\bar{s}_2 =$	$-\frac{3}{4}$	$-\frac{1}{4}^*$	$-\frac{1}{4}$

$|D| = 4.$ Optimal

F: $\frac{1}{4}$ (3, 1, 1)
  (2, 2, 2)
  (1, 3, 3)
  (0, 0, 0)

	1	$-s_2$	$-s_1$
$z =$	1	1	4
$x_1 =$	1	0	1
$\bar{x}_1 =$	4	2	-5
$x_2 =$	2	1	-1
$\bar{x}_3 =$	1	-1	-1
$\bar{x}_2 =$	3	-4	1

$|D| = 1.$ Optimal

Integer Matrix

Solution:

$z = 1 \quad x_1 = 1 \quad x_2 = 2$

Example 3.

This problem illustrates one way of doing these computations in integers throughout. Each $a_{i,j}$ is written as $A_{i,j}/|D|$ with $A_{i,j}$ (the numerator) an integer. Since the common D is known, only the $A_{i,j}$ are written in each array. The rules for pivot choice are the same as before and the $A_{i,j}$ can be used in place of the $a_{i,j}$ as only ratios are involved. Pivoting on A_{i_0,j_0} produces new $A'_{i,j}$ and a new D' as follows:

$$|D'| = |A_{i_0,j_0}|$$
$$A'_{i,j} = (A_{i,j} A_{i_0,j_0} - A_{i_0,j} A_{i,j_0})/\pm|D| \qquad i \neq i_0, \; j \neq j_0$$
$$A'_{i_0,j} = \pm A_{i_0,j} \qquad j \neq j_0$$
$$A'_{i,j_0} = \pm(-A_{i,j_0}) \qquad i \neq i_0$$
$$A'_{i_0,j_0} = \pm|D|,$$

the plus sign being used if A_{i_0,j_0} is positive, the minus if it is negative. Since all 2×2 subdeterminants of the array of $A_{i,j}$ are divisible by D, the division involved in getting $A'_{i,j}$ always produces an integer.

Maximize $z = x_1 + 2x_2 + 3x_3 + x_4 + x_5$

Subject to: $x_1 \qquad + 4x_3 + 2x_4 + x_5 \leq 41$

$\qquad 4x_1 + 3x_2 + x_3 - 4x_4 - x_5 \leq 47$

$|D| = 1$

Primal Feasible

	1	$-x_1$	$-x_2$	$-x_3$	$-x_4$	$-x_5$
$z =$	0	−1	−2	−3	−1	−1
$\overline{x}_1 =$	41	1	0	4	2	1*
$\overline{x}_2 =$	47	4	3	1	−4	−1

$|D| = 1$

	1	$-x_1$	$-x_2$	$-x_3$	$-x_4$	$-\overline{x}_1$
$z =$	41	0	−2	1	1	1
$x_5 =$	41	1	0	4	2	1
$\overline{x}_2 =$	88	5	3*	5	−2	1

$|D| = 3$

	1	$-x_1$	$-\overline{x}_2$	$-x_3$	$-x_4$	$-\overline{x}_1$
$z =$	299	10	2	13	−1	5
$x_5 =$	123	3	0	12	6*	3
$x_2 =$	88	5	1	5	−2	1

$|D| = 6$. Optimal

Solution:

$z = 106\frac{1}{2}$　$x_1 = 0$　$x_2 = 43$

$x_3 = 0$　$x_4 = 20\frac{1}{2}$　$x_5 = 0$

$\longrightarrow$

	1	$-x_1$	$-\overline{x}_2$	$-x_3$	$-x_5$	$-\overline{x}_1$
$z =$	639	21	4	30	1	11
$x_4 =$	123	3	0	12	3	3
$x_2 =$	258	12	2	18	2	4
$s_1 =$	−3	−3	−4	0	−1*	−5

$F: \frac{1}{6}$　(3, 3, 4, 0, 1, 5)　(0, 0, 4, 0, 4, 2)

$\qquad$ (0, 0, 2, 0, 2, 4)　(3, 3, 2, 0, 5, 1)

$\qquad$ (3, 3, 0, 0, 3, 3)　(0, 0, 0, 0, 0, 0)

Additional inequalities:

$\frac{1}{6}$　(6, 6, 2, 6, 2, 4)　(6, 6, 4, 6, 4, 2)　(6, 6, 6, 6, 6, 6)

			1	$-x_1$	$-\overline{x}_2$	$-x_3$	$-s_1$	$-\overline{x}_1$
$\|D\| = 1$. Optimal	$z =$		106	3	0	5	1	1
Integer Matrix	$x_4 =$		19	-1	-2	2	3	-2
$z = 106 \quad x_1 = 0 \quad x_2 = 42$	$x_2 =$		42	1	-1	3	2	-1
$x_3 = 0 \quad x_4 = 19 \quad x_5 = 3$	$x_5 =$		3	3	4	0	-6	5

REFERENCES

1. Dantzig, G., R. Fulkerson, and S. Johnson, "Solution of a Large Scale Traveling Salesman Problem," Journal of the Operations Research Society of America, Vol. 2, No. 4, 1954.
2. Markowitz, Harry M., and Alan S. Manne, "On the Solution of Discrete Programming Problems," Econometrica, Vol. 25, No. 1, 1957.
3. Gomory, Ralph E., "Outline of an Algorithm for Integer Solutions to Linear Programs," Bulletin of the American Mathematical Society, Vol. 64, No. 5, 1958.
3a. ——— "Solving Linear Programming Problems in Integers," Combinatorial Analysis, R. Bellman and M. Hall (ed.), Proceedings of Symposia in Applied Mathematics 10, American Mathematical Society, 1960.
4. Dantzig, George B., "Notes on Linear Programming: Part XLVII Solving Linear Programs in Integers," RAND Corporation, RM-2209, July 11, 1958.
5. ———, Alex Orden, and Philip Wolfe, "The Generalized Simplex Method for Minimizing a Linear Form under Linear Inequality Restraints," Pacific Journal of Mathematics, June 1955, Vol. 5, No. 2.
6. Tucker, A. W., "A Combinatorial Equivalence of Matrices," Combinatorial Analysis, R. Bellman and M. Hall (ed.), Proceedings of Symposia in Applied Mathematics 10, American Mathematical Society, 1960.
7. van der Waerden, B. L., Modern Algebra, Frederick Ungar Co., New York, Vol. II, pp. 106-107.
8. Gomory, Ralph E., "The Fortran Code for Integer Programming," forthcoming as a RAND Corporation report.
9. Beale, E. M. L., "A Method of Solving Linear Programming Problems When Some but Not All of the Variables Must Take Integral Values," Statistical Techniques Research Group Technical Report No. 19, Princeton, N.J., July, 1958.
10. Gomory, Ralph E., "An Algorithm for the Mixed Integer Problem," RAND Corporation, RM-2597, July 7, 1960.
11. Dantzig, George B., "Discrete Variable Extremum Problems," Operations Research, Vol. 5, No. 2, 1957.
12. ———, "On the Significance of Solving Linear Programming Problems

with Some Integer Variables," RAND Corporation report P-1486, September 8, 1958.

Fundamental References on the Simplex Method

Dantzig, G. B., "Maximization of a Linear Function of Variables Subject to Linear Inequalities," Chapter XXI of Activity Analysis of Production and Allocation, T. C. Koopmans (ed.), Cowles Commission Monograph 13, John Wiley & Sons, Inc., New York, 1951.

Lemke, C. E., "The Dual Method of Solving the Linear Programming Problem," Naval Research Logistics Quarterly, Vol. 1, No. 1, 1954.

For a Different View of the Simplex Method

Beale, E. M. L., "An Alternative Method for Linear Programming," Proceedings of the Cambridge Philosophical Society, Vol. 50, 1954, pp. 513-523.

Integer Quadratic Programming†

Hans P. Kunzi
Werner Oettli

1. INTRODUCTION

A number of procedures for solving both quadratic programming problems and integer programming problems now exist [1, 2, 3, 5]. Here we consider the combined problem. That is, we add to the ordinary constraints of a quadratic programming problem the requirement that the variables be integers. An approach to the general nonlinear-integral problem has been suggested by Kelly [4]. The procedure given here is designed to take advantage of the special properties enjoyed by problems with a convex quadratic objective function and linear constraints.

The problem in the form we shall consider it is:

$$\text{minimize } Q(x) = p'x + (1/2)x'Cx$$
$$\text{subject to } Ax \leq b$$
$$x \geq 0$$
$$x \text{ has integral components} \qquad (1\text{-}1)$$

In the above, p is a given n-vector, b is a given m-vector, x is an n-vector to be determined, C is an n by n positive definite matrix, and A is an m by n matrix. Transposes are denoted by primes. It is assumed that the set of all points x satisfying the constraints is bounded.

2. THE GEOMETRICAL INTERPRETATION

It is convenient to describe the process geometrically and illustrate it in two dimensions. Suppose that the constraint set is the (convex) polyhedron shown in Fig. 1. The point x_0 is the center of the family of ellipsoids, $Q(x) = $ constant; that is the point at which $Q(x)$ assumes its free (unconstrained) minimum. The problem is to find the smallest ellipsoid which passes through a lattice point lying in the polygon.

This will be done by solving a sequence of mixed integer problems. We should caution, however, that the objective function in these mixed integer

---

†We are indebted to R. L. Graves for a number of improvements in the present version.

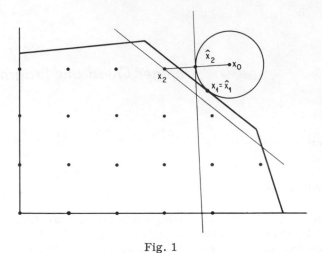

Fig. 1

problems is not itself required to be an integer so that our procedure
yields only approximate solutions with present techniques for mixed
integer problems.

To continue with the description, we first determine x_1, the point at
which the smallest ellipsoid, $Q(x)$ = constant, just touches the polygon.
Since C is positive definite, Q is strictly convex and this point is unique.
A next natural step would be to dilate the ellipsoid, $Q(x) = Q(x_1)$, relative to
x_0 until it first passes through an integer point of the polygonal domain.
The iteration procedure we propose to adopt instead consists in the dilation
not of this ellipsoid but rather of a polyhedral approximation of it. At step
k, this polyhedron, P_k, has k faces which are tangent to the ellipsoid. At
the first step, P_1 has one face. The polyhedron, then, is dilated until it
meets a lattice point of the given polygonal domain. The "stretching
parameter," λ, in terms of which the dilation is expressed, determines a
unique ellipsoid, say $Q(\lambda)$, which is, of course, tangent to the dilated polyhedron, $P_k(\lambda)$. Let x_{k+1} (at the first step this is x_2) be the lattice point encountered upon dilating P_k. Now x_0 and x_{k+1} determine a line which meets
the ellipsoid $Q(x) = Q(x_1)$ in a point. Call this point $\hat{x}_{k+1}$. We now construct
the line (more generally a hyperplane), which is tangent to the ellipsoid at
$\hat{x}_{k+1}$, and use this line to form a new approximating polyhedron, P_{k+1}, which
has k + 1 faces.

Now if $\hat{x}_{k+1} = x_{k+1}$, then the problem has been solved. This is true because the tangent polyhedron in which the ellipsoid is imbedded has passed
through no lattice points in the dilation process, and hence the ellipsoid itself certainly hasn't. Otherwise the new polyhedron, P_{k+1}, is properly contained in P_k. We now repeat the process by dilating P_{k+1} to obtain a lattice
point x_{k+2}. The procedure terminates in an optimal solution when a lattice
point appears for the second time because the point can be reached only by
the hyperplane which touched it before and this point lies on the dilated
ellipsoid.

3. THE ALGEBRAIC TREATMENT

Here we shall give a more formal presentation and exhibit explicitly the sequence of steps. The problem we wish to solve has the same solutions (the solution need not be unique) as the following problem.

$$\text{minimize } \lambda$$
$$\text{subject to } Ax \leq b$$
$$x \geq 0$$
$$x \quad \text{integral}$$
$$t'(x - x_0) \leq \lambda t'(\hat{x} - x_0) \tag{3-1}$$

The last inequality is to hold for all $\hat{x}$ such that $Q(\hat{x}) = Q(y)$ where y is the (unique) solution to

$$\text{minimize } Q(x)$$
$$\text{subject to } Ax \leq b$$
$$x \geq 0$$

The value of the t which is associated with an $\hat{x}$ is given by

$$t = p + C\hat{x}$$

To prove that a solution, x, to (1-1) is indeed a solution to (3-1), and to facilitate the exposition of the constructive procedure, we need the following sequence of lemmas. In them x_0 denotes the free minimum of $Q(x)$. We suppose it to be outside the constraint set. It is elementary to show that $x_0 = -C^{-1}p$.

Lemma 1. $t'(\hat{x} - x_0) = 2[Q(\hat{x}) - Q(x_0)]$

Proof: $t'(\hat{x} - x_0) = (p' + \hat{x}'C)(\hat{x} - x_0)$
$$= p'\hat{x} + x'C\hat{x} - p'x_0 - \hat{x}'Cx_0$$

Now $Cx_0 = -p$ and $Q(x_0) = (1/2)p'x_0$ and these substitutions give the desired result.

Definition: Given a vector x_a, let

$$\mu_a = [(Q(y) - Q(x_0))/(Q(x_a) - Q(x_0))]^{0.5}$$

and

$$\hat{x}_a = x_0 + \mu_a(x_a - x_0)$$

Lemma 2. $Q(\hat{x}_a) = Q(y)$. (That is $\hat{x}_a$ lies on the undilated ellipsoid.)

Proof: $Q(\hat{x}_a) = Q((1 - \mu_a)x_0 + \mu_a x_a)$
$$= (1 - \mu_a^2) Q(x_0) + \mu_a^2 Q(x_a) = Q(y).$$

Lemma 3. Given a vector x_a, the problem
$$\text{maximize } t'(x_a - x_0)$$
$$\text{subject to } Q(\hat{x}) = Q(y)$$
has the solution $\hat{x} = \hat{x}_a$.

Proof: $t'(x_a - x_0) = Q(x_a) + Q(\hat{x}) - 2Q(x_0) - (1/2)(x_a - \hat{x})' C(x_a - \hat{x})$
The only variable part of this expression involves the quadratic form C.
This form assumes a minimum value when $\hat{x} = \hat{x}_a$, and hence its negative
is a maximum there.

This shows that for a proposed solution to (3-1), say x_a, we need only
verify one "t" inequality, namely for $\hat{x} = \hat{x}_a$ since the left side of the relation assumes its greatest value for this value of $\hat{x}$ and the right side is a
constant.

Lemma 4. Let x_b, λ_b be a solution to (3-1).
Then $\lambda_b = 1/\mu_b$.

Proof: $\hat{x}_b - x_0 = \mu_b(x_b - x_0)$
$t_b'(\hat{x}_b - x_0) = \mu_b t_b'(x_b - x_0)$
$t_b'(x_b - x_0) = \lambda_b t_b'(\hat{x}_b - x_0)$.

The last equality is true because the left side assumes its largest value for
$\hat{x} = \hat{x}_b$ and λ_b is a minimum.

Theorem. Let a solution to (1-1) be denoted by x_a. Let
$\lambda_a = [t_a'(x_a - x_0)]/[t_a'(\hat{x}_a - x_0)]$. Then x_a, λ_a is a solution to (3-1). Conversely,
let x_b, λ_b be a solution to (3-1). Then x_b is a solution to (1-1).

Proof: Given x_a and λ_a, the hypothesis and lemma 3 yield
$t_a'(x_a - x_0) = \lambda_a t_a'(\hat{x}_a - x_0)$
$t'(x_a - x_0) \le \lambda_a t'(\hat{x} - x_0)$
Hence x_a, λ_a is a solution to (3-1). Given x_b, λ_b we must have $\lambda_b = \lambda_a$ because λ_a is a solution to (3-1). Using lemma 4, it is easy to show that

$$Q(x_b) = (1 - \lambda_b^2) Q(x_0) + \lambda_b^2 Q(\hat{x}_b).$$

A similar expression can be written for $Q(x_a)$. Since $Q(\hat{x}_b) = Q(y)$ and λ_b
$= \lambda_a$, $Q(x_b) = Q(x_a)$. This completes the proof.

Turning now to the constructive procedure, the first step is to find the
location of the free minimum of $Q(x)$. As indicated before this is

$$x_0 = -C^{-1}p$$

Then x_1 is the solution to the quadratic programming problem

$$\text{minimize } Q(x) = p'x + (1/2)x'Cx$$
$$\text{subject to } Ax \le b$$
$$x \ge 0$$

Then set $\hat{x}_1 = x_1$.

We wish to determine a sequence of integer-valued x_k which satisfy $Ax_k \leq b$ and lie on the dilations of hyperplanes tangent to the ellipsoid, $Q(x) = Q(x_1)$, and an accompanying sequence of $\hat{x}_k$ which lie on the ellipsoid and on the line joining x_k to x_0.

The general step in the procedure can be expressed as follows. Given the points x_j and $\hat{x}_j$ for $1 \leq j \leq k$, solve the mixed integer problem

minimize λ
subject to $Ax \leq b$
$$t_j'(x - x_0) \leq \lambda t_j'(\hat{x}_j - x_0); \qquad (j = 1, 2, \ldots, k)$$
$$x \geq 0, \lambda \geq 0$$
x integral, λ arbitrary

In this problem, t_j is the gradient vector given by

$$t_j = p + C\hat{x}_j$$

If we let

$$\alpha_j = t_j'(\hat{x}_j - x_0)$$

$$\beta_j = t_j'x_0$$

Then the problem can be expressed more succinctly as

minimize λ
subject to $Ax \leq b$
$$(t_j'x - \beta_j)/\alpha_j \leq \lambda; \qquad (j = 1, 2, \ldots, k)$$
$$x \neq 0, \lambda \neq 0$$
x integral, λ arbitrary

If the solution to this problem is denoted by x_{k+1}, λ_{k+1}, then $\hat{x}_{k+1}$ is given by

$$\hat{x}_{k+1} = x_0 + \mu_{k+1}(x_{k+1} - x_0)$$

$$\mu_{k+1} = [(Q(x_1) - Q(x_0))/(Q(x_{k+1}) - Q(x_0))]^{0.5}$$

Now if we find a vector, x_m, and scalar, λ_m, satisfying merely the one additional "t" constraint

$$t_m'(x_m - x_0) \leq \lambda_m t_m'(\hat{x}_m - x_0)$$

then lemma 3 insures that we have a solution because all of the other "t" constraints will be satisfied. Such a solution will be available if at some stage $x_m = x_k$ for $m > k$, because x_m satisfies the earlier kth relation

$$t_k'(x_m - x_0) \leq \lambda_m t_k'(\hat{x}_k - x_0)$$

and $\hat{x}_m = \hat{x}_k$, $t_m = t_k$ (ordinarily $\lambda_m > \lambda_k$). There are only a finite number of integer points to consider, since the constraint set is bounded. Thus at some stage $x_m = x_k$. The only reason for choosing x_1 as the solution to the noninteger problem is to ensure that an integral point in the constraint set will be found in the process of moving the tangent hyperplane from x_1. It is perfectly possible to start with an integral point in the constraint set.

It is worth observing that this procedure adds additional constraints or cutting planes just as ordinary integer programming does. (In the end only one of them is needed.) Thus the dual method can be used as it is in ordinary integer programming.

There are serious approximation problems since this is a mixed integer problem with a nonintegral objective function. For the mixed integer finiteness proofs to apply, it is necessary to replace the functional by $N\lambda$ (say $N = 1000$) and require that $N\lambda$ be an integer. Then the procedures of either Gomory or Dinkelbach can be applied.

REFERENCES

1. Beale, E. M. L., "On Quadratic Programming," Naval Research Logistics Quarterly, Vol. 6, 1959, pp. 227-243.
2. Dinkelbach, private communication.
3. Gomory, R. E., "Mixed Integer Programming," The RAND Corporation, Feb. 10, 1959.
4. Kelley, J. E., "The Cutting-Plane Method for Solving Convex Programs," J. Soc. Indust. Appl. Math., Vol. 8, No. 4, Dec. 1960, pp. 703-712.
5. Wolfe, P., "The Simplex Method for Quadratic Programming," Econometrica, Vol. 27, No. 3, 1959.

ON DIAGONALIZATION METHODS IN INTEGER PROGRAMMING

Richard Van Slyke and *Roger Wets*

ABSTRACT

An important area for improvement in existing integer programming codes is in the easy generation of efficient cutting hyperplanes; here we approach this problem using a triangular canonical form. First an algorithm is given based on Gomory's all-integer integer programming algorithm, which constitutes a first step in this direction. This procedure is a practical analog of a deepest cut method discussed in the second part. Finally, a brief outline and flow diagram for the algorithm are given and illustrated.

We assume that we have at hand an integer program where all the coefficients and constant terms are integers. The functional is to be maximized. The problem can be written in a parametric form due to Tucker:

Maximize x_0 subject to x_j integer, $j = 0, \ldots, n$; $x_j \geq 0$,

$j = 1, \ldots, n$; and

$$x_0 = b_0 + c_0 t_0 + c_1 t_1 + \ldots + c_k t_k$$
$$x_1 = b_1 + a_{10} t_0 + a_{11} t_1 + \ldots + a_{1k} t_k$$
$$\vdots$$
$$x_m = b_m + a_{m0} t_0 + a_{m1} t_1 + \ldots + a_{mk} t_k \tag{1}$$

Then a simple transformation is made to the following equivalent problem

Maximize x_0 where $x_j \geq 0$, $(j = 1, \ldots, n)$; and x_j are integers $(j = 0, \ldots, n)$ subject to

$$x_0 = b_0 - t_0$$
$$x_1 = b_1 + a_{10} t_0 - t_1$$
$$x_2 = b_2 + a_{20} t_0 + a_{21} t_1 - t_2.$$
$$\vdots$$
$$x_{k+1} = b_{k+1} + a_{k+1,0} t_0 + a_{k+1,1} t_1 + a_{k+1,2} t_2 + \cdots - t_{k+1}$$
$$x_{k+2} = b_{k+2} + a_{k+2,0} t_0 + a_{k+2,1} t_1 + a_{k+2,2} t_2 + \cdots + a_{k+2,k+1} t_{k+1}$$
$$\vdots$$
$$x_n = b_n + a_{n0} t_0 + a_{n1} t_1 + a_{n2} t_2 + \cdots + a_{nk+1} t_{k+1} \tag{2}$$

Because the columns of (2) are ordered lexicographically, "efficient cuts" can be easily found.

A simplified variant of Gomory's all-integer integer programming algorithm leads to the solution in a finite number of iterations.

An Accelerated Euclidean Algorithm for Integer Linear Programming

Glenn T. Martin

THE PROBLEM

Many optimization problems may be formulated as linear programming problems in which the solution variables must take on integer values. Development of linear programming into a routine mathematical tool has intensified the search for associated computational procedures to handle the integer programming problem. Until recently, however, progress has been meager both in the area of mathematical theory and in the area of application. But in 1958, R. E. Gomory [1] proposed a rigorous solution procedure which was shown to converge in a finite number of steps. Later he proposed a modification of this method as an "all-integer algorithm" [2]. Both these techniques make use of the simplex procedure and apply principles of the Euclidean Algorithm [3]. In each case a set of suitable "cutting planes" is applied to the system in such a way that non-integer solutions are occluded and the desired integer solution ultimately found.

Both of Gomory's techniques have met with limited success in application. Nonetheless, many computational difficulties have been encountered even on very small problems. Larger problems—very modest by normal linear programming standards—often persistently refuse to converge. It seems, therefore, that a means to accelerate convergence is necessary if reasonably complex problems are to be routinely solved.

An Accelerated Euclidean Algorithm has been investigated as a means of reducing computational effort involved in solving integer linear programming problems. The procedure is a direct extension of Gomory's original proposal. The technique will be illustrated and modifications to the earlier technique pointed out by use of a small example.

Example Problem

Minimize

$$z = -2x_1 - 3x_2 \tag{1}$$

Subject to

$$2x_1 + 5x_2 \leq 8$$

$$3x_1 + 2x_2 \leq 9 \tag{2}$$

and

$$x_1, x_2 = 0, 1, 2, \ldots \tag{3}$$

The variables x_3 and x_4 are added as slack variables and the array shown in Fig. 1. The identity columns are omitted and basis vectors are indicated by row identification.

Procedure

A. Apply the (composite) simplex algorithm to (1) and (2). If (3) is met the desired solution has been attained; otherwise

B. Apply the Accelerated Euclidean Algorithm, steps B1 to B7, until an integer solution is attained, then reapply the simplex algorithm as in step A. Thus:

1. Select a noninteger row vector, p, from the set.
2. Abstract the "Gomory" restraint, s, from p. This is the positive fractional components of the elements of p.
3. Determine k, the dual simplex pivot column for the row, s.
4. Compute p', the Gaussian transform of s on p only (contrast to earlier procedure which transformed the entire set).
5. Continue to abstract s' restraints and transform p' until the k component of p' becomes integer. Note that the index, k, as determined in step B3 is retained throughout this process. A special algorithm has been devised for carrying out this step. (This also contrasts to the earlier procedure.)
6. Using the original restraint, p, and its final form, p'', perform a "reverse inversion," i.e., a reverse Gaussian transformation, to find the "consolidated restraint," r, which generates p'' from p.
7. Append r to the entire set and perform the indicated Gaussian transformation. Iterate this process beginning with step B1 until an all-integer solution is attained. Then return to the simplex algorithm (step A).

Accordingly, in our example, the simplex algorithm [4, 5] is applied and the resulting optimal-feasible solution displayed in Fig. 2. D is the de-

INITIAL MATRIX

	b	x_1	x_2	
z		2	3	
x_3	8	2	5	$|D| = 1$
x_4	9	3	2	

Fig. 1

SIMPLEX SOLUTION 1

	$\underline{b}$	$\underline{x_4}$	$\underline{x_3}$	
z	$-76/11$	$-4/11$	$-5/11$	
x_2	$6/11$	$-2/11$	$3/11$	
x_1	$29/11$	$5/11$	$-2/11$	$\lvert D \rvert = 11$
s	$-7/11$	$-5/11$	$-9/11*$	

$$p = x_1, \; k = x_3$$

Fig. 2

terminant of the matrix, the product of all pivot elements. Since the solution is not integer, a noninteger row, called p, having the largest fractional component in b is selected. The modulo one components are extracted and appended as s, however, the only use made of this row at this time is to select k, the simplex dual method pivot column [6].

Now p is subjected to accelerated reduction via the following algorithm. (Primes refer to the next subsequent stage of numbers.)

$$a_p = I_p + a_p^+/\lvert D \rvert$$
$$a_{pk} = a^*/\lvert D \rvert \quad \text{(definition)}$$
$$\lvert D' \rvert = a_{pk}^+$$
$$a_{pk}' = a^*/\lvert D' \rvert$$
$$a_p' = I_p + (a_p^+/\lvert D \rvert)\,(\lvert D' \rvert - a^*)/\lvert D' \rvert$$

Since $(\lvert D' \rvert - a^*)/\lvert D \rvert =$ an integer, it is convenient to split the p components, a_p, into integers, I_p, and positive fractional components, $a_p^+/\lvert D \rvert$, and operate simply on the latter, splitting out any integers generated and adding to the other integers. Finally, when a_{pk} becomes integer the residual components are added to form the transformed row, p''. This process is tabulated in Fig. 3. The p'' is result of applying five Gomory restraint stages to p.

ACCELERATED REDUCTION 1

$\underline{D}$	$\underline{D'}$	$\dfrac{\lvert D' \rvert - a^*}{\lvert DD' \rvert}$	(k) x_3	FRACTIONS b	x_4	INTEGERS b	x_4
11	9	$1/9$	$-2/9$	$7/9$	$5/9$	2	0
9	7	$1/7$	$-2/7$	$7/7$	$5/7$	2	0
7	5	$1/5$	$-2/5$	0	$5/5$	3	0
5	3	$1/3$	$-2/3$	0	0	3	1
3	1	$1/1$	-2	0	0	3	1

$$p'' = \begin{array}{ccc} b & x_4 & x_3 \\ 3 & 1 & -2 \end{array}$$

Fig. 3

Now we do a "reverse inversion" step; thus,

$$a_{rk} = -a_{pk}/a_{pk}'' = -|D''|/|D|$$
$$a_r = (a_p - a_p'') \, a_{rk}/a_{pk}$$
$$= (a_p - a_p'')/(-a_{pk}'')$$

This operation is summarized in Fig. 4. The resulting restraint and its application to the system is shown in Fig. 5. Since this is integer, we return to the simplex procedure.

The process of integerization rendered the solution nonoptimal; therefore, a new simplex solution is generated in Fig. 6. This is noninteger, so we select a p row, extract s and determine k (in this case we have deliberately violated the criteria of selecting the largest fractional component of b).

Figure 7 shows the accelerated reduction, and Fig. 8 shows the reverse inversion step for the new restraint. Its addition to the system and the result is displayed in Fig. 9. Since this satisfies both the simplex and the integer requirements, the final solution has been obtained.

REVERSE INVERSION 1

		b	x_4	(k) x_3
p	=	29/11	5/11	−2/11
p''	=	3	1	−2*
p − p''	=	−4/11	−6/11	----
r	=	−2/11	−3/11	−1/11

Fig. 4

APPLICATION OF r 1

	b	x_4	x_3	
z	−76/11	−4/11	−5/11	
x_2	6/11	−2/11	3/11	$|D| = 11$
x_1	29/11	5/11	−2/11	
s_1	− 2/11	−3/11	−1/11	

⇩

	b	x_4	s_1	
z	−6	1	−5	
x_2	0	−1	3	$|D| = 1$
x_1	3	1	−2	
x_3	2	3*	−11	

Fig. 5

SIMPLEX SOLUTION 2

	$\underline{b}$	$\underline{x_3}$	$\underline{s_1}$	
z	$-20/3$	$-1/3$	$-4/3$	
x_2	$2/3$	$1/3$	$-2/3$	$|D| = 3$
x_1	$7/3$	$-1/3$	$5/3$	
x_4	$2/3$	$+1/3$	$-11/3$	
s	$-1/3$	$-2/3*$	$-2/3$	

$$p = x_1, \ k = x_3$$

Fig. 6

ACCELERATED REDUCTION 2

$|\underline{D}|$	$|\underline{D'}|$	$\dfrac{|D'| - a*}{|DD'|}$	$\underline{x_4}$	FRACTIONS $\underline{b}$	$\underline{s_1}$	INTEGERS $\underline{b}$	$\underline{s_1}$
3	2	$1/2$	$-1/2$	$1/2$	$2/2$	2	1
2	1	$1/1$	-1	$1/1$	0	2	2

$$p'' = \begin{array}{ccc} b & x_4 & s_1 \\ 3 & -1 & 2 \end{array}$$

Fig. 7

REVERSE INVERSION 2

		$\underline{b}$	(k) $\underline{x_4}$	$\underline{s_1}$
p	=	$7/3$	$-1/3$	$5/3$
p''	=	3	$-1*$	2
p − p''	=	$-2/3$	----	$-1/3$
r	=	$-2/3$	$-1/3$	$-1/3$

Fig. 8

Reduction of Positive a*

It is noted that in the accelerated reduction step, fractional components are always interpreted modulo one at each stage. The signs of $(|D'| - a*)/|DD'|$ and of fractions must be algebraically maintained. Any negative fractions are interpreted modulo one and the resulting negative integer added to the integer component. Fig. 10 illustrates this with positive a*.

DISCUSSION

It is evident that the strongest "cutting plane" available from a particular row with a particular pivot column is likely to represent a

APPLICATION OF r 2

	$\underline{b}$	$\underline{x_4}$	$\underline{s_1}$	
z	$-20/3$	$-1/3$	$-4/3$	
x_2	$2/3$	$1/3$	$-2/3$	
x_1	$7/3$	$-1/3$	$5/3$	$|D| = 3$
x_3	$2/3$	$-1/3$	$-11/3$	
s_2	$-2/3$	$-1/3*$	$-1/3$	

⇩

	$\underline{b}$	$\underline{s_2}$	$\underline{s_1}$	
z	-6	-1	-1	
x_2	0	1	-1	
x_1	3	-1	2	$|D| = 1$
x_4	0	1	-4	
x_3	2	-3	$+1$	

Fig. 9

ACCELERATED REDUCTION WITH POSITIVE a*

	$\underline{b}$	$\underline{x_1}$	$\underline{x_2}$
$p =$	$11/4$	$1/4$	$7/4*$

$|\underline{D}|$	$|\underline{D'}|$	$\dfrac{\|D'\| - a*}{\|DD'\|}$	(k) x_2	FRACTIONS b	x_1	INTEGERS b	x_1
4	3	$-1/3$	$7/3$	$-3/3$	$-1/3$	2	0
				0	$2/3$	1	-1
3	1	$-2/1$	$7/1$	0	-4	1	-1

		$\underline{b}$	$\underline{x_1}$	$\underline{x_2}$
p	$=$	$11/4$	$1/4$	$7/4$
p"	$=$	1	-5	$7*$
p $-$ p"	$=$	$7/4$	$21/4$	----
r	$=$	$-1/4$	$-3/4$	$-1/4$

Fig. 10

complex multiple-sum of the restraints immediately apparent in a non-integer system. Since the original procedures for choosing a restraint primarily examined only those fairly readily apparent, obviously the prospect of a "good" choice was quite remote.

In selecting a noninteger row, we simply take the row containing the largest available fractional component of interest. It is not clear that this is necessary or even helpful with the Accelerated Euclidean Algorithm, i.e., a random choice may do as well, or better. We simply don't know.

The procedure used here operates much like the previous technique, however, (a) restraints are applied only to one row until the pivot column element becomes integer, with later application to the entire set, and (b) this process of applying restraints is allowed to destroy optimality as well as feasibility. Thus a composite simplex algorithm is essential to effective use of the new procedure.

Computing Experience

We have solved only a handful of problems via this algorithm. We can report however that for small problems which we easily solved by earlier methods, the new procedure has proved much more efficient in all cases. Perhaps 75 per cent of the "integerizing" iterations were typically saved (although this is not necessarily meaningful because of possible non-representative problems). More importantly, problems which we found impossible to handle with earlier procedures have generally yielded to the new technique provided digital difficulties could be avoided. In this category is a 54×442 system which is the largest problem we have attacked.

CONCLUSION

The Accelerated Euclidean Algorithm seems to offer computational advantages over earlier Euclidean methods for integer linear programming. However, more comprehensive experience is needed before a thorough evaluation of this early promise can be made.

REFERENCES

1. Gomory, R. E., "An Algorithm for Integer Solutions to Linear Programs," This volume, see also IBM Mathematics Research Project Technical Report No. 1, Princeton, Nov. 17, 1958.
2. Gomory, R. E., "All-Integer Programming Algorithm," IBM Research Report RC-189, Jan. 29, 1960.
3. Gelford, A. O., "The Solution of Equations in Integers" (translated from the Russian by J. R. Roberts), W. H. Freeman and Company).
4. Dantzig, G. B., "Maximization of a Linear Function of Variables Subject to Inequalities," Activity Analysis of Production and Allocation, (T. C. Koopmans, ed.), Wiley and Sons, 1951, Chap. XXI, pp. 339–347.
5. Charnes, A., W. W. Cooper, and A. Henderson, "Introduction to Linear Programming," Wiley and Sons, 1953.
6. Lemke, C. E., "The Dual Method of Solving the Linear Programming Problem," Naval Research Logistics Quarterly, Vol. 1, 1954, pp. 36–47.

Flows in Networks

D. R. Fulkerson

This survey will summarize, in a very brief way, that part of linear programming theory encompassed by the phrase "transportation problems" or "network flow problems." The latter name better describes the mathematical content of the subject and is less committed to one domain of application. This paper will not say too much about applications, but will instead stress some of the more important notions and theorems in this subject.

Before getting into some of these concepts and theorems, a word should be said about the history of network flow problems. Just where the subject may properly be said to have started depends on how much latitude is allowed in interpreting the phrase "flows in networks." Certain static minimal cost transportation models were independently formulated and studied by Hitchcock [13], Kantorovitch [15, 16] and Koopmans [18] in the 1940's. A few years later, when linear programming began to make itself known as an organized discipline, G. B. Dantzig showed how his simplex method could be simplified and made more effective for this class of problems [1]. It would not be inaccurate to say that the subject really began with the work of these men on the very practical problem of transporting a commodity from certain points of supply to other points of demand in a way to minimize shipping cost. However, dismissing the formulational and applied aspects of the topic, and with the advantages of hindsight, one can go back a few years earlier to work of P. Hall on set representatives [12], or Konig, Egervary and Menger [17] on linear graphs, and relate this work in pure mathematics to the practically oriented subject of flows in networks also. One can even go further back to the Maxwell-Kirchoff theory of electrical networks, although this is not a linear problem, and say the subject began there. Actually, the earliest reference I know of to work that can be regarded as in this area is a paper by Monge in 1781.

So much for history. We now turn to some of the main concepts and theorems about network flows.

BASIC CONCEPTS

Figure 1 shows a network and introduces some notation. The six circles in the figure are called nodes. They are indexed by i, i running

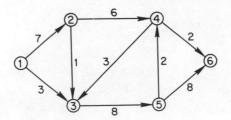

<u>Nodes</u> i, i = 1, ···, n

<u>Arcs</u> ij (from i to j), i, j = 1, ···, n

<u>Arc capacities</u> $c_{ij} \geq 0$

Fig. 1

from 1 to n. In addition there are directed arcs, denoted by ordered pairs (i, j), to be interpreted "from i to j," i and j running from 1 to n. There are also arc capacities, nonnegative numbers denoted by c_{ij}. For instance, the arc (1,2) has capacity 7; the arc (2,4) has capacity 6. Capacity simply means an upper bound on the amount of flow that can take place in an arc in the direction of its orientation in some steady state situation. For instance, 8 units per unit time can pass from 3 to 5.

It turns out that it really doesn't make any difference, for most flow problems, whether oriented arcs or unoriented arcs are assumed. In some problems it does make a real difference, but we'll assume directed arcs uless otherwise stated.

Figure 2 shows a flow through the network from the node 1 on the left

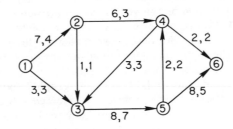

<u>Flow</u> f <u>from</u> 1 (source) <u>to</u> n (sink) <u>of value</u> v

(1) $\sum_{j} (f_{ij} - f_{ji}) = \begin{cases} v & i = 1 \\ 0 & i = 2, \cdots, n-1 \\ -v & i = n \end{cases}$

(2) $0 \leq f_{ij} \leq c_{ij}$

<u>Problem</u>: construct flow from source to sink of maximal value

Fig. 2

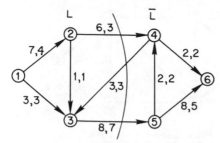

Cut separating source and sink: partition L, $\overline{L}$ of nodes with source in L, sink in $\overline{L}$

From (1) and (2),

$$v = \sum_{\substack{i \text{ in } L \\ j \text{ in } \overline{L}}} (f_{ij} - f_{ji}) \le \sum_{\substack{i \text{ in } L \\ j \text{ in } \overline{L}}} c_{ij}$$

(Cut capacity)

Fig. 3

to node 6 on the right. This flow is an assignment of numbers to the arcs of the network—here shown by the second number on each arc—such that for any intermediate node (here, nodes 2, 3, 4, 5), conservation holds, that is, flow-in equals flow-out. For example, at node 2 there are 4 units coming in and $3 + 1 = 4$ units going out. Because of the conservation condition at nodes 2, 3, 4 and 5, the net flow of 7 units out of node 1 is equal to the net flow of 7 units into node 6. In general, Eqs. (1) describe a flow $f = (f_{ij})$ from source to sink of value v, that is, v units get through the network. In addition there are capacity constraints and nonnegativity requirements (2).

Given this formulation, a very natural problem that suggests itself is: Push as much as possible through the network. That is, maximize the variable v subject to the equations (1) and inequalities (2). This is probably the most fundamental problem about flows in networks, and we shall state some of the basic theorems about this problem. But in order to do this, the notions illustrated in Figs. 3 and 4 are needed.

Figure 3 introduces the notion of a cut in a network. The nodes of the network are split into two sets L and $\overline{L}$, one of which contains the source and the other the sink. This division is called a cut separating source and sink. If the flow equations are added up over the nodes in the source-set of a cut, then the inequalities (2) yield the result shown in Fig. 3. The value v of a flow f is equal to the net flow across any cut, and is hence bounded above by the capacity of the cut. We shall see in a moment that equality holds (i.e., the upper bound is achieved) for some flow and some cut.

Figure 4 illustrates one way of increasing the value of a flow; namely, by using what might be called a flow-augmenting path, shown by the dotted arcs, which form a path from source to sink. Some arcs are traversed

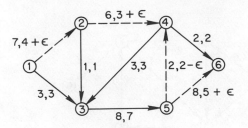

Flow augmenting path

Fig. 4

with their orientation, some against their orientation, in going from source to sink. In order for a path to be flow-augmenting, we want the property that for the forward arcs (those traversed with their orientation), the arc flow is less than capacity, whereas for the reverse arcs of the path (those traversed against their orientation), the arc flow is positive. Thus if the flow is changed by adding $\epsilon > 0$ to the flow in forward arcs of the path and subtracting ϵ from the flow in reverse arcs, a new flow is obtained whose value is ϵ units greater than the old flow. The largest value for ϵ in Fig. 4 is $\epsilon = 2$ (the bind coming on the reverse arc), so the new flow has value 9. It turns out that it suffices to look for flow augmenting paths in order to maximize flow through a network [3].

Figure 5 shows the flow that is obtained if the change $\epsilon = 2$ is made along the flow-augmenting path in Fig. 4. Now observe the cut shown by the wavy line. Every arc that goes from source-side to sink-side in this cut is carrying flow at capacity. On the other hand, any arc that comes back across the cut in the wrong way carries no flow. Hence equality holds in the inequality of Fig. 3, and this flow is consequently maximal, while the cut is minimal. This illustrates the most fundamental theorem about maximal flow.

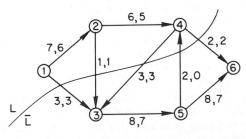

Maximal flow

Fig. 5

THEOREMS ON MAXIMAL FLOWS

There are several important theorems about maximal flow. The first, shown in Fig. 6, says that the situation illustrated in Fig. 5 is general.

One of the several proofs [3] of this theorem yields the other two theorems of Fig. 6 as corollaries. The content of the construction theorem is: To force more through a network, it suffices to look for a path that augments the present flow. To make a real construction out of this, some good way of searching for a flow-augmenting path is needed. There are such ways, combinatorial in nature, that are quite good computationally.

The integrity theorem follows from the construction theorem, since if all arc capacities are integers, and the initial flow is integral, then the flow change ϵ made along a path will be an integer, yielding a new integral flow. Of course, more fundamentally, the integrity theorem follows from the fact that the constraint matrix of this linear program has the total unimodularity property: Every subdeterminant has value $+1$, -1, or 0. But it is not necessary to look at determinants in order to prove the theorem. It drops out of the proof of the max-flow min-cut theorem, as does the construction theorem.

MULTI-COMMODITY FLOWS

We've been talking about a flow of a single commodity from source to sink. A multi-commodity flow problem [2, 4] is illustrated in Fig. 7. There are several sources, indicated by the s's, and several sinks, indicated by the t's, with a pairing between sources and sinks. Source 1 ships to sink 1; source 2 ships to sink 2; source 3 ships to sink 3, but the three simultaneous flows share capacities on arcs. This problem doesn't have the nice simple features that the single-commodity problem has. A hint that this is so can be gotten by looking at the examples in Fig. 7. Suppose each arc has unit capacity in the left network, for instance, and it is desired to force as much as possible through the network in this multi-commodity fashion. With integer flows, the best one can do is a flow of

Max-flow min-cut theorem: for any network, the maximal flow value from source to sink is equal to the minimal cut capacity of all cuts separating source and sink

Construction theorem: a flow f is maximal if and only if there is no f-augmenting path

Integrity theorem: if all arc capacities are integers, there is an integral maximal flow

Fig. 6

MULTI-COMMODITY FLOW PROBLEMS

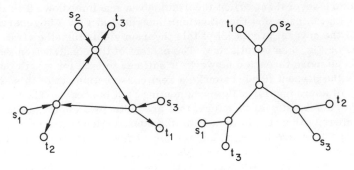

Fig. 7

value 1, since a 1-unit flow of each commodity blocks flow for the other two commodities. On the other hand, using fractions, one can send a half-unit of each commodity, giving a total flow of 3/2. The right network has the same features as the left, but for the undirected case.

SOME COMBINATORIAL THEOREMS

Consider the single-commodity problem shown in Fig. 8. Suppose supplies of a commodity are available at certain points in a network, and demands are made at other points. In the network shown (ignoring the dotted

FEASIBILITY OF SUPPLIES AND DEMANDS

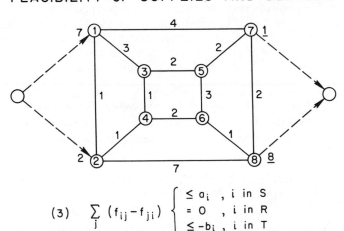

$$(3) \quad \sum_j (f_{ij} - f_{ji}) \begin{cases} \leq a_i & , \ i \ \text{in} \ S \\ = 0 & , \ i \ \text{in} \ R \\ \leq -b_i & , \ i \ \text{in} \ T \end{cases}$$

$$(2) \quad 0 \leq f_{ij} \leq c_{ij}$$

Fig. 8

arcs), the supplies are 7 units at node 1, 2 units at node 2, and the demands are 1 unit at node 7, 8 units at node 8. When can the demands be satisfied from the supplies? This question was asked and answered by Gale several years ago [10]. The idea is to convert this problem to a maximal flow problem by adding a first fictitious node—the source node—and another fictitious node—the sink node—and putting in the dotted arcs as indicated. Now interpret the supplies and demands as capacities of these arcs in the obvious way, and ask: Can 9 units be moved from source to sink? If they can, clearly both sink arcs are saturated and the demands are satisfied. So the question can always be answered by solving a maximal flow problem. If this analysis is extended a bit further, an interesting theorem drops out of this situation, as illustrated in Fig. 9.

The necessity of the condition in the supply-demand theorem is obvious and there's no interest there. The sufficiency is not obvious and is quite interesting. To paraphrase it: Select any subset of the demand nodes and ask whether enough can be put into that subset to meet the sum of the demands over the subset without worrying where the flows go individually. If this can be done for all subsets of demand nodes, then the supply-demand constraints are feasible. This is a nice generalization of a well-known theorem in combinatorial mathematics due to P. Hall, which has to do with systems of distinct representatives for sets [12]. This theorem is stated at the bottom of the figure. To interpret it a different way, one might think of the sets as being jobs, and the elements as men, with the object being to assign men to jobs. The men are qualified only for certain jobs. For example, man 1 is qualified for jobs a, b and c, etc. Then ask if it is possible to supply men to these jobs, one man to each job and no man doing more than one job, when given such a configuration. Hall's theorem

Supply-demand theorem: the supply-demand constraints (2) and (3) are feasible if and only if, for every subset $T' \subseteq T$ of demand nodes, there is a flow (depending on T') that meets the aggregate demand over T' without violating the supply limitations at nodes of S

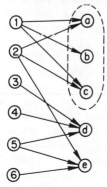

Distinct representatives theorem: given a family of n subsets of some set, there is a system of distinct representatives for this family if and only if every k of the subsets collectively contain at least k distinct elements, $k = 1, \cdots, n$

Fig. 9

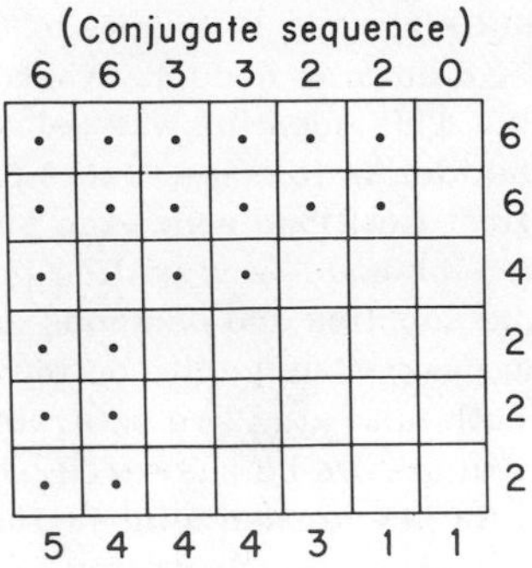

(Conjugate sequence)

	6	6	3	3	2	2	0	
	•	•	•	•	•	•		6
	•	•	•	•	•	•		6
	•	•	•	•				4
	•	•						2
	•	•						2
	•	•						2

5   4   4   4   3   1   1

Existence theorem for $(0,1)$-matrix having specified row and column sums. There is an m by n $(0,1)$-matrix having row sums a_i, $i = 1, \cdots, m$, and column sums b_j, $j = 1, \cdots, n$, if and only if $\sum_{j=1}^{k} b_j \leq \sum_{j=1}^{k} a_j^*$, $k = 1, \cdots, n$.

Here $b_1 \geq b_2 \geq \cdots \geq b_n$

Fig. 10

says: Take any subset of the jobs (such as indicated by the dotted oval in the figure) and examine all of the men who are qualified for some job in that subset; if there are enough men (that is, k men if k jobs were singled out) who are qualified for some job in the subset, and if this is true for all subsets of jobs, then one can indeed assign men to jobs. Here it is not possible because the dotted subset of these jobs leads back to only two men. Again, of course, the necessity is obvious. The sufficiency is the interesting part.

To prove Hall's theorem from the supply-demand theorem, the integrity theorem mentioned previously is needed in order to single out an integral flow. That's one of the uses of the integrity theorem; it provides a flow approach to many combinatorial problems.

Another combinatorial problem that can be solved using flows is illustrated in Fig. 10. It may not be the easiest way to solve it, but it is a mechanical way. That is one of the advantages of using flows on such a problem: If the problem can be formulated in terms of flows, then little subsequent imagination is required. The problem here is to construct a $(0,1)$-matrix having stipulated row and column sums. Of course, if just a nonnegative matrix is required rather than a $(0,1)$-matrix, the conditions are simple: the total of the row sums must equal the total of the column sums. But for a $(0,1)$-matrix, the situation is not that simple. The theorem, due to Ryser [21] and Gale [10], says the following. First, arrange the columns in monotone decreasing order. Now take the row sums and represent them by dots placed as far to the left as possible. Count the dots in the columns: 6, 6, 3, 3, 2, 2, 0. This sequence is conjugate to the row-sum sequence, that is, the two sequences are conjugate

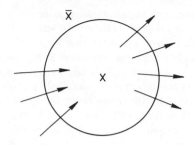

Circulation <u>theorem</u>: there is a flow f satisfying the constraints

$$\sum_{j} (f_{ij} - f_{ji}) = 0, \text{ all nodes } i,$$

$$0 \le l_{ij} \le f_{ij} \le c_{ij}, \text{ all arcs } ij,$$

if and only if, for every subset X of nodes,

$$\sum_{\substack{i \text{ in } \bar{X} \\ j \text{ in } X}} l_{ij} \le \sum_{\substack{i \text{ in } X \\ j \text{ in } \bar{X}}} c_{ij}$$

Fig. 11

partitions of the same integer. In the figure, the conjugate sequence is denoted by a_j^*. Such a $(0,1)$-matrix exists if and only if the partial sums of the column-sum sequence are dominated by the partial sums of the row-conjugate sequence. Here there is a $(0,1)$-matrix having the given row and column sums.

There is a very simple rule for constructing such a matrix. Simply take any column and put its 1's in the rows having the biggest sums,

MINIMAL COST FLOWS

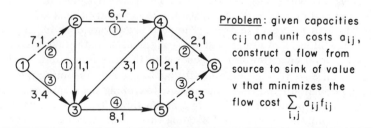

Problem: given capacities c_{ij} and unit costs a_{ij}, construct a flow from source to sink of value v that minimizes the flow cost $\sum_{i,j} a_{ij} f_{ij}$

Construction <u>theorem</u> : let f be a minimal cost flow of value v. Then the flow f′ obtained from f by adding $\in > 0$ to the flow in forward arcs of a minimal cost f-augmenting path, and subtracting $\in$ from the flow in reverse arcs of this path, is a minimal cost flow of value $v + \in$

Fig. 12

delete the column, reduce the appropriate row sums, and repeat the procedure in the reduced problem. This rule will construct such a matrix if there is one, and will lead to trouble otherwise. If this rule is applied by first selecting the column having smallest sum, then next smallest, and so on, the resulting matrix has some rather remarkable properties [9].

Figure 11 shows another interesting feasibility theorem due to Hoffman [14], which is concerned not with flows from source to sink but rather with circulations. Assume flow in equals flow out at every node, and put a lower bound on flow in each arc, denoted by l_{ij} here, as well as an upper bound, and ask: When can you satisfy these constraints? The resulting theorem is one of Hall-type. The constraints are feasible if and only if, for every subset X of nodes, the sum of the lower bounds on arcs pointing into X does not exceed the sum of capacities on arcs pointing out of X. Again this theorem can be proved using the max-flow min-cut theorem.

It should be remarked that the integrity theorem holds for the feasibility situations that have been presented; that is, if the given data are integers, and if there is a feasible flow, then there is an integral feasible flow.

MINIMAL COST FLOWS

Another important problem concerning single-commodity flows is the minimal cost flow problem. In Fig. 12, a network is given with arc capacities and a source and sink. Also a cost per unit flow for each arc is given. (The second number of each pair in the figure is the cost, the first number is the capacity, and the circled number the flow.) Then ask: How can v units be sent from source to sink at minimal cost? (The figure shows a minimal cost flow with $v = 5$.) Perhaps the most basic theorem about this problem is the construction theorem stated in the figure. Take f, which is assumed to be a minimal cost flow of a certain value. Look for a flow augmenting path with respect to f that has the least path cost of all flow-augmenting paths with respect to f. The path cost here (the dotted path) is obtained by summing the costs for forward arcs, and subtracting the sum of costs for reverse arcs. The path shown has cost 10. If you alter the flow along a minimal cost flow-augmenting path, then the new flow is a minimal cost flow corresponding to the new flow value. So to solve minimal cost flow problems, all that is needed, assuming the process has been started, is a routine for searching out a minimal cost flow-augmenting path with respect to a given flow. There are very efficient combinatorial methods for doing this. And starting the process is no problem if all arc costs are nonnegative.

There are many applications of minimal cost flows. Conspicuous among them are the Hitchcock problem and PERT-scheduling problems. Another application to maximal dynamic flows is described in [6]. Suppose a network is given where each arc of the network has a capacity and also has a traversal time. The object is to send as much through the network as possible in a given time interval. If capacities are constant over time, there's a very simple way of doing this as a minimal cost flow problem.

MULTITERMINAL FLOWS

Figures 13 and 14 get into another area that has been explored primarily by Gomory and Hu [11]. Here the concern is with multiterminal flows; this to be distinguished from the multicommodity flows mentioned earlier, in the sense that, while attention will be focused on many flows,

MULTI-TERMINAL FLOWS

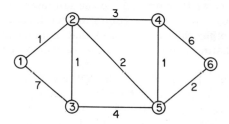

Problems:

(a) Let v_{ij} denote the maximal flow value between i and j. Determine the flow value function $v = (v_{ij})$ efficiently.

(b) What are conditions on a given $v = (v_{ij})$ in order that it come from a network?

Fig. 13

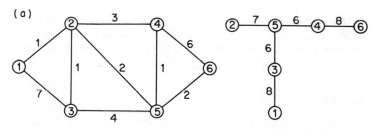

(b)

A symmetric, nonnegative $v = (v_{ij})$ is realizable as the flow value function of an undirected network if and only if the "triangle" inequality

$$v_{ij} \geq \min (v_{ik}, v_{kj})$$

holds for all i, j, k

Fig. 14

we shall not be dealing with simultaneous flows. Instead, questions are asked about all pairs of nodes taken as source and sink for a given network. The results here are for undirected networks, and are very pretty.

Gomory and Hu considered several problems. One is this: Suppose we let v_{ij} denote the maximal flow value between nodes i and j. How do you determine the flow value function v in an efficient manner? Clearly, $v = (v_{ij})$ can be determined by solving $n(n-1)/2$ single-terminal flow problems, but it is possible to do a whole lot better.

The second problem is this: Given $v = (v_{ij})$, when is v the flow value function of some network?

Let's look at (b) first. It says: A symmetric, nonnegative v is realizable as the flow value function of an undirected network if and only if a kind of "triangle" inequality holds: For any triple of nodes i, j and k, then v_{ij} must be greater than or equal to the minimum of (v_{ik}, v_{kj}). This triangle inequality puts very severe limitations on functions v that are realizable. Among other things, it implies that, numerically, v can take on at most $(n-1)$ distinct values if n is the number of nodes in the network.

We turn now to (a). The intent here is that any network is flow-equivalent to a tree. An equivalent tree for the example is shown. For instance, suppose you ask yourself: What's the maximal flow between 1 and 4 in this network? Go to the equivalent tree and proceed from 1 to 4 by the unique path joining them, and take the minimum of the numbers you encounter—here 6—and that's the maximal flow value. The number 6 is the capacity of the cut separating 1 and 3 from 2, 4, 5, 6 (or the cut separating 1, 2, 3, 5 from 4 and 6) in the original network. Thus there are only $(n-1)$ cuts that are relevant in solving the multi-terminal maximal flow problem for all pairs of nodes, and each of these is represented by an arc of the equivalent tree. Moreover, such a cut-tree can be constructed by solving precisely $(n-1)$ single-terminal maximal flow problems, as described in [11].

This survey of basic concepts and results about flows in networks has necessarily omitted everything in the way of detail and also has not even mentioned much substantial work in this field. I hope that it has at least imparted some knowledge and feeling for the subject.

REFERENCES

1. Dantzig, G. B., "Application of the Simplex Method to a Transportation Problem," Activity Analysis of Production and Allocation, Cowles Commission Monograph 13, Wiley (1951), pp. 359-373.
2. Ford, L. R., Jr. and D. R. Fulkerson, "Maximal Flow through a Network," Can. J. Math., Vol. 8, 1956, pp. 399-404.
3. Ford, L. R., Jr. and D. R. Fulkerson, "A Simple Algorithm for Finding Maximal Network Flows and an Application to the Hitchcock Problem," Can. J. Math., Vol. 9, 1957, pp. 210-218.
4. Ford, L. R., Jr. and D. R. Fulkerson, "A Suggested Computation for

Maximal Multi-commodity Network Flows, Man. Sci., Vol. 5, 1958, pp. 97-101.

5. Ford, L. R., Jr. and D. R. Fulkerson, "Network Flow and Systems of Representatives," Can. J. Math., Vol. 10, 1958, pp. 78-85.

6. Ford, L. R., Jr. and D. R. Fulkerson, "Constructing Maximal Dynamic Flows from Static Flows," Op. Res., Vol. 6, 1958 pp. 419-433.

7. Ford, L. R., Jr. and D. R. Fulkerson, Flows in Networks, Princeton University Press (1962).

8. Fulkerson, D. R., "A Network Flow Feasibility Theorem and Combinatorial Applications," Can. J. Math., Vol. 11, 1959, pp. 440-451.

9. Fulkerson, D. R. and H. J. Ryser, "Multiplicities and Minimal Widths for (0,1)-Matrices," to appear in Can. J. Math.

10. Gale, D., "A Theorem on Flows in Networks," Pac. J. Math., Vol. 7, 1957, pp. 1073-1082.

11. Gomory, R. E., and T. C. Hu, "Multi-terminal Network Flows," J. of the Society for Industrial and Applied Mathematics, Vol. 9, 1961, pp. 551-570.

12. Hall, P., "On Representatives of Subsets," J. Lond. Math. Soc., Vol. 10, 1935, pp. 26-30.

13. Hitchcock, F. L., "The Distribution of a Product from Several Sources to Numerous Localities," Jour. Math. and Phy., Vol. 20, 1941, pp. 224-230.

14. Hoffman, A. J., "Some Recent Applications of the Theory of Linear Inequalities to Extremal Combinatorial Analysis," Proc. Symposia on Applied Math., Vol. 10, 1960.

15. Kantorovitch, L., "On the Translocation of Masses," Comp. Rend. (Doklady) Acad. Sci., Vol. 37, 1942, pp. 199-201.

16. Kantorovitch, L., and M. K. Gavurin, "The Application of Mathematical Methods in Problems of Freight Flow Analysis," Collection of Problems Concerned with Increasing the Effectiveness of Transports, Publications of the Akademic Nauk SSSR, 1949, pp. 110-138.

17. König, D., Theorie der Endlichen und Unendlichen Graphen, Chelsea, New York (1950).

18. Koopmans, T. C., and S. Reiter, "A Model of Transportation," Activity Analysis of Production and Allocation, Cowles Commission Monograph 13, Wiley (1951), pp. 222-259.

19. Kuhn, H. W., "The Hungarian Method for the Assignment Problem," Nav. Res. Log. Q., Vol. 2, 1955, pp. 83-97.

20. Orden, A., "The Transshipment Problem," Man. Sci., Vol. 3, 1956, pp. 276-285.

21. Ryser, H. J., "Combinatorial Properties of Matrices of Zeros and Ones," Can. J. Math., Vol. 9, 1957, pp. 371-377.

MULTI-COMMODITY NETWORK FLOWS†

T. C. Hu

ABSTRACT

A network is a set of nodes N_i connected by branches with nonnegative branch capacities b_{ij} which indicates the maximum amount of flow that can pass through the branch from N_i to N_j. Given all b_{ij}, there is a maximum flow $f(i;j)$ from N_i to N_j using all branches. The max flow min cut theorem of Ford and Fulkerson [1] is to find the maximum flow of one commodity. The present paper deals with simultaneous flows of two commodities in a network.

Let $f(k;k')$ be the value of the kth flow from N_k to $N_{k'}$. Let $c(k;k')$ be the capacity of a minimum cut separating N_k and $N_{k'}$; $c(1-2; 1'-2')$ be the capacity of a minimum cut with N_1, N_2 in one component and $N_{1'}, N_{2'}$ in the other component; $c(1-2'; 1'-2)$ be the capacity of a minimum cut with $N_1, N_{2'}$ in one component and $N_{1'}, N_2$ in the other component.

Under the assumption that $b_{ij} = b_{ji}$, the two flows are feasible if and only if

$$f(1;1') \leq c(1;1')$$

$$f(2;2') \leq c(2;2')$$

$$f(1;1') + f(2;2') \leq \min [c(1-2; 1'-2'), c(1-2'; 1'-2)]$$

and

$$\max f(1;1') + f(2;2') = \min [c(1-2; 1'-2'), c(1-2'; 1'-2)].$$

An algorithm similar to the labeling method for constructing the two flows is obtained.

REFERENCES

1. Ford, L.R., Jr. and D. R. Fulkerson, "Maximum Flow Through A Network," Canadian Journal of Mathematics, Vol. 8, 1956, pp. 399-404.

†This paper will appear as an IBM Research Report

TRANSPORTATION PROBLEMS WITH DISTRIBUTED LOADS

M. D. McIlroy

ABSTRACT

Let F be a distribution of load over a space X; let $d(x - x_0)$ be the cost of servicing a load at x from a source at x_0; and let x_i, i = 1, 2, ..., n, be given locations of n sources. We seek an optimal assignment of load to sources, according to distributions Φ_i, minimizing

$$\sum_i \int_X d(x - x_i) \, d\Phi_i$$

subject to the constraints that all loads in any set S are served

$$\sum_i \int_S d\Phi_i = \int_S dF$$

and that the capacity of source x_i is limited by M_i

$$\int_X d\Phi_i \leq M_i$$

An optimal solution consists in a set of exclusive and exhaustive regions R_i which form the supports of Φ_i. Points on the boundary between R_i and R_j satisfy

$$d(x - x_i) - d(x - x_j) = const$$

(In particular, with cost proportional to distance, each source serves a simply connected region whose boundaries are hyperbolas.)

The regions are characterized by linear programming dual "potentials," V_i, which determine the boundary loci according to

$$d(x - x_i) - d(x - x_j) = V_i - V_j$$

In terms of potentials, the problem of finding the n distributions Φ_i is equivalent to finding n numbers V_i (from which regions R_i follow by the preceding formula) such that

$$V_i \quad\;\; \leq 0$$

$$\int_{R_i} dF \leq M_i$$

with the complementary slackness condition that strict inequality in the first formula is accompanied by equality in the second.

Due to their geometrical simplicity, distributed transportation problems often admit rough-and-ready solution techniques. Such methods based on our duality theory are discussed.

LEAST COST ESTIMATING AND SCHEDULING
WITH LIMITED RESOURCES

C. F. Fey

ABSTRACT

J. E. Kelley and F. D. Fulkerson developed algorithms for determining least cost project schedules for projects composed of many activities which must be performed in certain sequences. They assume that unlimited resources are available.

In practice, only a limited amount of scarce resources is available at any given moment. This paper describes an algorithm for generating least cost project schedules when the available resources are limited. An algorithm for one limited resource is developed in detail.

The algorithm requires a project defined by a network of activities, the cost-time relationship for each activity, and the amount of scarce resources available at any time. Given that the project must be completed in a certain time, schedules are determined which minimize the project cost under the constraints imposed by the scarce resource. A series of these minimum cost schedules is generated, each differing from its predecessor by the time allotted to the project. The set of schedules spans all feasible project durations.

MATHEMATICAL PROGRAMMING SOLUTION OF TRAVELING SALESMAN EXAMPLES

Frederick Bock

ABSTRACT

A mathematical problem which he designated the messenger problem (Botenproblem) was stated by Karl Menger [1] on February 5, 1930, at a mathematical colloquium in Vienna as follows (in translation):

> We designate as the Messenger Problem (since this problem is encountered by every postal messenger, as well as by many travelers) the task of finding, for a finite number of points whose pairwise distances are known, the shortest path connecting the points. This problem is naturally always solvable by making a finite number of trials. Rules are not known which would reduce the number of trials below the number of permutations of the given points. The rule, that one should first go from the starting point to the nearest point, then to the point nearest this, etc., does not in general result in the shortest path.

Renamed the traveling salesman problem, this problem in various versions has received much attention in recent years because of both theoretical interest and practical importance. However, the methods so far proposed lack in power and elegance as compared with algorithms for related problems such as the assignment problem and the minimum tree problem.

Mathematical programming solutions have been obtained for more than 30 examples of the following traveling salesman problem, including all examples found in the literature: Given an $n \times n$ matrix of nonnegative integers c_{ij} (some of which may be arbitrarily large), find values x_{ij} that minimize

$$z = \sum_{i,j \in S} c_{ij} x_{ij} \tag{1}$$

and satisfy
1. Primary constraints
   a. Matrix constraint

$$\sum_{i,j \in S} x_{ij} = n = b_1 \tag{2}$$

   b. Line constraints
      i. Row constraints

$$\sum_{j\in S} x_{ij} \le 1 = b_i \qquad i \in S \tag{3}$$

ii. Column constraints

$$\sum_{i\in S} x_{ij} \le 1 = b_j \qquad j \in S \tag{4}$$

c. Submatrix constraints

$$\sum_{i,j\in S_k} x_{ij} \le n_k - 1 = b_k \qquad k \in Q \tag{5}$$

d. Boolean constraints

$$x_{ij} \in \{0,1\} \qquad i,j \in S \tag{6}$$

2. Secondary constraint

$$\sum_{i,j\in S} a_{ij} x_{ij} \le b_2 \tag{7}$$

S denotes the set of matrix indices, $\{1, 2, \ldots, n\}$. S_k denotes a proper subset of S having n_k elements. Q is the set of indices over which k ranges, i.e., $\{1, 2, \ldots, (2^n - 2)\}$. The secondary constraint (7) is a linear inequality implied by the nonlinear (Boolean) constraints (6) in conjunction with the linear constraints (2)-(5). A secondary constraint is required in some examples to eliminate fractional solutions in the x_{ij} that satisfy all primary linear constraints and yield a smaller value of z than does any integer solution. Nonnegative integer values of the a_{ij} and b_2 of the secondary constraint are developed as necessary in the solution of particular examples; initially they are zero valued.

The dual problem is: For values of b_1, b_i, b_j, b_k, b_2, and a_{ij} as defined above in connection with an n × n matrix of data c_{ij}, find values u_1, u_i, u_j, u_k, and u_2 that maximize

$$w = u_1 b_1 + \sum_{i\in S} u_i b_i + \sum_{j\in S} u_j b_j + \sum_{k\in Q} u_k b_k + u_2 b_2 \tag{8}$$

and satisfy

$$u_1 + u_i + u_j + \sum_{k\in Q} a_{ijk} u_k + a_{ij} u_2 \le c_{ij} \qquad i,j \in S \tag{9}$$

The coefficients a_{ijk} have the value 1 if $i,j \in S_k$ and otherwise 0. Add auxiliary integer variables y_1, y_i, y_j, y_k, y_2, and v_{ij} to the left sides of constraints (2), (3), (4), (5), (7), and (9) respectively to measure infeasibility and slack and to convert inequalities to equations. Restrict u_1 to be a nonnegative integer, u_i, u_j, u_k, and u_2 to be nonpositive integers. In any optimum feasible solution $y_1 = y_i = y_j = y_2 = 0$, $y_k \geq 0$, $v_{ij} \geq 0$, $uy = vx = 0$ for all subscripts, and $z = w$.

The method developed for this problem is an extension of the Hungarian method for the assignment problem [2, 3]; the latter is defined by (1)-(6) above with the omission of submatrix constraints (5). The present method has three phases and throughout shares these characteristics with the Hungarian method: it is dual feasible, primal feasible in the Boolean constraints, and all integer; at each iteration there is exhaustive search, limited to those cells ij with $v_{ij} = 0$, resulting in a maximal set of $x_{ij} = 1$ compatible with respect to the constraints being enforced, and a minimal cover defined by unit changes in the u's, except u_1, with $\Sigma x - n = \Sigma \Delta u$. The cover is then applied with maximum multiplicity, permitting a corresponding increase in u_1 and a strict increase in w. The search and revaluation are iterated until demonstration of infeasibility, attainment of the desired solution, or (as at present) termination of the phase.

Phase 1. By (5) make c_{ij} arbitrarily large for $i = j$. Comply with (3), (4), (6). Find the minimum assignment by the Hungarian method. Covers consist of lines only. Terminate with (2)-(6), but not (5), satisfied. At most, nonzero weights u_1, $n - 1$ of u_i, and $n - 1$ of u_j are necessary.

Phase 2. Change one x_{ij} from 1 to 0 in each subcycle resulting from phase 1. Comply with (3)-(6). Covers consist of lines and submatrices; the latter may occur in a negative sense (relaxation of u_k) as well as in a positive sense. Weighted submatrices are always pairwise disjoint or contained one in the other. Terminate with (3)-(6) but not (2) satisfied. The latter cannot be satisfied because there is no minimal cover consisting of lines and submatrices and there is a fractional solution better than any integer solution. At most, nonzero weights u_1, $n - 1$ of u_i, $n - 1$ of u_j, and $n - 3$ of u_k are necessary.

Phase 3. Form increments to the secondary constraint (7) by making Δa_{ij} the sum of (1 if $v_{ij} = 0$) plus (1 for each submatrix k such that $a_{ijk} = 1$ and $u_k < 0$), and Δb_2 the sum of x_{ij} for $i,j \in S$ plus the sum of b_k for $k \in Q$ and $u_k < 0$. Comply with (3)-(7). Covers consist of increments to the secondary constraint together with relaxation of nonzero u_k. At most, $3n - 3$ nonzero weights in all are necessary, i.e., u_1, $n - 1$ of u_i, $n - 1$ of u_j, $n - 3$ of u_k, and u_2.

REFERENCES

1. Menger, K., "Botenproblem," in Ergebnisse eines Mathematischen Kolloquiums, Heft 2 (ed. K. Menger), B. G. Teubner (1932). See pp 11-12, 9th Colloquium.
2. Kuhn, H. W., "The Hungarian Method for the Assignment Problem," Naval Research Logistics Quarterly, Vol. 2, 1955, pp. 83-97.
3. Kuhn, H. W., "Variants of the Hungarian Method for Assignment Problems," Naval Research Logistics Quarterly, Vol. 3, 1956, pp. 253-258.

NETWORK ALGORITHMS FOR COMBINATORIAL AND DISCRETE VARIABLE OPTIMIZATION PROBLEMS

John W. Suurballe

ABSTRACT

A mathematical technique which shows considerable potential for representing and solving discrete variable problems uses the concept of a directed network and the shortest path through it. The many applications of this method are not yet widely known; it is the purpose of this paper to present some results in shortest and K^{th} shortest route algorithms, and illustrate their application by obtaining algorithms for several well-known optimization problems of current interest in industry and operations research. These are the traveling salesman, assignment, and more complex, related problems; a combinatorial wiring problem; a job-shop scheduling problem; and problems of system construction for maximum economy.

Informally, the "shortest route in a network" problem is as follows: There is given a collection of nodes, and directed branches between pairs of nodes, forming a network or maze. In some way appropriate to the problem, an origin node A and destination node B are given, and we are concerned with the various paths from A to B, observing always the "one-way" rule specified by the arrows. Each branch in the network has a distance associated with it, and the distance along a path from A to B is the sum of distances of all branches used in that path. The shortest route problem is one of finding (efficiently) the path or paths from A to B with minimal distance.

Historically, the idea and method of finding the shortest route in a network was first presented as an application of linear programming to discrete extremem problems by G. B. Dantzig in 1956. Since Dantzig's paper, several more efficient algorithms have been developed for finding shortest routes.

Our network representations of the above combinatorial problems can be divided into two types. In the first type we have an "exact" representation—exact in the sense that every path in the network is one of the acceptable alternatives in the problem, every alternative is a path in the network, and the sum of distances along a network path is exactly the cost associated with the corresponding alternative.

Using a node-ordering property of our particular networks, a shortest route algorithm is developed and applied to obtain the following results:

1. Network algorithms for the wiring problem, and the assignment problem, using an N-cube model.

2. The optimum location of relay points (or supply points) in a given discrete set of potential locations, for a communication (supply) system with interrelated choice constraints.

The network algorithms result in neat tabular arrangements in which addition, subtraction, and comparison are the only numerical operations.

In the second of our two types of network representation, a problem is not represented exactly but is imbedded in a network and represented inexactly in the sense that all acceptable alternatives are network paths, but not all network paths are acceptable alternatives. In these problems the shortest route algorithms must include additional constraints which automatically rejects unwanted network paths when they turn out to be optimal. To solve this problem generally, some new results in shortest route algorithms are developed. This material is applied, along with certain network representations, to get the following results:

1. Algorithm for K^{th} Shortest Routes in a Network.
2. Network algorithms for the traveling salesman, assignment, and related problems. The traveling salesman algorithm provides a neat example and is given in detail.
3. Network algorithms for the job-shop scheduling problem, allowing set-up times for both jobs and machines, which depend in general on the order of operation. This application is more difficult, and only sketched.

Some refinements and general comments on the network algorithms are given.